ADAM AND HIS WORKS

ADAM AND HIS WORKS

Collected Stories of
PAUL GOODMAN

VINTAGE BOOKS
A Division of Random House
NEW YORK

for Beethoven, whose piano sonatas,
and Hawthorne, whose stories,
were my chief models

Contents

ADAM AND HIS WORKS

JEREMY OWEN

※　Says Thoreau in a letter: "The blacksmiths met together looking grim and voted to have a thunderbolt, if they could only get someone to launch it; but all the while there was not one man among them who could make anything better than a horse-shoe nail."

But this has not been my experience. I make a fine occasional poem when they give me an Occasion.

I

"Hey, Jeremy, when do we eat?" hinted O'Donell loudly. He was the Chevrolet agent and had recently gotten Jeremy an honest buy, so he felt at home in his little restaurant.

But Jeremy was looking blankly at the meat fried on the grill that he had mechanically turned off. He did not start, as if his thoughts had been elsewhere. They were nowhere. He made the sandwich and brought the dish. Astoundingly he did not bring the coffee.

The auto salesman *was* astounded. He looked up with sudden eyes, like a small boy who knows that something is wrong if the routine is interrupted. He was not a sharp observer and he imagined that Jeremy was preoccupied; he did not see that he was ceasing to be occupied at all. Perhaps he did see it, but could not accept the terrible fact, "Mama isn't going to feed me any more." Their eyes met. O'Donell was abashed to ask for his coffee. But he had to have coffee. "Hey, Jeremy, do you still make that good coffee?" he called pleasantly.

Jeremy was a candid observer and caught the lie. Making an effort of good will, he brought him his coffee. Without apology.

"You in love, Jer'my?" said O'Donell pleasantly. But the perplexity on his forehead said, "What's wrong, Jeremy?"

Jeremy responded to his forehead and not to his words. His impulse was simply to take off his apron and walk out; instead he dutifully spelled it out, "I don't want to serve you any more . . . I don't mean *you*, Red Hugh—" As soon as he had said the words, he realized that he had indeed withdrawn from these people and was in a crisis. The sweat stood on his face.

The remark had a finality that the salesman could only disregard. He sank his teeth in the meat that was, as always, the best, seasoned with a thumb of dry mustard, blackened bits of garlic, and a dab of creamy butter; and he took a sip of the coffee that was the best in that county.

II

Jeremy Owen's was a jewel of a short-order restaurant; by luck the small town happened to possess it—and what a difference it made! Jeremy's sign said Good Food without quotation marks, a fact not an opinion.

After trying other jobs, the young man had hit on this way to make a living. He had no special talents, no particular interests (not in food either), but he had a good appetite himself, good senses, intelligence, and a beautiful serviceable soul; he fed them as he fed himself, taking the trouble. Truck drivers and commercial travelers arranged the schedule to eat at Jeremy Owen's, and he made plenty of money. But he had no interest in making money. He wouldn't feed a man if he didn't like him, but this rarely happened, for people tended to be at their best at his little tables. Jeremy had no conceit about this either. He saw that he had simply gravitated, as if by a deliberate choice, to an elementary role in life that could not fail if he performed at all. He was Mother Nature. He grinned when he first thought of the analogy. (He had a wide grin that flashed when something was neat, even if it was grim.)

Jeremy Owen didn't look like Mother Nature. He was five foot ten and rather spare, with the plain good looks of his frank and serviceable character, with blue eyes and chestnut hair not neatly kempt, and with something unusual from time to time in his expression that might be borderline-insane.

III

They had trooped out, after the lunch hour, the last hot apple pie à la mode. He went to the doorway and looked after them with stupefaction.

Across Main Street, Alex was on a ladder changing the sign on the movie theater. Lola was window-shopping the silver dress. Red Hugh disappearing into Auto Sales. The 2:10 bus pulled in front of the drug store and the basketball team mounted with their satchels. 2:14. On all this Jeremy looked, and realized that he was not *serious*. Those fellows working in their businesses were ambitious to make money; they were married men. Lola was set on making a marriage in a few months, and would succeed because she wanted to. The basketball team wanted to win. To him money and marriage meant nothing, and there was no game that he wanted to win.

To a short-sighted view, Jeremy *was* serious, for he was giving a service that they needed and he was doing it outstandingly. But that view would prove false, for he was not interested in these people, to serve them. They did not interest *him*. Just because he was not conceited about his abilities, nor ashamed of his worthlessness, he was able to pose to himself the naked awful fact: that the people of his town, who were some of them fine people against whom he bore no grudge, for he was successful and had no cause of resentment—those people were of no interest to him, and therefore he could hardly continue to serve them.

But he did not know any other town, he was in a crisis. As yet, however, he felt only stupefaction, as if it were they, and not his own nature, that amazed him. He did not yet panic.

Alex, on his ladder, had spelled out the name of the movie. Jeremy did not take it in as a word, though it was the very movie they had all been heatedly discussing at lunch. Instead—there swept over him a wave of nausea, as if he had been eating bad food, force-feeding himself. When it passed, and the pure taste returned to his mouth, he had a flashing insight: he had been existing among these people by making allowances. Their entertainment was *not* entertainment for him. Their movie stars were not teasing images for him, and the stories had nothing to do with *his* problems. Why pretend any longer? But he had been making allowances for them, for their business and their entertainment, in order to have his town at all, a people and place. If he did not share these fantasies, what fantasies could he share? (In fact, he had not gone to the movie in a year; he was already hopelessly out of touch.)

He did not like to be contemptuous—it made no sense —what was the use of a small triumph when he was the big loser? But—just look at that unlovely street! It did not flatter your eyes! the unproportioned buildings, dingily colored and without unity of form or material; the bleak road through, where the immodest cars drove too fast; the lousy chain grocer—like ten thousand other uninteresting places. Jeremy realized, with naive surprise, that his own little place was attractive to him because he had himself made it so. It did not yet occur to him to become angry and change the street. Instead, he became uneasy with romantic longing, and sank into gloom.

IV

He closed for the afternoon and went fishing.

He was afraid that there was "something wrong with him," meaning that he was going crazy. But he had a test of his sanity. If Dyer's Pond and the pretty woods around it would also seem mean and unattractive to him—especially at the end of September—then certainly he was far gone.

Jeremy did not know many poems but he had by heart one that had been printed in the county paper:

Dyer's Pond

You're a sweet limpid pond
to trudge a mile around
    or swim across you idly
    that mile divided by π.

The hatchets of boy scouts
ring out like rifle shots
    through the scrubby pines
    where yellow sun shines,

and through the water where we stand
we see white pebbles on the sand
    and green pickerel about our feet
    nosing if this be likely meat.

(By his measurement, the swim across the pond was 300 yards and not 560, a "mile divided by π," but Jeremy saw that the poet was right to put it neatly, and this was for him a great literary discovery.)

The insanity-test was negative. The pond was as attractive as ever. The cottonwoods were yellow, the pines dark. It was hot Indian summer and he soon kicked off his clothes and took a swim. He felt better. He was not estranged from the *world,* for he could always go to Dyer's Pond! Today he scrutinized the purple flowers, the dying weeds, the single-minded ants. It was all of a piece—with his own body—practical, like Paradise. But he was lonely.

Alas! when the human beings appeared in their station-wagon on the other shore—a couple of families and assorted youngsters—there was a tumultuous hiding in the thickets to change into bathing-suits, with piercing jokes. This offended Jeremy; life again had him by the throat, stupefied, estranged. He clenched his fists and determined to swim across and lecture them on their behavior, naked as he was.

He bethought himself. "*They* seem to be sociable and happy; it's I who am lonely and in dismay. Who asks me?

Why should I give them a hard time when they couldn't care less?" Yet he swam in their direction anyway, and when he was about sixty yards offshore he shouted: "For Chrissake! why in hell you need bathing-suits to swim in a pond like this?"

"Can't hear you! I can't hear you!" shouted a man. "What you say?" He waded out in the water. "You say can we lend you a bathing-suit? . . . Hey, do we have an extra bathing-suit?"

"Why don't you swim bare-ass?!" shouted Jeremy in a fury.

"Oh. Why don't you mind your own business, Owen?"

The conversation set off a renewed volley of laughter, and Jeremy was stung and swam away.

It was not that the others embarrassed him, or interfered with him in any way at all. That would have made him fight. He sunned himself on the beach quite as if they weren't there. But how did it come about, he wondered, that he, with the same background as his townsmen, was unlike them? He did not doubt himself. He *knew* that their mores made no sense. He concluded baffled: he simply did not know enough to answer the question, why people behaved as they did when they knew better.

As he was returning into town, however, happening suddenly on a knot of people, he was possessed as by a demon by an evil thought that human beings were like roaches huddled in their dirty spots, that scurry when you flash a light. This never happened in his restaurant.

V

For a week the passion of Jeremy Owen had a most curious effect on his menus. Since he was not interested in the diners, he tried to interest himself in the cooking. He began to offer fancy dishes studiously copied from Escoffier, and spent hours at night concocting the white stock for the sauces. It was an empty gesture, because he was not an artist.

Amazed, his clients obediently ate what he put before them. But the small town, so lucky in its jewel of a short-order diner, hardly needed or appreciated a learned

French cuisine, nor was it very good. Even Jeremy had to laugh at his efforts.

VI

He described the incident at the pond to Julia.

"The man was right," she said. "How *is* it your business if they want to wear bathing-suits?"

"Can't you see? They don't take it seriously or they'd be indignant at *me* being naked."

"Of course they don't take it seriously. It's not a big deal any more. Everybody knows *that*."

"But they *still* wear the bathing-suits!"

"It's for the children," she explained. . . . "Why, what's the matter, Jerry?"

He had fallen silent. Finally, "It's not interesting," he said thickly, "when they behave like that."

The words fell between them dully. What he was seeing was generation after generation, down, down, down. He quietly began to panic.

"What did you hope for?" her voice rose. "Did you want them to lynch you for shocking them, when you don't shock them? Would that be—interesting?"

"Why are you shouting at me?" he said.

"You don't have much sense of humor," she said and laughed.

Her laughter was swallowed in the silence. He was looking at her. She became anxious and touched his forearm. The touch made her amorous, but him cold. They were upstairs at his place.

"Look, Jerry," she said, "everybody knows I spend two, three nights a week here. Does anybody say anything—at the Company—or make me any trouble? It's not a big deal any more. How do they stand in your way?"

She knew that something bad was happening. He was looking at her, so to speak, objectively. In fact his mind was racing, not helter-skelter but leaping from one vanquished position to another, as a mechanized army leaps ahead with lightning prongs and swallows up France. *They* were not interesting, *she* was not interesting, *this* was not interesting. He had often asked himself why he did not marry her, or when he was going to marry her. She played her cards skillfully; one of the things he admired in her was her skill, even though he was the prey. He was lustful and forward, he had tried a good sampling of the women, but he always found that it was with Julia that it worked out best. Nevertheless he avoided committing himself. Now he knew (he felt he knew) that it was by a deep instinct of self-preservation. With her too he had been making allowances. Can you marry some one, making allowances?

He was ashamed. He had been lying to her. Not because he had sometimes acted as though he loved her or might get to love her, for that is an honorable experiment; but because he was really making allowances for her.

Rallying to his gentlemanly honor, he took her hand, as if he were responding. At once she rebounded. "What was that you called out?" she said happily. "Bare-ass! *I* like to swim bare-ass!" She put his hand under her shirt.

Now he felt his panic. His eyes were glaring and the sweat appeared on his brow. For he felt no animal desire. He did not begin to. Without love, the promise of love— the essence of love is its on-going promise—there is no lust. He took her body in his arms but it was not interesting. He was not used to this absence of feeling, and he could not help but interpret it as a maiming. He thought that this was what he was panicky about. By iron self-control he willed his body to respond. But while they were making love, he kept thinking, "No one is to blame! no one is to blame! I am not made for this world. It is as if they sent me to the wrong planet."

She, of course, knew that he was slipping away from her and she was invaded by a chaos of sentiments, fear and woe, recrimination and self-recrimination; included in which, however, was also a motherly concern for the man she loved.

VII

Now on October 4 (1957) the men launched and sent into orbit our first man-made satellite, sharing in heavenly motion, freely falling around the world once an hour. In space.

When Jeremy heard about it in his country town, he was mad with joy and pride. As an American, he was disappointed that Russians had made the first successful launching, but this feeling was overwhelmed by his love (and indeed relief) for mankind, who had again done something magnificent, worthy of enthusiasm without making allowances. Something interesting! The names kept repeating on his tongue when he read them in the newspapers, Copernicus and Kepler, Galileo and Newton. These astronomers were for him romance, and there was nobody in that county, or in that state, who was so proud and happy as Jeremy Owen.

The exploit also frightened him. To think of the hundreds of men on the far-off steppe, and our own soldiers and sailors on the shore in Florida, single-mindedly active like the ants at the pond. To do it! to do it! swept up in obedient activity! So he alternately chilled and was afire. He saw the rocket rushing aloft, and finally achieving its swift unhurried ellipse. It was hourly signaling to us in our language, saying beep.

Pounding on the latest edition, he sought out Red Hugh in his salesroom. "Well! how's about it?" he crowed. "And what do you think o' that?! It says here—"

But the Irishman's reaction to the new moon was an odd one. Jeremy found it touching. Faced with a real novelty, the cautious Donegal superstitions of Red Hugh's childhood rose to the surface. "I dunno," he said dubiously, "I don't like us goin' in there where we're not invited. My way o' thinkin', people shouldn't step out o' their place. When I was a boy, we knew our place."

Jeremy roared with joy and began to beat him on the head and shoulders with the newspaper. "It's *our* place, Irishman, it's *our* place! Do you think we picked the lock and walked in? Kepler and Newton! Do you think we're whirling up there without trying for it, wishing for it, working at it, till we figured out all the laws of motion? Copernicus and Galileo! Why, they *opened* the door for us and said, 'Boy, welcome home!' "

When he cried out this, that entering into space was

like coming home, Jeremy blushed scarlet; and Red Hugh, flustered by his enthusiasm and being pounded by the newspaper, blushed too.

All day at the restaurant, however, Jeremy had the melancholy opportunity to listen to the responses of the average man to this wonder of Man. Unable to let the subject drop, he greeted each newcomer with the glad tidings; and he kept tuning the radio to the small moon's hourly beep, for it was a busy moon that came by often. Alas some persons didn't care about Fellow Traveler at all; others felt nothing but chagrin that the Russians had beat us to it and won a victory of propaganda; and others knowingly pointed out that the satellite proved that our enemies had an Intercontinental Ballistic Missile with a Nuclear Warhead—the polysyllables rolled off the tongue.

"But *men* did it," said Jeremy pathetically, and he repeated the magic names Copernicus and Galileo, Kepler and Isaac Newton.

"Yeah, and the crazy Jew Einstein."

Jeremy looked at him with stupefaction. Yet he was not disheartened; they could not take away his moon.

It was not till late in the afternoon that he got a normal response. A youth came in for a hamburger after the basketball practice. "Say, Jer'my," he said, "what you think about this satellite?"

"God bless you!" said Jeremy. "Yes!"

"You bet, Yes!"

"Isn't it great?"

"That sure is great, because it says here in ten years we're gonna have a man up in a rocket on the way to the planet Mars."

"That's right," said Jeremy, "that's what they say."

"I'm gonna be that man," said the youth seriously.

"I believe you are," said Jeremy seriously, and the tears of pride began to stream down his cheeks as he looked at the youth of lofty aspiration.

"Gee, Jer'my," said the youth frankly and without embarrassment, "I feel like bustin into tears about that satellite too, but I wouldn't dast to cry in public and all. Gee, Jer'my." He looked at the man as if he were as wonderful as the satellite, and suddenly, fearfully, he bolted out the door.

Fifteen minutes later he came back calmly for his hamburger, but the place was closed and on the door was the sign:

> CLOSED
>
> JEREMY OWEN WON'T
> SERVE FOOD IN THIS TOWN
> UNTIL FURTHER NOTICE.

VIII

He was bent on leaving the town. He was not yet sure that he wanted to leave Julia. He called her up and they sat in a corner in the tavern. He persisted in talking about the Fellow Traveler.

Ordinarily Julia would easily have shared his enthusiasm, the way a loving woman shares in such things, by complacently admiring the exploits and enthusiasms of her baby: he with his eyes on the machinery, she with her eyes on his face. But now just her love was hurt and threatened. She was anxious, finally frantic. It was she who was the child and needed attention and reassurance, which he did not have to give. She hated the artificial satellite. She was jealous of it.

He became mournful. He did not mind her spiteful remarks, which were simply stupid and unlike her; but she was clinging to him when he was bent on freedom. He felt that he was going to do something brutal.

She sat like a block of resentment, intent on her own hurt feelings, and unable to look at him and say the simple sentence that would have made sense, "Let's *us* go to Outer Space! there's nothing here." Ordinarily this would have been an easy sentence to say, for the town was indifferent to her, it was only Jeremy that mattered.

Instead of doing a brutal act, he tried to sneak away from her by feeling remorseful. "I'm sorry, Julie—I see I made you fall in love with me. That was wrong. Wrong. A woman like you—a woman like you deserves to have a steady man who can take care of her, but I'm going crazy and I can't even take care of myself. Naturally you want to get married—. Who in hell do I think I am!" he exclaimed. "If *I* don't care for what other people care for, is that *their* fault? Jeremy Owen doesn't go for Lana Turner. Big! deal! Is it Red Hugh O'Donell's duty in life to be interesting to Jeremy Owen? It's not *my* fault either!" he shouted.

"What on earth have I got to do with Lana Turner and Red Hugh O'Donell?" she said, offended.

"Oh yes! oh yes! it's all the same."

"What's all the same? I think you *are* going crazy."

With a shaking hand he lit a cigarette, puffed on it, enveloped his head and shoulders in a cloud of smoke.

"I closed up the diner," he said, "and I'm going to New York."

"Take me with you!"

"No."

The tip of his cigarette was glowing in the heart of the swirl of smoke. As the smoke wafted toward the door on the draft, his eyes appeared, hard. He could see his eyes mirrored in the drop of tear hanging on her cheek. The small word he had said was hanging in the room between their heads. "No."

IX

That night the sky was mercifully veiled in cloud, so that Jeremy did not have to look for the little moon, which he could not have seen anyway. Instead, he himself walked in interminable circles, in and out of town. To an onlooker —but there was no onlooker—it would have been problematic whether or not he would last in possession of his sanity till dawn, having quit his job, rejected his woman, and no longer making allowances.

His mood swung from enthusiasm to stupefaction, from glad surprise that it was so to unbelief that it could be as it was. Having suddenly decided no longer to be interested when he was not interested, Jeremy Owen was like Adam awaking, to whom everything was a surprise. But who can endure that?

Jeremy was not a church-goer; yet in this crisis of his existence when, arbitrarily, he was going to New York on the first train in the morning, he reverted to an archaic pattern of his childhood and fell on his knees to pray to God. Alongside the bed. He grinned at himself, though wryly, because it was neat. But his behavior was more peculiarly appropriate than he was aware of, it reverted to his ancestors in Connecticut, religious reformers; the borderline-insane strain was an ancient one. They too, out of the blue, used to make a public gesture and bear witness according to their consciences.

He had come back to his lonely dwelling to catch a little sleep. On an impulse he lit a candle to see by, for that seemed to him to be a warm and "real" light. He felt that his day's joy was holy and that he was "wrestling" and making a "clean decision." Then he was kneeling and the candlelight shone from the table on his wedge-shaped profile and unruly hair.

The content of his prayer was astoundingly American. "Creator Spirit," he prayed, "do not make me, with my new feelings, stand out as too different from the rest of the people. Granted that I am most often right in my judgments, and they are wrong, let me either be persuasive to others or come to respect them anyway as also having views worthy of men. Otherwise I cannot be democratic. But I cannot be myself unless I believe that all men are equal. O God Creator of the world! do have made your world so that we are essentially equal and can give and take and come to an agreement. Amen.

"You know I'm not afraid," he said further to God, "to stand out alone for what I think. How could I do otherwise, in your spirit? I am strong and stubborn enough to suffer isolation, envy or disdain, and prejudices and penalties. But all this makes sense only if finally I and my people do not fundamentally differ. (May it be in my time! but as is your will.) O God! what is the use of your truth if I lose by it my people? Certainly you can't mean anything like that!"

It was good old-fashioned wrestling with God, that usually came to recriminations and taking Him to task.

"Good," said Jeremy and climbed into bed, "that'll work."

He was confident because his prayer was sincere. It cast the burden off his own shoulders, no matter where or on whom or even into the deep blue sea. And sure enough, he at once got his answer, in the form of a salutary admonition: "Jeremy Owen!" something said to him, "you'd do much better for yourself, young man, if you'd stop being the mother of the multitude. You are *not* Mother Nature. Really, the sky won't fall down, nor anybody starve, if you take a vacation, even if you *never* came back." With this ironical reflection, he fell happily asleep.

X

It was on the 10th of October that I met Jeremy at the Museum of Modern Art on 53rd Street, looking, or trying to look, at the big *Water Lilies* of Monet on the third floor, the same picture as was destroyed in a fire a few months later. I could see that the young man was highly excited by the picture—as well he might be—he kept changing his position to get it into focus.

He turned to me impulsively. "How you get to *see* that picture?" he asked.

I pointed out to him, sourly, that it wasn't his fault, the picture itself was poorly hung. Typical Modern Museum slovenliness with all their slickness. It was too big for the room it was in, it needed a back-up to see the impression. I showed him where, from the adjoining room, one could get a kind of good glimpse, at an angle, through the doorway.

"I guess that's what we always get," he said wryly, and riveted my attention, "a glimpse, at an angle, through the doorway, if the other people get out of the way. . . . Are there more pictures like that?"

I assumed that he meant *Water Lilies* by Monet and I assured him that there were many, including the remarkable ones, even bigger than this, at the Orangerie in Paris. (I spared telling him that those were so miserably lit that they looked like mud.) His face fell, he did not have the means to go to Paris. Then I understood that by pictures like that he did not necessarily mean *Water Lilies* by Monet, but any pictures in which there shone the work and devotion and intellect of Man, not otherwise, as I soon learned, than we (Copernicus, Kepler, etc.) had whirled our moon in space.

"Oh, if that's what you mean! we have fifty great works of art right here in New York City!" I said proudly. "A few in this very museum." I steered him toward the *Three Musicians*. I urged him by no means to miss the Tlingit Blanket at the Museum of the American Indian, nor the Unicorn in the Cloisters, and there was an Easter Island head in Natural History, where he could also take in the dinosaurs on the top floor.

Jeremy was drunken on the display, the *proofs*, of the grandeur of mankind. He was insatiable for more and more and more, like a man who has been lost in a desert, endlessly thirsty and who ought not to drink so fast. I watched him sidelong. He was a borderline schizophrenic, all right, but I listened carefully to his syntax and I was pretty sure he wouldn't break down. He was glaringly using the monuments of our magnificence in order to ward off a catastrophic response to the newsy fact that we do not live in Paradise. It certainly was going to persist as a fact, and he'd certainly have to keep hustling. But what gave me confidence for him was his beautiful serviceableness. He had finally come to the idea that if he did not find us lovely enough, he'd set about to make us lovely. I bowed to him.

We had coffee and sandwiches on the roof. I was ashamed how poor the food was, especially when he told me that he used to run a restaurant himself—I could imagine that it was a solid little restaurant. I was not personally ashamed at the ugly view of the mid-town street —it wasn't my fault; my brother and I have never stopped nagging for a Master Plan—but I was distressed at it for him.

"No no!" said Jeremy, "your city's immense. When you go round it in the steamboat. It's only when you get in the streets that it's no good."

"Ah, you took the boat ride!" I said, pleased, for my Hudson shows off well, when it doesn't stink.

. . . "Look, Jeremy," I said finally, tentatively—I

wanted to calm him down but not break his spirit—
"Granted some of these pictures are wonderful—but you
must bear in mind—that they are only works of art." Being an artist myself, I could say this. "Men are *good* at
art-works. Other works too—bridges, and your rocket,
and, you know, the Salk vaccine, antibiotics, and all that
jazz. Oh, when we have something to work at, we're first
rate. You don't even need to get fancy: just look at the
fellow seriously fixing his car, or two men working seriously on the same job. They're absorbed, cooperative;
they're human. But it's quite a different matter, you know,
if you're looking at the human animals themselves, in
their lives, their projects—especially if you *don't* have
something to work at—do you follow me?"

"Living is no different from pictures," said Jeremy
Owen. "You've got to work at it, and it's all by grace. It's
there, but it's rare." He gave me his frank grin. He was
sane as a hammer. "I see you're trying to calm me
down but not break my spirit. Really, it's not necessary.
Don't make allowances for me." He touched me with
his hand. "Thanks. I like you," said Jeremy Owen.

XI

The youths hanging around the corners made him uneasy. They existed in his home town too, who could not
find work and also did not want to, but they were few
and each one seemed to be a special case ultimately dis-
soluble by friendly heckling or somebody's giving him a
job willy-nilly—or by their leaving town. With a start
Jeremy realized that the youngsters who left town came
to New York.

In New York these young men were not special cases.
They formed a class in the city, with their own class prop-
erties of disaffection, degeneration of skills, drinking,
drugs, and finally their own literature.

Indeed, the discovery of classes, classes of people with
characteristic troubles, was the most surprising experience that Jeremy Owen had in his visit to New York. In
New York there were so many people. Back home, he
was aware of personal problems; here overnight, for he

was quick, he became a sociologist. But whereas formerly he would have thought that this new way of having his problems, as universal in the nature of things,
would make them abstract and impersonal, to his amazement he found that, on the contrary, they became even
more grindingly personal, intransigent, hard. And if
you could confront them, noble.

Ignorant himself, he was appalled by the ignorance of
these youths. They had never noticed that there were
tides in the Hudson River, not to speak of knowing the
causes of tides. They did not know who the Mayor was.
They did not know the principle of an electric motor.
They could not fix a bicycle.

On the corner of the street he lived on, hung out a
gang of Puerto Rican lads. One of them had a shining
new bicycle and all were soon wildly pedaling it. Jeremy
was charmed by this generous camaraderie, as if all property belonged to all. But he quickly saw that there *was* no
community, no mutual pleasure or mutual concern, but
each one was simply proving his prowess and demanding
an equal go in order not to be belittled. All were so fearful of everything that they could not afford to be affectionate to any one. There was a crash; a few spokes of the
bike were broken, and the wheel knocked out of line. The
fellows formed a circle around the accident and looked at
it a moment. The owner angrily kicked the rider, a
smaller boy, who was hurt. *"Perdida—"* they said, and
went away leaving the bicycle and the hurt boy in the gutter.

Jeremy was at a loss. The bicycle was lying there. He
began to call them back—he would show them how to
fix it, fix it for them. He pulled up short as if some one
had caught him by the shoulder in an iron grip. He was
not to be the feeder of the multitude. He was *not* to be
their bicycle repairman.

But the bicycle was lying there. It was shining, it was
brand new, it was as beautiful as a bicycle. The hurt boy
was sitting on the curb rubbing his knee. Jeremy looked
at this and looked at that. "I'd take the bike myself," he
thought, "but what do I need with a bicycle? Is the boy
badly hurt? Am I his nurse?"

He wished that he had some special talent that he had

to exercise—the "talent that is death to hide," as Milton said; or that some problem of the world, not his problem, puzzled and intrigued him, so that he could work at it; or that, as some did, he took satisfaction in pleasing himself. Then he could evade this dilemma of either having to work in conditions not interesting to a man, or of having no job at all. It was a general dilemma, for they were surplus. In 1957, nobody desperately needed you or me.

None of his wishes was true; he had no special talent, no special interest, no urge to please himself. His disposition was not assertive but serviceable. But he had a balky strain that said, "I won't."

He touched the abandoned bicycle with the toe of his shoe. At this moment Jeremy Owen would have put his fist through a wall. . . . He turned away.

Quick as a flash, nimble as could be, as soon as his back was turned, the hurt boy had leaped up and dragged the bicycle into a basement. Jeremy caught it out of the corner of his eye and he was enchanted. All problems were solved! The boy *wanted* the bicycle!

His mood swung to the euphoric and he continued his walk up the street. He looked back and there, where there had been a hurt boy and an abandoned bicycle, now was nothing at all, the empty street. Jeremy laughed with pleasure, it was so dandy. The problem had vanished.

XII

On his own stoop was Julia sitting, smoking a cigarette, wearing a red bell-hop's cap, a black velvet jacket, and a skirt of the yellow plaid of her clan. She had been watching him as he watched, and she was pleased that he was enjoying it.

He started. "You've been watching me down the block," he said, "and you seem to be pleased that I was enjoying it."

"Yes," she admitted.

"That's remarkable, for you to be pleased at that."

Nevertheless, he felt that he ought to be severe, for obviously it would not do for her to come pursuing him, as she had done. Why it would not do, was not clear to him. "Why have you followed me here?" he said severely. "Explain yourself. I said No, I wouldn't bring you to New York."

"You didn't bring me, I came after you," she said simply. "When you left, there was no use my staying behind. I came as soon as I got paid."

"And what are you going to do if I don't want you here?" he said brutally, wondering at his words, for he was, rather, sexually aroused as he looked at her; he wanted to touch her and was complacent about not having to sleep alone again that night.

"I don't think that's likely," she said bravely, or maybe simply, for his look was evident. "Unless you try hard against it—like a sailor on the town—it's impossible not to like the woman you enjoy yourself with."

"What the devil do you know about sailors on the town!" he said, amused.

"I figure it this way," she said. "Before I left, I figured it out. Either he'll have me around—from time to time—" Her eyes moistened. "Or he—you—won't—in which case I'm no worse off anyway—without. Isn't that logical?" She could not smile.

He sat down beside her on the step and put an arm around her waist. Dutifully to himself, he went over her speech, how and why she came, what she thought likely, and how she figured. No matter which way he turned it, her argument made lovely sense.

"What are you thinking?" she said.

"I am turning what you say this way and that."

"Ah, you are twisting it and turning it!" She bit her lips.

"No, I'm not twisting it," he said, surprised but not indignant. "Come upstairs, Julie. Have you eaten?"

XIII

Jeremy had never read the play *Everyman*, nor had it been played in his town. But he knew the name *Everyman*, although he imagined, somewhat off the mark, that it was a story of every man's life rather than his death. Now being in New York, where there were so many people, he was powerfully seized by the dramatic idea of the fate that belonged to Everyman. Not the luck or bad luck, the talent or beauty or only average gifts, or the stupidity or ugliness, that mark this man as different from that man, but those facts of life which happen to Everyman, so that every man would say that you were talking about *him*. Likely that would be a melancholy story, for by and large one did not see mankind cutting a glorious figure in New York City, winter of 1957.

"Where are you going, Everyman?" said Jeremy, to the man who was going but was willing to stay a moment and exchange the time of day.

"Looking for a job," said Everyman.

"Yes, everybody's got to do something," said Jeremy. "*I* seem to be conducting a Public Opinion Survey. What kind of work do *you* want to do?"

"I beg your pardon?"

"What do you like? what are you good at? You say you're looking for a job."

"I don't think you size up the situation, stranger," said Everyman. "You sound like from up in the mountains. Around here, there *aren't* many jobs fit for a man to do, and if you want to get anything at all, you'd better omit that kind of thinking, I mean what you like and what you're good at. Once in a blue moon you'll find a man here doing what suits him; but he ain't Everyman."

"Do you mean that Everyman is spending his working life doing what's no good?"

"That's right. Forty years, forty hour week."

"Hm. . . . What's the matter, Everyman?"

"Well, to be frank with you, I'm lonely."

"Ah, you mean you don't have enough sex? I've heard about that."

"*You* are frank. No, I didn't mean that. But that too. I don't think you'll find many in New York as get enough as is good for them. What I meant was just lonely. I don't love anybody. I don't feel they love me, though I guess I may be wrong. You ever been in love?"

"I don't think so," said Jeremy. "But leave me out of this."

"I been in love, a few times. And whenever I was in love, it didn't work out. The damnedest thing. This one didn't happen to like me; another one, her brother beat the tar out of her and I had to stand by; another one the father beat the tar out of *me*. Another one, my furlough was up and afterward she had made other arrangements. Oh, nothing unusual, just what happens to Everyman. But do you know what it adds up to?"

"What does it add up to, Everyman?"

"Since I never been able to get this simple thing I want when I want it, I've become convinced that the world isn't ordered for the best. Now that saps your confidence. There are lots of things possible to people who have been lucky in love that are impossible to me because I have no faith. If God couldn't provide better for such a simple thing, that terrific want and need of mine sometime— well, I don't know."

"Don't you believe in God, Everyman?"

"I don't know. I tell you, I don't know. That's one of the things you'll learn if you go around questioning Everyman, I'm ignorant. I don't know the first things. What to teach my children, nor how to get them to learn it if I knew. I don't know how to fix the machines I use every day. They get me in wars, but how in hell should I know what's it about? It's too big and far. (By the way, they don't know either; what's in the papers is bullshit.) Naturally I can't live this way, continually confused; so soon I know all about everything, it's all in the papers. Any taxi driver will tell you. Especially if you're a New Yorker like Everyman, we're notorious for it. Do *you* know anything?" he asked curiously.

Jeremy pondered it. "I've just begun," he said carefully. "I think I have learned a few *small* things."

"Will you tell me?" said Everyman eagerly, "and be my guide? and be my best man by my side?"

"When I am more sure of myself, Everyman. I swear it," said Jeremy.

"Well, I'm not getting any younger," said Everyman, and they walked along in silence.

"Why are you limping, Everyman?"

"Cause I'm lame, stupid. Had an accident as a child."

"Oh, that was tough luck."

"Tough luck? No, not at all. It's in the nature of things. Everybody's got something."

"Really? Isn't that exaggerated?" said Jeremy.

"How! exaggerated! Open your eyes, man. One has migraine, one has ulcers. They're all chronics. This one's alcoholic, this one's queer, and this one's what they call a psychopathic personality and lands in jail. Some of 'em can't get it up and more than 50 per cent of the women are frigid. The average children are stuck with their parents, and the orphans and foundlings grow up cold. Just figure it out, man. If there's two per cent of this and five per cent of that and three and a half per cent of the other, it soon adds up to a whopping hundred and eighty-eight per cent of the whole jolly population. Do you mean to tell me there's nothing wrong with *you?* You're a liar! *I'm* one of the lucky ones!" boasted Everyman, "I'm just lame. I can work and walk, even if I won't run no mile in three fifty like an Australian. I grant you," he said morosely, "we're not very interesting—the lame, the ailing and neurotic—they never surprise you. But nobody is to blame! No—one—is—to—blame. We're just not made for this world. As if they sent us to the wrong planet. You take it easy, buddy."

And Everyman went off, raucously singing *The Ballad of the Hurricane*:

When you was little, man, your mama
    threw out the baby with the bath,
you ain't got the equipment
    to beat your feet and laugh.

So sit down there and drink your beer
    and don't be bothering
the people drinking with their friends
    so gay and good-looking.

Don't snap out of it, buddy,
    stay with it till it hurts,
because you only live once
    you might as well know the worst.

No, look, he said, my situation
    is delicate. He frowned.

I gotta stay here in the center
   o all these winds rushin around,

a hundred twenty miles an hour
   around the edges, knock you silly,
where here I sit as calm as calm
   and the sky is sunny.

But he bowed to Fate, and a mile an hour
   he drifted out the door northwest
by the compass that he wore
   dangling from his vest.

That was the blast that wrecked my house
   and knocked the spire off Old North Church,
it drowned a man in Providence
   and left New London in the lurch.

Mighty trees with dirty roots
   at the break of day
with chickens roosting in the leaves
   floated in Narragansett Bay.

After that flood at daybreak
   our town was dirty and washed
and we walked the streets in wonder
   to look at what was smashed.

XIV

"Are you still questioning Everyman, Everyman?" I said to Jeremy.

He nodded dumbly.

"What did he tell you this time?"

"He said that Everyman has no real job and no faith, lousy sex, and he's ignorant and crippled."

"Oh?"

"And he went off singing about a drunk who thought he was a Hurricane, and he was."

"Yes. *The Ballad of the Hurricane*."

"But I have hammered out of it a slogan!" said Jeremy passionately, and the sweat rolled off his face as if he were literally hammering a tough metal. "Foster Excellence! Approve of it, even if it hurts, and give it chances to be used. I came here to learn something to tell him, and I've already found one thing."

TERRY FLEMING—
OR, ARE YOU PLANNING
A UNIVERSE?

I

Mother told Terry that his father was dead. But when he grew old enough to read and to ferret in the trunk, he found newspaper clippings that his father was in jail. He was excited. His father was not dead but alive, not nothing but a person, not nowhere but in a place called jail. He was angry with his mother anyway, now he was angry with her because she tried to hide his living father. She kept secrets from him, he kept his secret from her; but he had the advantage, because he knew.

His father and his father's plight were wonderful to Terry and he bragged to his mates in school. "My father is in a tremendous jail. It goes on more'n fifty miles. It's far away." His schoolmates were doubtful how to take this novelty. Those to whom the word jail meant something guilty and frightening were stirred to awe and envy —what is forbidden is delightful without limits. The thought of this ecstasy communicated itself from them to Terry. He radiated privilege.

He bragged to his teacher Miss Agostino that his father was in the great jail. She started and Terry was convinced that he had something unbelievable. He insisted, to enjoy the reaction again and again. But when she showed signs of sympathy, he felt contempt and anger and said, "What do you know about jails, you old maid?"

To preserve his little glory he made a devaluating judgment of them all.

His schoolmates, fortified by information from home, conspired to take him down a peg, and at the corner after lunch they greeted him with the cry, "Your daddy's a jail-bird."

But Terry said serenely, "What do you know about jails? My daddy's alive. My daddy's alive and in jail. Even my mom tried to keep it secret from me, but I found it out by reading. It's in the papers. He's not nowhere. Yeow! my daddy's alive, he's in jail."

II

Terry's father, Dick Fleming, was inured. Whether in fear or perverse hope, he could not foresee any extraordinary punishment that they could inflict on him that would not be indifferent, indifferently sad, to him. When he first reached this condition, his attitude was exasperating to the prison authorities; it seemed to be insolent, defiant and provocative, a show of force to be met with force. But there was no increment of rebellion on his part and even a superficial observer could see that his attitude was not a judgment of them nor of his relation to them, but of a certain relation to himself. Now to create such an inward-turning relation was just the purpose of their reformatory, and therefore usually they now let him be.

Whether punished or let be in his cage, Dick Fleming felt no anger. He had achieved a control of his feelings that prevented fruitless anger from rising and disturbing the pleasure of surcease from pain. The worst pain would be to repeat the process of bursting with anger and swallowing the anger. Of turning four colors: red, black, white and purple. For there is the red of boiling anger, the black of settled wrath, the white of blazing fury, and the purple of suppressed rage.

The expense of soul in repeating this fruitless procession of the angers was too exhausting to endure. Dick was preoccupied with avoiding the pain of the rising of the instinctive reaction of anger, and he was inured to the hurt, usual or extraordinary, that they inflicted on him. He did not fear anything but the obliterating fury itself.

But when he slept, he dreamed of dark fire. We others dream of fire with its forms and colors and licking its objects: houses burning, explosions and bolts of electricity. But the fire that Dick dreamed of was more like the dark fire of physics, an invisible mass not even hot because it touches no objects—the fire itself, filling a space where nothing else can be, except that occasionally there is a white flash and annihilation because of some flaw in the perfect vacuum.

III

"My father is a king," thought Terry. "Enemies have locked him in jail. They have cruel guards and use heavy stone and iron to keep him unknown. But his dignity shines.

"They gave me to a gypsy. My real mother is dead."

Terry was too prudent to brag to his schoolmates that his father was this important person. His knowledge of it enabled him sometimes to withdraw from stupid competitions with a distant smile. But the secret of it isolated him from his friends and he had no other confidants.

Terry did not betray to the woman he housed with that he knew she was a gypsy.

"Also, my father has a daughter, my older sister," thought Terry. "She is beautiful and she has let-down hair. She is not in jail, but she has a way of getting in to see our father. She works on the outside with our party. She is the one I must get in touch with, to know what to do next."

But it was not the case that Terry met with his sister on any corner, although he had a suspicion that certain persons, by their dignity, belonged to their party; but he was too prudent to be forward. What he recognized clearly, however, by their pretended dignity and their cruelty, were the enemies. He learned to mark how they had usurped privileges and were abusing them. The enemies did not aim any special attacks at Terry himself because he kept his secret too well, that it was *his* father who was the king. Terry saw that most of the kids were ignorant sheep who did not know what was going on, and they were the most abused.

Sometimes he was buoyed up by hope. At other times,

especially in the anxious dark before sleep, Terry felt that the enemy regime was becoming the accepted order of things: the king was literally rotting away in jail and it was too late to rescue him. The world was closing in and there was no way of making a break-through, even if he would meet his sister.

Most of the day he was neither elated nor anxious but masturbated with dogged courage.

IV. HINTS ON PLANNING A UNIVERSE

Are you planning a Universe? Are you thinking of creating a Universe? Here are some *do's* and *don'ts* to bear in mind. If you follow these simple suggestions, you will have a better chance of being content with your Universe.

Don't have any "chosen people." The fancied advantages of such an arrangement are far less than the complications that arise.

Do have a good supply of material on hand, so that at the last minute you don't have to skimp on whole realms of being.

Don't try to settle everything beforehand. Pace yourself for a continuing interest in the thing so that it can work itself out.

Don't be vindictive, just because something breaks.

If you're planning a Universe. If you're thinking of creating a Universe.

Do be patient. *Don't* get disgusted right off. Try to keep it going. *Don't* plunge into a series of sketches like artists who tear off the pages.

Don't hide your face too completely, otherwise soon you yourself won't know what goes on.

Be as subtle as you want, but *don't* be mean.

Don't have any "chosen people."

If you follow these simple suggestions you will have a better chance of being content with your Universe.

Don't let it get mathematically complicated. Try to keep it clear what is nature and what is accident.

Don't hurry, putting in a week's work and forgetting it on the shelf. It's a very expensive hobby.

But *do* let yourself go, according to your whim. Remem-

ber that it's your show from the beginning to the end.
Don't have any "chosen people."

If you're planning a Universe. If you're thinking of creating a Universe. Here are some *do's* and *don'ts*. Follow these simple suggestions and you will have a better chance of not being appalled by your Universe.

New York City
June 1947

A CEREMONIAL

※ *"Oui, le culte promis à des Cérémonials, songez quel il peut être!"*

MALLARMÉ

I. VIOLA AND THE ALDERMAN

A breezy May morning (not long after the establishment among us of reasonable institutions), a section of decrepit billboards along the highway was called to the attention of Alderman Manly Morison. He was out walking in the breeze when he came on a small black girl, Viola, letting fly with a rock at the sheet-metal billboard: *Bang!* After this percussion she kept time with her forefinger: "1-1-1,2,3-1-1-1,2,3"; then she screeched at the top of her voice: *"Eeeeee! Iiiii!"* and then again let fly with a rock: *Bang!* while antique flakes of paste and paper showered to the ground.

"Bang!" said Alderman Morison.

"No, *Eeeee!* stupid. Can't you keep a steady beak? 1-1-1-and 2."

She almost burst into tears and ran away, so rudely awakened out of music and dancing. But curiosity prevailed and she asked, "Hey, what all wuh them tin fences for?"

"Those?" Now suddenly it came to the Alderman's memory that they had been billboards for advertising, to make profits by persuading people to buy certain products. As he thought of the advertisements, those curious works of painting and poetry, and of the institution, the Alderman turned pale and lifted his hand to his brow in dizziness. He could not think of those times without becoming confused. "Oh, those," he faltered, "were just used for pasting up paintings and things."

"Paintings!" said Viola contemptuously. It was not her thing.

—One of the billboards had shown a huge sexy pirate naked to the waist carrying off a smirking girl in a gossamer nightgown. Above, in italic type, was the legend: *Nature in the Raw Is Seldom Mild.* Below: LUCKY STRIKES (a brand of cigarettes)—*"It's Toasted!"*

Another billboard had displayed a farmer leaning on a rake with glasses on the tip of his nose and symmetrical patches on his overalls, reading to his pink-cheeked white-haired wife holding in her hands an apple-pie, a letter from their son: *". . . Am doing swell! just bought a Ford V-8."* Below: "CONSULT YOUR LOCAL FORD DEALER."

The third billboard at Christmas season had borne the poster of a mother in a mauve dress with newly marcelled blond hair and just the faintest suggestion of a halo, perhaps only a highlight, gingerly holding a darling baby with face taken from a contemporary infant cinema star, Baby Kelly. Against the deep rose background shone two golden candles. Underneath in tasteful Gothic letters was the legend: "SHEFFIELD FARMS (milk products) wishes you a Merry Xmas and a Happy New Year."

The fourth billboard said peremptorily: BUY REM (a kind of cough syrup).

"What are yuh *cryin'* about?" cried Viola, astonished to see tears rolling down the Alderman's cheeks.

"Look here, black girl," said Manly, "suppose a big sign there said 'Chew Juicy Fruit!' what would you do?"

"Who, me?"

"I mean, supposing the sign jumped up and down and did acrobatic exercises—" said Manly, and he laughed.

"What are yuh *laughin'* about?" said Viola. But she was not unwilling to join in, first uncertainly, then with a high clear peal of laughter. She let fly another rock: *Bang!*

"Do you mind, kid," said Manly, "if we have the fence knocked down this afternoon? it blocks the view along the road."

"Yes, it does," said Viola judiciously. "You asking my advice?"

"Well, you seem to be using it?"

"Oh, only this much. Don't need it all. I don't *really* need none of it."

"We'll have to get together some kind of program," said the Alderman.

"Program! Just to knock down a tin fence—"

These historic sentences, which I have imitated pretty crudely, were spoken on the morning of May 9, 19—.

Manly Morison and Viola clambered through the hedge to see what was behind the billboard. From tatters of paper hanging from the metal Manly could see that one of the advertisements had been the following, founded on an evil sentiment of fear:

A young girl is shown in tears, because no boy could call her, because she had not rented a telephone from the Bell Telephone Corporation.

What should there be in the field behind the antique billboard but the meadow flowers—

> *white-eyelashed daisies and gold buttercups*
> *and devil's-paintbrushes in fire dipt.*

There was a linden sapling we shall refer to again. The wind had swept away the last wisps of cloud, and the sky was a *breathing* blue. So blue, day of lovely glory. The grass and weeds, so early in the year, were almost knee deep. With an exclamation of delight, Viola picked up an antique milk bottle, full of soil.

"What do you want with that, girl?"

"It has a *squeak* note," said the girl, making it tinkle.

"Don't you have any regular instruments to play, girl?" asked the Alderman.

"Oh, yes, I play the viola," said Viola.

II.   ADDRESS BY MEYER LEIBOW

The afternoon's program began about four-thirty. People got these ceremonies together quickly. Almost a hundred chairs were set up in front of the billboards on the now little used highway. The children, for the most part, were playing a ball game in the field a few hundred meters off, but they silently returned whenever anything was of interest.

Three of the billboards were to be pushed down; the fourth, on the right, was to be preserved (really for Viola) and it was draped with a yellow curtain.

Meyer Leibow made an address somewhat as follows:

"Spinoza said there's no use upbraiding the past. Yet I'd like to point out how insulting these old signboards were; and I guess I'll have to induce, therefore, that some of us were very undignified to take so many insults without flinching. Finally, I intend to make a remark about the color yellow.

"These advertising signs operated on an hypothesis of how we'd react. Namely, the advertisers believed that if they merely brought a certain name to our attention, we'd pay out money for something. Stimulus! Response! Can you imagine such a belief?

"Furthermore, some of the signs used to scream *Buy! Buy!* Yet how many of us ever stopped to say: 'I beg your pardon, are you addressing me? Would it not be more polite to say "If you please—" or wait till you are asked, or even, perhaps, wait till we are introduced?' But a citizen would walk along the street and jump out of his skin when something shrieked, 'Hey, you! Do! Don't! Give! Buy! Use! Hurry!'

"Other signs became even more insulting by adopting a familiar attitude: 'Listen, Buddy, let me give you a tip—' or 'Say, don't miss it on your life!' or 'Ain't got time for loose talk, folks, but they got taste and plenty to spare!' The theory here was that if we'd develop a chummy attitude to Campbell's soup, we just couldn't help pay out money.

"The idea was to make people well-disposed and the advertisers had a theory as to what would make people feel well-disposed. One thing that could not fail was to show a picture of a blonde little girl or an apple-cheeked boy with torn pants. As Delmore Schwartz remarked, whenever a baby appeared on a movie screen everybody said '*Ah!*' (something like the end of the skyrocket cheer the young men do). Therefore folks would pay out money. Another way to attract attentive observation, so the fateful name of Hennafoam Shampoo could sink into the soul, was to display secondary sexual activity, such as the exchange of ardent looks. Therefore folks would pay out money. It was the belief of advertisers that the mind worked in this way.

"It was essential in putting the buyer in the right frame of mind to suggest to him the right social status, namely one grade above (as they used to say) what he could ever attain. The theory was that a person would feel that if he bought such and such an article he as good as belonged to the next economic class. Therefore he would pay out money. This was a sad insult.

"Besides, there were catchy rhymes, such as:

> Cooties love
> bewhiskered places,
> but Cuties love
> the smoothest faces—
> USE BURMA SHAVE!

And there were many deep-thought mottoes and slogans, such as: 'Not a Cough in a Carload' or 'Next to myself I like B.V.D.'s best' or 'Eventually—Why not Now?' And it was considered good by these theorists of our common human nature to use elegant diction, such as 'Always Luckies Please.' To give credit where credit is due, it was they who invented a new usage of grammar, the comparative absolute, as to say: 'I *prefer* Tasty Bread,' or 'Kraft Cheese is *Superior*.'

"Aware that we were rational as well as passionate, they made philosophy, too, the handmaiden of commerce. 'Nature in the Raw Is Seldom Mild,' posited one product that had a patent process. 'Nature's Best After All!' countered its rival, displaying the effigy of a miss in riding togs feeding sugar to a thoroughbred horse. Therefore people would pay out money.

"Science and common sense were not exempt. Young Mathew Goodman, I remember, had an absurd collection of advertisements that proclaimed 'Here's proof!' and showed you a cartoon.

"But it was believed that by sufficient repetition, assertions in the teeth of the most ordinary experience would come to be credited."

As Meyer declared that this or that theory of the advertisers was an insult to our common nature, some of the older men and women shifted in their seats, for sometimes they had not been proof against these very advertisements. They therefore listened with attention to the simple speech.

"What a sad case!" exclaimed Meyer, "that science, ordinary sentiment, painting, our dear English tongue—should all have been made to serve so ruthlessly. Everything, to be sure, might sometimes have to serve—to serve life and freedom—but not so ruthlessly.

"We often find, I think, that things serve best by not having to serve.

"What a nervous time it was when every perception along the road was designed to influence some far-off behavior! I am surprised that there were not more automobile accidents. We most often have peace, I think, in enjoying each thing in itself."

He turned to the draped billboard. "Therefore let me call your attention to this color—this color yellow—this yellow—" he said, turning to regard the yellow curtain with attentive sensation. "No, do not consider it too attentively—it is not important enough.

"No, I'd better bring my remarks to a close. When I'm sitting down I can let my mind roam as much as I please. So to conclude: I have of course touched only a single aspect of this ancient evil of advertising. I have not spoken of unproductive effort and the expense of the creative soul; I have not touched on the creation of immoderate desires, the fixing of the habit of publicity, and so on. Yet given all these things, how is it that these advertisements, so insulting, so nervous, were able to survive? The answer, my loves, is that they *did not!*

"Today we are demolishing these boards."

Hereat Meyer again took his seat in the audience.

There was no applause for these remarks, since what was there to rejoice in in such remarks? It was often hard for a speaker to know whether he had gotten across. But it didn't matter.

III

The next number on the program was the purpose of it all, and the boys came drifting in from the field, hoping for more action and less talk. It being nearly five, tea and cakes were passed around.

"Will the gentlemen carpenters please come forward and take charge and explain the proceedings," said Alderman Morison.

Three fellows rose, rolling up their sleeves, and came forward. Two at once disappeared behind the billboards. Their spokesman, a short stout type, wrapped his cigar in a piece of paper and put it in his breastpocket. He said: "Well, we first sawed through the supports in the back, leaving a few props. Then we cut through these posts here in front, down on the bottom here." He indicated where wedges had been cut from the posts, as lumberjacks do with great pine trees. "Now, then, when I push in front, at the same time they'll pull away the props in back with cords—and down she'll go! all except that end one that's being kept." He indicated the one on the right, draped with the lemon-yellow curtain.

When he finished this explanation, the people broke into a volley of applause—until the two in the back reappeared at the edge, grinning.

"O.K., boys—" said Tony Bridges, the spokesman. The children had gone around the back to watch. *"Ready?"* cried Tony.

"Ready!" cried they.

"Here *goes!* One—two—and *three!"* and with a great shove he gave his weight to the billboard.

With a crack that made the audience jump, it went down, sounding a dull *bunnnnng!* as it landed, amid a cloud of dust, disclosing the grassy field and the meadow flowers.

But there in the field, center of all eyes, the two young carpenters standing on ladders were surprisingly holding stretched a maroon curtain. What was behind it? This was the question everyone asked himself. (It was of course the linden sapling.) Some observed with simpler pleasure the maroon curtain and the lemon-yellow curtain. They took one thing at a time.

"Our friend—Gregory Dido—" announced Manly Morison, his voice broken with emotion.

And in fact, when this artist and poet and statesman, and philosopher, came to the front, all stood up for a moment. It was a rare chance to see him.

"I just thought," said the aged man in his beautiful easy tone, "that when something appears from behind a curtain, or when there is a frame round it, we consider it more easily, more in itself, as my friend Meyer was just saying. All right, lads, drop the curtain," he said to the lads on the ladders.

They disclosed the quiet tree with its heart-shaped leaves and a few cream-colored blossoms in the sunlight.

This tree, at first, excited only wonder, almost disappointment; until it became apparent, just by looking at it, that the utmost tiny leaves and petals were organs of the invisible roots. Such as it was, this tree in seclusion had come to its present being, behind a fence. Here it was, this linden tree, when the maroon curtain dropped.

Loudly we applauded. "Bravo! bravo!" cried some. There was thunderous handclapping. Even Dido and Meyer Leibow, who had spent a long time considering the tree in the morning, were moved anew. The children, in the field, did not fully understand the occasion for it, but they added their cheers and joyous jumping. This continued for three or four minutes, during which time the linden tree stood appreciative.

"It's a hit!" said Gregory. "We'll have to try it in the theaters: a tree alone in the middle of the stage."

"It wouldn't work," said Meyer, "taken away from its natural meadow."

"I am not so sure of that!" said Gregory.

We leaned forward, hoping to hear a further exchange of arguments between the two.

But no! The next number on the program was not a dialectical skirmish, but a little poem of gratification composed that day by Harry Walker, fourteen. Dark-haired Harry, dangling a fielder's glove from his wrist, unfolded a soiled sheet of paper which he took from his hip pocket; and although the other boys made a few sotto-voce remarks, he read in a firm and manly voice, as follows, stressing the periods:

"Today in center field although
   I shouted to the others playing ball,
   there was not any sound at all.
The meadow flowers softly grow

in the knee-deep grass. The meadow flowers
   grow softly in the knee-deep grass
   I do not know how many hours pass.
I do not know how many hours

the meadow flowers grow softly in
   the knee-deep grass. There is not any
   sound at all. I do not know how many
hours pass. There is a din

of baseball. Is no sound at all.
   I do not know how many hours pass
   the meadow flowers in the knee-deep grass
   grow softly without any sound at all."

There was no applause also for this effort, except from the children. It was not considered convenient to applaud young boys. Having used up his courage, Harry awkwardly stuffed the paper in his pocket; but as he was going away, Dido drew him near and said in a low voice, "It is true, it is true!—the meadow flowers grow softly in the knee-deep grass"; so that the boy blushed deep red, and when the others wanted to know what Dido had said, he wouldn't tell, he would never tell.

"All the same, it's a sad way to play ball!" said Meyer to Gregory, "he probably can't field."

"No, otherwise he'd be put in right field, not center."

"Hm. Tell me, Joey," Meyer asked one of the kids, "what position does Harry Walker play on his ball team?"

"He holds down the hot-corner for the Bears," said Joey.

Dido grinned.

"Little liar!" said Mike.

The members of the famous string quartet, who had traveled over a hundred miles to come to this ceremonial, were setting up their music stands.

For it was a principle (one of those established by Gregory Dido) generally followed throughout the land, that there was never a public gathering without excellent music. That is why there are so many musicians.

But since the music was this afternoon of so serious a kind—namely one of the later works of Beethoven—the children and several of the adults went to occupy themselves elsewhere for half an hour. Tony Bridges took his cigar from his pocket and lit it, to enjoy the music and his cigar both.

The quartet tuned their instruments, dropping the plucked notes and the searching tones into the deepening silence.

They played several deep, slow chords—major and minor triads—until the spirit of simple harmony spread among the listeners in the late afternoon: for what advantage is it to surprise with complicated music an unprepared soul?

IV.   CAVATINA

And the four began to play the long quartet of Beethoven, opus 130, in B-flat major. While they are playing let us withdraw from representing their real activity (for there is no describing these tones); but just represent the performers, and a few of the auditors, and the power of music.

The second violinist, Dickie M'Nall, was then a youth in the period of form and fire. That is, after study, taking his work to bed and for long walks with himself, and expounding it in discussions, he would arrive at a formal analysis of the whole; and now, in executing his part, he attacked this form, outline and details, with the utmost passion. Self-centered, centering on this imagined ideal, he sat as if alone, constructing the edifice of the second violin.

The violist, Maritimus, was a profound intelligence. He was the synoptic soul of this famous quartet, who, in a sense, played the four instruments. Indeed, it was an experience to see Maritimus look up, with a glance of dark eyes, at M'Nall or Mrs. Troy—and moderate. It was he who gave the broad lines of what M'Nall studied. The youth and Maritimus were sexual friends; it did not make difficulties, but understanding—when they were playing music. Otherwise, M'Nall has told me, so so.

Mrs. Troy, the 'cellist, was the heroine of the civil war, the mother of two now grown daughters and a small son, a strong and simple musician. I do not mention these things at random, for she held her instrument between her knees and bowed it in a firm and matronly way, playing music as if it were drawing breath, and sometimes joking with Maritimus, whom she had first met when he was a sailor. About such a person as this, one can *say* very little.

The first violinist was Herman Schneider. About his playing, in which there is no distinction between the playing of the sounds and the form, one can never say enough. It is like anything in nature growing, the linden tree. A strange illusion grew from this playing, that after a piece was over and the other sounds faded, the line of the first violin seemed to persist in the air, almost visible, like a kind of ghost. Once the other three broke off in the middle to hear him alone, this happened.

So these were the four who were playing: Herman Schneider, first violin, Dickie M'Nall, second violin, Charles Maritimus, viola, and Martha Aaron Troy, 'cellist.

Dido, with head bent haggardly on his chest, was hardly listening. He was thinking, with horror and fatigue, of his blighted life. And, I hate to say it, when the quartet came to the smiling, morosely repetitive Dance *alla tedesca,* tears began to stream down his lined cheeks, no doubt (he thought) for Beethoven.

At the Dance *alla tedesca,* small black Viola, who had been painfully following the score in a book, began to hum so loud that Mrs. Troy told her to shut up and called her up to turn pages instead.

I too was there. But I was not very attentive to Beethoven. Beside my usual task of noticing, which I have learned to live with, I was perplexed by a problem about the performers. It sounded to me, although I *knew* I was in error, that the others were more musical than Herman Schneider. His playing did not have any idea, it did not seem to "add up" to anything.

But if I had listened only and not thought at all, I

would have been wiser; and so it came about when they began the *Cavatina*.

Tony Bridges, with moving finger, hearing, was a true critic, his attention *crowding* into his ears.

After the fourth movement there was a pause, a full half minute. The glance of Maritimus held us all. (I think, now that he is dead, that it was a *kind* glance, one with the feeling of our kind.) When he lowered his eyes, they played the deathless *Cavatina*.

Then any one might, if he came by, have observed the power of music. For the people were as if asleep or dead —relaxed—some with open sightless eyes, as if they had been slain with violence and suddenness. An arm in an awkward position; no grace left to these mere bodies. A passer-by would have been amazed if he were unacquainted with such causes. And even I was able to hear the deathless *Cavatina* without evaluation. The power of the impassible musicians was not resented, though we all had the habit of freedom, which we had suffered for. A very small child came from the field and started with fright, seeing all asleep or dead. At the turn of the melody,

2nd Viol.

some of the dead shed tears. Ludwig Beethoven had been brought in his fifty-second year to such a turn of the melody. Music looses the soul so flow the tears; soon breathing is formal with the song.

V

The last number on the program comprised the re-dedication of the billboard left standing, again in some remarks by Gregory Dido, whom we were inevitably exploiting, since he was a rarity. By this time it was late in the afternoon, the ovoid sun low on the hill, tinging the linen on the lines.

"I don't quite see the point of preserving this relic," said Gregory. "It's a kind of gloating over the past. But they tell me some child here has a use for it, is using it. This one." This got some laughter but, as we know, it happened to be true.

"Our friend Morison asked me to decorate the board," said Dido. "I've done so the simplest way I could think of. Certainly somebody else would do better, but it doesn't much matter—it's a country billboard. But maybe there *is* something in my idea.

"In public vehicles we might post an occasional poem, a mathematical theorem, an account of the reasoning behind a beautiful physical experiment. Anything, I mean to say, embodying a simple worth-while act of thought. Something to think about, to re-think, while you're riding on a bus. If you're in the mood.

"I'm not sure how far I'd stretch this, to billboards and so forth. We can make too much of a production. *What is the right amount?*"

Ah! *that* was the question!— But at this moment the sun set and Gregory remarked, "You see, the day has ended again."

Having said so, he could not bring himself to break the silence of the pure daylight of the beginning of evening; so he merely made a gesture, and a couple of lads climbed up and loosed the yellow curtain overhanging the board. There was disclosed a sentence elegantly printed and a large circle, as follows:

WHEN A LINE MOVES
WITH ONE END
FIXED,THE POSI-
TIONS OF THE
OTHER END DE-
SCRIBE A FORM
INTERESTING TO SEE

This was what was hidden behind the lemon-yellow curtain, just as behind the maroon was a linden tree.

"The word 'describe' is too fancy," thought Miss Campbell, teacher of English.

VI

High over the hill gleamed Venus, afterthought of the Sun. The meeting broke up.

I don't think I've caught the exact spirit of this first May ninth celebration, which began on that day so casually, and has since become the prototype of our "May Ninth." Such was the origin of the maroon and lemon, the linden tree, reading the poems of Dido and Harry Walker, and the hoops. I have failed especially, I know, to imitate the social peace and easy subtility. Trying to be archaic, I get pedantic.

What is the spirit of May Ninth? Different people emphasize different things: some the radical turning away from the centrifugal culture of pre-revolutionary days, others the unexpected conserving of that culture. Some call May Ninth the Holiday of the Arts, and of course it is. Others, more Zenny, say it is "dedicated to each moment enjoyed in itself."

To my mind the chief miracle of that day was the easy mutual acceptance, *while they were alive,* among such exact minds, profound and sad minds, as Dido, Meyer Leibow, Martha Aaron Troy, Maritimus; and harsh critics like myself; and simpler folk happier than any of us. —We generally take our friends at their best only after they're dead.

What is new in May Ninth—it is as old as music and science—is the coupling of fastidiousness and love. When evening fell on the first May Ninth, and the planet Hesperus hung in the sky, there was most of love.

Chicago
1937

THE FACTS OF LIFE

Childish Ronnie Morris has a wife Martha and a daughter Marcia, aged nine.

Ronnie is middle-aged, ten years older than ourselves; and he has invented a wonderful scheme to milk money from those who make $20,000 a year: he sells them Fine Editions with odd associations, as *The Golden Ass* bound in donkey's hide or *The New Testament* signed by the designer in the blood of a lamb. (He is childish enough to go through with such a profitable idea, instead of dismissing it like the rest of us fools.) He has a two-masted sailboat. In a business way, he knows Picasso and Thomas Benton, and is the expert at the Club in the trade-secrets of the Muses. In the acts of love, he is medium; he went to Dartmouth; but he is only moderately fixated on the period when he was fifth oar, for he had had a prior period of lust, which has saved him for philosophy and the arts rather than the brokerage.

Martha Morris is an Andalusian type. When she arranges flowers she keeps them under control with wires. She drives at high speeds. Her relations with Ronnie are ordinary, she is her little daughter's friend, and every Christmas she and Marcia design a gift-volume for Ronnie's clientèle. She is more political than her husband, her position dramatically to the left of the right wing of the liberal center, a tendency that used to have thirty seats in Paris. And they have written ads about Martha's teeth as they flash under her nose.

Now little Marcia goes to the University Progressive School where many of her schoolmates have fathers in the embassies, but Marcia, too, has been to the Near East in search of that lamb. At school they are taught to express themselves freely, and Marcia is good at collages.

Marcia has a fight in school today with one of the little gentlemen, her contemporaries. He breaks her photographic plate. The fight is about the nature of chickens' eggs. She stamps on his foot. Being a girl, she still has an advantage in mental age and more words to say; she says a sentence in French. He can't punch her in the nose because it is ungentlemanly. He is inhibited from drawing on his best knowledge because it is dirty; but worse, it is gloomily indistinct, and even on these matters she seems to have more definite information and is about to mention it.

"Shut up!" he argues, "shut up! you're just an old-time Jew."

This perplexing observation, of which she understands neither head nor tail, brings her to a pause; for up to now, at least with Harry—though certainly not with Terry or Larry—she has maintained a queenly advantage. But he has stopped her by drawing on absolutely new information.

In this crisis, she does a reckless thing: she dismisses his remark from her mind and launches into a tirade that devastatingly combines contempt and the ability to form complete sentences, till Harry goes away in order not to cry. A reckless, a dangerous thing: because what we thus dismiss enters the regions of anxiety, of loss and unfulfilled desire, and there makes strange friends. It is the prologue to fanatic interests and to falling in love. How new and otherwise real it will be on its next appearance!

Marcia calls her mother sometimes Momsy and sometimes Martha.

"What did Harry mean," she asks her, "when he called me an old-time shoe?"

"Jew?"

"Yes, he stated I was just an old-time Joo."

Across the woman's face passes, for ever so many reasons, a perceptible tightening. "Oh oh!" feels Marcia along her ears and scalp. She is confirmed and doubly confirmed in the suspicions she did not know she had. When she now has to express herself with colored chalks, new and curious objects will swim into the foreground alongside the pool, the clock will become a grandfather's clock, and all be painted Prussian blue, even though Miss Coyle is trying to cajole especially the girls into using warm bright colors because that is their natural bent.

"Well, he was right, you are a Jewess," says Martha. "It's nothing to be ashamed of."

"Said Joo, not Juice."

"A Jew is a boy; a Jewess is a girl."

"Oh! there are two kinds!"

It's worse and worse. She never thought that Harry was up on anything, but perhaps even his veiled hints conceal something. She feels, it seems inescapable, that boys have a power, surely not obvious in school—and the grownups even take it for granted! She sees it every day, that these same boys when they become men are superior to the women. Yet men's clothes don't *express* anything, and actresses are better than actors. But just this *contradiction* confirms it all the more, for the explanations of contradictions are in the indistinct region. Connected with what? Marcia is already working on a system of the mysteries. Especially when Momsy now tries to tell her some reasonable anecdote about Jewesses and Jews, just like a previous astringent account of the chickens and the flowers.

Martha never happens to have told little Marcia that they are all Jews.

"Is Ronnie a Joo?"

"Of course."

"Are Louis and Bernie Joos?"

"Louis is a Jew but Bernie is a Gentile."

It's a lie, thinks Marcia; they are both the same. They are both effeminate. Why is Martha lying to her?

"What is ser-cum-si-zhum?" asks Marcia, calling the lie.

This inquisition has become intolerable to Martha. "Good night, Marcia," she explains.

"Is Rosina a Juice?" Marcia cries, asking about Ronnie's mistress.

"Marcia! I said good night!"

"Tell me! tell me! is Rosina Juice?"

"No."

"Ah!"

"Why 'Ah!'?"

"Good night, Momsy," says Marcia, kissing her.

Since the habits are formed speediest when there is necessity and yet conscious and deliberate adjustment is embarrassing or tedious, Martha has speedily and long ago learned the few adjustments belonging to Jews of a certain class of money. The other hotel; not on this list; the right to more chic and modernity, but please no associations with Betsy Ross in tableaux. Of course habits learned by this mechanism are subject to amazing breaches, when submerged desire suddenly asserts itself and the son of Jacob becomes Belmont or Ronnie becomes, as he is, an honorary colonel in the militia. But on the whole, since money is so exchangeable, there are very few special adjustments. They never even came to Marcia's keen perception, especially since none of the Jews whom she is so often with without knowing it, ever mentions them. But there are other meanings, archaically forgotten.

"Since you have to put up with the handicap whether you like it or not," decides Mrs. Ronnie Morris, "why not make an advantage of it, and be proud of it?" She is writing out a check for a subscription to *The Menorah Journal,* the *Harper's* magazine of reformed Jews.

"Never heard such a stupid argument in my life!" says Ronnie. He is very angry, like anyone who has played the game like a gentleman and then finds that the other side goes too far and calls his daughter an old-time Jew. "What's the use of *pretending* you're a Jew, when you're *not* a Jew?" he shouts.

"We are Jews. Don't shout," says Martha.

"I'll go to school and punch that brat's nose."

"Don't."

"Do I pay three hundred dollars a year for him to tell Marcia that she's a Jew?"

"But we are Jews," says Martha, with a new loyalty.

"Since when?" says Ronnie scientifically. "To be a Jew means one of three things: It means first a certain race; but there isn't any Jewish race in anthropology. Look at me, do I look like a Jewish race?"

He looks like a highly brushed and polished moujik.

"No. Secondly: it means a nationality. But even if some Jews think they have a nationality, do I? I went to Jerusalem to pick out a Gentile lamb. Anyway, I can't speak the language. Hebrew isn't the same as Yiddish, you know, even though it looks the same; but I can't speak that either.

"Third: it's a religion. So you see," he concludes, "it's not a matter of not *wanting* to be a Jew or trying to *hide* that you're a Jew, but you *can't* be a Jew if you're *not* a Jew!"

"Don't be a fool," says Martha. "A person's a Jew if his grandparents were Jews; even one's enough sometimes, depending."

"What sense does that make?"

"Do you think it's by accident," says Martha flatly, "that your mama and papa came to marry Jews and we married Jews?"

She means, thinks Ronnie, when all desire is toward Gentiles, toward retroussé noses and moon-face Hungarians. Does she mean Rosina? She means Bernie.

"I'll ask Louis," says Ronnie; for though he holds sway at the luncheon club, all his ideas come from this poet.

"He's taking Marshy to the Picassos tomorrow."

"Let him tell her, then."

"What! are you going to let your daughter find out the facts from a stranger?"

Having slept on it all night, by morning the little girl has contrived the following working theory:

In the beginning, of course, all babies are alike. Her deep-seated conviction on this point has never been in the least shaken by Momsy's anecdotes about the chickens, for it is plain to observe that all babies are alike. But then comes the moment when the thing is cut off the girls. When this takes place, is not yet clear; but it is planned from the beginning, because you can tell by the names;

although sometimes even there is a change of names; with some names you still can't tell; and others are easy to change, like Robert and Roberta or Bernie and Bernice. All of this is an old story.

But now, there are some *chosen* ones, who are supposed to be cut but somehow they get off. Why? They are only *partly* cut—and this is ser-cum-si-zhum, because they use a scissors. These are Joos. For a moment, starting from "Louis," Marcia thinks that she can tell by the names, but then when she thinks of "Ronnie" and of "Terry" and "Larry," two boys in school whom she now knows are Joos (in fact, Terry is and Larry is not), she sees that she can't. The *last* names are connected with marrying and have nothing to do with ser-cum-si-zhum.

Now, she sees in a flash, it is *better* to be a Joo, for then you still have the secret power and the thing, but at the same time you can be cleverer like a girl. This is why Larry and Terry are always able to beat her, they have an unfair advantage; but Harry, the dope, is only a boy and not a Joo.

There are also differences among Joos; for instance, Louis is much smarter than Papa. But this *proves* it, for Louis is more like Martha; that is, they cut the *best* amount off him, but not so much from Papa. Anyway, she hates Louis and loves her poor papa. Suddenly an enormous love for poor Harry suffuses her and she begins to tremble and want to go to school; he has so much secret power.

But more important—still lying in bed, Marcia begins to think about herself—what is a Juice? and besides all these, there are Gen-tiles. (1. [G-] *Scrip*. One not a Jew.) Martha and Marcia are Juice and Bernie is a Gen-tile. Oh! what a mean thing to say about poor Bernie, that he is not even a Juice, but even worse than a girl; he is not even clever. It is nice of Louis to be so kind to him. So it seems that things go in the following order: Boys, Joos, Juices, Girls, Gen-tiles. Except that it is smartest to be a Joo. But what is it? What is it that they did to Marcia to be a Juice? As she lets her fingers move between her thighs, she breaks into a cold sweat. With a violent dismissal, she leaps from bed.

While she is eating breakfast, an awful emptiness for

her boy Harry spreads within her, and she bursts into tears.

Louis, who is intelligent, often cannot resist being cruel and supercilious to Ronnie, so that Ronnie feels like punching him in the nose—but then suddenly, at a poignant touch, even suggested by his own monologue, he relapses into natural melancholia. "To me of course," says he, "your Jewish problem doesn't exist. My paternal parent twelfth removed was Joseph Karo, the author of the *Shulchan Aruch,* or *Table* of the observances; he had established the lineage back to Joseph son of Eli, so that according to the Gentile gospels, we go back to David the son of Jesse and further; but you're a Russian Jew. On my mother's side, I am related to the convert Leo the Hebrew; but that blood throughout is tainted by conversions; my three cousins, Georges de Duchesse, Georges Catala, and Georges Catala-de Duchesse were all converts of Maritain. My cousin Georges Catala-de Duchesse is the Abbot of St. Germain-des-Prés, an *idol*-worshiper, as I told him last summer. It ought to be clear by now, I said, that only Maimonides conceived the relation of God and Man in a way helpful to the Modern Age. This is my faith. If every Jew would read the *Mishnah Torah,* he would become a perfect snob," says Louis Parigi with pride, "he would set tradition against tradition and not take the insults lying down or by appealing merely to good sense! In our poetry both the Parigis and the de Duchesses look for inspiration to the Prophets. My cousin Georges de Duchesse, on the very eve of his baptism, wrote his rime royal *Habakuk;* 'Habakuk,' as Voltaire said, 'était capable de tout!' But in writing my *Anacreontics* I have drawn on the dipsomaniac rhythms of your Chassidim. By the way, my cousin Georges Catala was married to an eighth removed descendant of the Vilna Gaon, her suicide was the cause of his conversion, which goes to show what comes of marrying with the Ashkenazim. (Are you also related to the Vilna Gaon, like all the other Lithuanians?) On the National issue, I am, like Judah ha-Levi, an allegorical Zionist; but the pathetic desire of a temporal habitation—this destroys, as I see it, just our distinction from the *Goyim*"—(he pronounces *Go-yeem* as if he had stepped from a fastness in Aragon where never a foreign Jew had once set foot);—"but God said —but *God* said," says Louis, raising a forefinger, "Make *Succoth*, Booths." At this quotation, suddenly, he sinks into gloom. "But," he finishes airily, "except the purity of our Jewish morals, what defense do I have against adultery and sodomy?"

It is especially this breezy ending that makes Ronnie punch him in the nose—almost. It's hard to put up with somebody else's thing.

In the afternoon, in front of the impassive checkerboard of *The Three Musicians,* the little girl again bursts into tears. Louis, who has with some skill been pointing out to her only such features of the difficult paintings as she is adequate to, an underfed and melancholy face, a marvelous mother bathed in rose, the fact that in 1920 the colors are no longer blended, and enveloping it all in fanciful anecdotes—he looks at her in stupefaction.

"It's not fair! It's not fair!" she sobs.

They are alone in the room.

"What's not fair, dear?" says Louis.

"It's not fair 'cause it's a myst'ry, and I won't *ever* be able to understand it."

"Why you've been understanding it very well, Marcia. What you said about the colors I didn't see myself, because you're a painter and I'm not."

"You're *lying* to me—'cause it's a secret myst'ry, and I won't ever be able to understand it 'cause I'm only a girl, even if I'm a Juice."

? ?

"I understand about the colors and the poor boy, but I can't understand it *all,* 'cause they cut my thing off when I was little and Picass' is a man— An' I have nothing left but to be a nurse or a ballerina."

He takes her hand, for the tears are rolling down her cheeks.

"—I won't ever be able to make 'em with a myst'ry if I live to be a million years old."

She hides her face in her other arm, and she cries with the pent-up anxiety of her third to her ninth years.

The guard hastily goes into the other gallery.

On the walls, the impassive objects stare from side to side.

The tears glisten in Louis's eyes. "This Holy Spirit," he says—he thinks he says—"is given to us and not made by us. It's not my fault if I cannot any more."

"Ah," she says (he thinks), "maybe if it weren't for the Bernies and the Jackies, the prophetic voice of the Lord of Hosts would not prove so disheartened at the third and fourth verse."

"What a despicable argument!" he cries (he thinks), "if I'm finally tired of that boy, why don't I think so right off and not need these thin arguments to bolster up my courage? Stop staring, you," says he to the unblinking middle Musician, "or I'll punch you in the nose."

"Look, Marshy," he says reasonably to the little girl whose hand he is holding tight, "you can't expect to make pictures like this right off! You have to develop your power. Just as when you learn to play the piano, you have to begin with finger exercises."

"Oh!" she cries and pulls her hand away. "How could he tell so quick?" she thinks in terror; "Momsy couldn't tell."

"See, this one is easy to understand," he says, pointing to those Three Musicians. "You see, this is an oboe."

"What's a Obo?"

"An oboe is a kind of wooden instrument with stops. This part is what the oboe looks like from underneath, which you can't ordinarily see. This is a guitar; he broke it into two pieces in order to make the pattern here with this red business.—"

"Can you, Louis?" she seizes his hand, "I mean, can you? Can you develop your power by finger exercises?" ? ?

"Can you? Can you?"

"Certainly. Every day you'll be able to paint a little better."

"Hurrah!"

Two women come in, tittering at a pyramidal creature that is like one of the works of the Six Days.

But the silence is twangling with the music of the gui-

tars, with the guitars of Catalonia, with the cubist harmony by which the acrobats drift away.

On the school field, the fourth-year boys, in maroon
sweatsuits, are playing the in-tra-mur-al ball game,
while Mr. Donlin is umpiring and keeping order. From
time to time some of the little boys have their minds on
the game. When his side is at bat, Harry is sitting on the
lowest bench of the stands and Marcia bounces pebbles
on him from above. Outside the iron fence, Timmy and
Page McCroskey, who go to Holy Name Academy, are
staring at the clean and distinguished boys within. Mr.
Donlin looks a perfect fool, full of manly baby-talk such
as, "Goooood try!" or "C'mon *Terry,* let's see what you
can do!" Sometimes he loses his temper. One of the boys
takes off his clothes and to the amazement of the Irish
boys discloses his delicate limbs in another maroon uniform of shorts and a shirt with a big U. Amid a chorus
of complaints, Mr. Donlin has to assert his authority to
keep the children from exposing themselves to the cold
air.

"Mr. Donlin, Mr. Donlin," mimic the two outside the
bars, "kin I take off my drawers?"

A local merchant-prince, a great contributor to the
University, has the exclusive franchise for the manufac-
ture and sale of these many uniforms. Timmy and Page
and their friends call the U-school the Jew-school. They
are envious of the boundless wealth inside the bars and of
the fact that the girls and boys go to school together.
"Why doncha let the girls play with youse?" shouts little
Timmy. Page, who is a year younger and much bolder,
cries, "Mr. Donlin, kin I take off my drawers and show
the girls my prick?"

On the large field, which is used for the high-school
games, the baseball, thrown by weak arms and tapped by
little bats, makes little hops and arcs. Terry, distracted by
the remark from the fence, drops a little pop-fly and
the runners stream across the plate. Mr. Donlin advances to the fence, shouting without profanity, go away
or he'll punch them in the nose. From a little distance,

they shout in chorus "Jew School, Jew School!" and some of the little scholars, who at other times announce proudly that they go to the University P'rgressive School (as if they went to college), now turn pink. "Play ball!" shouts Mr. Donlin in a manly voice.

Now all the little feelings are afire.

Marcia and Harry, however, have heard nothing. They have now progressed from the first stage of touching-yet-not-touching by throwing things at each other, to the next stage of punching and pulling shoelaces.

To the Irish boys, so systematically kept in order by their father and by the priest and Brothers to whom even their mother defers, there is no way of doubting that non-Catholics enjoy a full sexual freedom. They *know*, in fact, that the Reformation began with fornication; and even more enviable are the Jews, as is proved by the anti-Semitism, otherwise incomprehensible, that forms so large a part of the instruction by the Brothers. And along with this yearning, they observe this wealth and beauty and privilege through the bars. So is consolidated that deep sentiment of inferiority which will tomorrow need fire-arms to soothe.

To the little rich boys, on the other hand, it is obvious that freedom lies outside the bars among those wild boys whose dirty language makes them tremble with terror and stirs unconquerable lust in each one when he is alone; who can stay out late and wear hats decorated with paper clips and beg for pennies from strangers. So even before the first clash, the rich boys feel physically and morally powerless and would like to be the slaves of the poor ones, whom it will require all the machinery of the state to treat with an iron hand.

But why should I make the case any simpler than is necessary? For Timmy also hates little Page, just as he hates the Brothers in school; and among the U-boys there are the families going up and the families falling down, and the case, for instance, of tubby Billy, whose parents are slipping and climbing at the same time, and who will tomorrow be satisfied and avenged by burning for a hustler if his name happens to be Woodrow, until with a sinking heart he one day learns that Woodrow isn't a family name, but a war name, after President Wilson.

Fascinated, Timmy is watching Marcia wrestling with Harry and pulling his hair, while he is trying to concentrate on his teammate at bat: "Make it be a good one! Make it be a good one!" he cries; and then he chases Marcia up the stands. Pressed between the bars till he is white, Timmy follows them with his stare, above him, through the stands. But she jumps down and runs across the field toward the building, and then they both disappear. Poor Timmy stares at the gray door which has just closed.— So in each heart are fixed the types of love, after the girls who seem to be easy, who have the reputation of being available, who are easy and available in idea though never in fact. The Jewish girls to the Irish boys like Timmy, and the Irish girls to the Jewish boys like Ronnie, and the sailors to Louis. But for the most part, it is just one's own kind that is really available (and really desirable, and deeply forbidden!), and that we live with in the end, as Ronnie with Martha, and Louis with Bernie; these are no doubt also types of love, but too repressed to give us any pleasure.

"Knock knock!" cries Page McCroskey.

"Play ball!" shouts Mr. Donlin.

"Knock knock, Mr. Donlin, knock knock!" he screams.

"Don't pay any attention, play ball," says Mr. Donlin.

"Who's there?" answers Larry.

"Cohen!"

"Don't pay any attention!" cries Mr. Donlin.

"Cohen who?" answers a voice.

"Who said it?" shouts Mr. Donlin.

"Cohen fuck yourself!" cry Page and Timmy together. One of the boys throws a stone at them.

"You cocksuckers!" says Timmy, casting his eyes about for some resource.

"Shut up, McCroskey," says Terry, "or I'll tell somethin' on you, but I don't want to make you shamed."

"Do you believe that pile o' shit that O'Hara said?" says Timmy wildly.

"Naw, I *saw* it!" says Terry.

"What did O'Hara say?" says Page.

A foul ball jumps out over the fence.

"H'yaann! H'yaann!" sing Page and Timmy and run down the block with the ball, grasping off their hats.

"Where's Harry Riesling? He's supposed to be coaching on first," says the beaten Mr. Donlin.

But Marcia and Harry are in one of the empty rooms where they have never been before (it is part of the high school), and she is telling him all about Picass'. He explains to her that he likes Terry and Larry swell, but he hates his big brother; but he promises just not to notice him any more. "He probably hates your papa as much as you hate *him*," Marcia observes judiciously, "so that's something you know on *him*." This insight, this knowledge, casts such an angel light on Harry's usually puzzled countenance that Marcia turns and stares at him. He explains to her that he likes geography and history, but Miss Jensen doesn't make it interesting the way Mr. Bee used to, and that's why he's not smart. When Marcia tells him that she was in Egypt and the Near-East (as opposed to the Far-East), he is struck with admiration. But different now is his admiration and his pleasure and pride in her ability to form complete sentences, as if she were a teacher whom he can kiss and lick and not even have to stand up and recite, from the animosity he felt yesterday when she was so goddamned smart. She draws on the blackboard the dolphins playing on the *Ile de France*'s prow.

"There are geniuses in every race," says Ronnie passionately, with all the energy of his desire for Rosina; "but both per capita and absolutely there are more of them among the Jews."

"I thought you said there was no Jewish race?"

"There's not, but facts are facts, and you can't get around it. Einstein, Ehrlich, Freud."

"Yes, the Jews are always going in for syphilis or psychoanalysis or the fourth dimension," says Martha.

"Picasso—"

"Ha, the same thing!"

"Proust—"

"There you have it!" says Martha triumphantly. "I'm not saying the Jews are not geniuses, but they're *queer*, they're just queer, that's all."

"What about Dali? He's not a Jew."

"Will you please tell me what you're trying to prove by that? I thought you were trying to prove that all the Jews, including yourself, were geniuses."

"No, but you said that Proust and Picasso were Jews."

"*I* said it? *I* said it?"

"I didn't say you said it especially; they *are* Jews, *half-Jews.*"

"Oh, don't be a fool."

Ronnie says nothing.

"And let me tell you another thing," says Martha, "you Jews are not doing yourselves any favor by putting yourselves forward so much. If Felix Frankfurter is so smart as he's supposed to be, he knows that especially just now there's no place for another Jew on the Supreme Court bench. Every Jew that gets on the Supreme Court makes it just so much harder for us and Marcia. Where do you think I'm going to be able to send her to college?"

"That's a fine way of looking at it!" cries Ronnie. "It's true enough," he thinks; but Martha has always been ahead of him on national and international affairs.

"You're a Jew, so all right!" says Mrs. Ronnie Morris née de Havilland. "It's nothing to be ashamed of. But why bring it up in public? Who asks you?"

"Who?" says Ronnie, bewildered.

"But trust a Jew to put himself forward as if he were something peculiar! If it weren't for the Jews there wouldn't be any anti-Semitism."

"Who?" asks Ronnie.

New York City
1940

LITTLE BERT, INTERVENING

I.

His sister Lucy clambered over the stone fence to get the buttercups with longer stems, although nailed on the apple-tree was the sign "Beware Bull." Her dress was colored faded nearly white and she had formal curls that hung on her shoulders. From out his hiding place, the bull sauntered in their direction, indecisive, like the drunken man on Ninth Avenue. The small boy opened his mouth past his ears and screamed Help! it is still ringing high A-flat. But this outcry only made Lucy freeze and look in all directions. But their companion the farmboy Dan, who wore overalls, jumped over the stones, took her by the hand, and led her back across, while a flush of admiration and gratitude colored Little Bert's cheeks and a pang of envy smote him between the eyes.

There was a well on the farm with a hood and a windlass, and sitting nearby Lucy was braiding the daisies and long-stemmed buttercups into a garland. She wove some daisies into a starry circlet and placed it on Bert's hair where it tickled. With big eyes Dan was watching the city-girl who did city-things and his thighs were trembling to his embarrassment. Soon the grown-up boy and girl walked behind the house and did not reappear.

Little Bert became fearful and suspicious. His anxiety grew. Sauntering near, as if indecisively but he was in the grip of decision, he wandered around the L of the white house, and the two were kissing in the angle of the L. Without a word he slipped his arms between them, around her waist. In this way he intervened, effected a rescue, shared. He shared in the secret. He did not notice, and did notice, if the big boy had a hard-on. With violent spite Dan twisted Bert's left arm behind his back. The tears and sweat started into Bert's face but he would not cry out. But Lucy said in anger and alarm, and with the compassion for all hurt things that was forever hers, "Don't! you're hurting him." Dan was confused, abashed. "No, he didn't hurt me," said Little Bert.

Trembling in every joint, and his fingers clumsily fumbling, Dan turned aside to pee. His trembling and confusion communicated themselves to Bert and he watched him with open mouth, and also with blinding envy that fails to notice facts.

II.

Now Auntie Dora, the guardian of the children in their visit at the farm, was at the piano composing *The Lucille Waltz*. She had no children of her own, though she had married several times, but she was considered excellent with children because she was loving and firm. Indeed, she was sentimental and cruel, perversely lascivious and vindictively guilty.

The piano was equipped with a special pedal that allowed the upper register to twang like a guitar.

Having completed the pretty *Lucille Waltz,* Auntie Dora was now furiously shouting at real Lucy and beating her about the head and shoulders, while Bert was cowering behind the wicker-chair—confused, in pain, excited. "Some one is beaten, not I—" But he already could not remember whether Auntie Dora was beating her because of the kissing or because of the wild charging of the bull. *Who* had told? *What* had he told?

Back in the city, Little Bert had driven Papa away in vain, because Mama was now seeing Mr. Gericke and that was why they were exiled to this farm.

"Don't! you're hurting her!" cried the little boy manfully intervening. "Don't hit her any more." It was frightful, the crazy woman had picked up an iron poker. Bert thought, "She can't *mean* to hit her with that—that might *really* hurt her." He went between, intervening, shielding his head under his left forearm. He said, "You're bad, Auntie Dora. You made *The Lucille Waltz,* but you hit Lucy."

But Papa's sister in fact brought down the poker on his arm, only once, but it really hurt. There was an unfillable void in his wail. He was not going to be able to stop. He implored, "Don't hit me any more. You meant it."

III.

His gritty eyes veiled with their dust flirtatious smiles and the flowers of the field. This dust lies there opaque between his sight and the objects of sight, intervening, rescuing him from the vividness of the meant. He began to be nearsighted.

Little Bert's forearm was breaking with fatigue as he masturbated, calling up the day's images unmeant and therefore unexciting. They threatened him about his naughtiness, but he strongly willed not to take them seriously.

He woke up wailing at midnight in order to make it impossible for other people to sleep.

At daybreak when he awoke, they were shouting in the next room about money and how the crying child made it impossible for other people to sleep. Little Bert narrowed to a pointed grin his wide quadrilateral mouth of pain. He stretched his happy grin taut from ear to ear, he was making plenty of trouble.

Auntie Dora came in and at once began to open the drawers and pack the clothes in the valises. Lucy moved about slowly as if unwilling, and Bert knew why. *He* was not unwilling to return home suddenly and surprise Mama. He was disgusted by the milk warm from the cow.

IV.

But oh!—O Garden of cornflowers and daisies, and where the piano twangles like a guitar—they were *really* going away. The horse was harnessed to the trap. Looking, looking, the sobbing child was stretching out his arms in longing. Auntie Dora sat stiff; their hostess was thin-lipped; the farmboy helped with the valises with the dumb willingness of the baffled. The horse had a patient fat behind that slowly swung as they started off. Bert and Lucy both silently stretched their necks to look back; they avoided touching each other on the seat.

Little Bert was going back to the city, to intervene with a new purposiveness.

As a man unwillingly—but why then does he do it?—boards the train again and again taking him from a station that promises a little comfort.

(There is a small but real happiness in going among fieldflowers.)

His hands are stretched out—will his fists ever come pounding down?

Why do you tell your hopes or your troubles to me? I cannot take them seriously, as if they were meant.

Dutifully, I have brought together lovers, and saved the marriages of wives and husbands, intervening like a physician watching the fever-chart, watching the way of it like the figures on a fever-chart.

BATHERS AT WESTOVER POND

※ In respectful memory of Hawthorne

I.

There were two men in the moonlight, arguing in low tones. The jealous husband was lying in wait. His elderly friend was trying to get him to go into the house.

Suddenly, both fists, the angry man pounded on the barn door. Inside, animals stirred. "I can't help it," he said choking, "it has me by the throat."

"Maybe you have *it* by the throat," suggested his friend, the doctor.

"O have a heart, Manny! don't give me moral lectures when I'm in trouble."

Carefully watching and biding his time, the way you handle the wilful drunk, the jealous, the doctor said nothing. Through the trees shone the moon, on the buildings, the mailboxes, the road around the bend. "Well, Mark Armisted?" the doctor said finally.

"Don't *call* my name!" the farmer gasped. "*How* can I appear? Yes, I have *it* by the throat. I spend *hours,* do you hear me? thinking up *schemes,* to *prevent* her from being happy. I!" As if it could not happen to him. "But when I eat it, it sticks." He began to cough. "She was supposed to be back by ten." It was ten fifteen. "Maybe there isn't even anything between them. She never *told* me." He had never asked her. He was again assailed with remorse. He coughed. The image that always came to him was Desdemona; he had seen the opera. "I understand," he said, "we can no longer live according to the usual ideas—there are no usual ideas. . . ."

"It's you who have ideas. Why don't you simply face it? you are suffering and you *don't* understand it, that makes it all the worse."

"All the worse!" echoed the farmer and the tears finally welled into his eyes. What he wanted was, after all, sympathy; not out of self-pity but to assure him that he was not isolated in his evil frame of mind. The scene blurred for him.

"I'm sorry you're in trouble, Mark," said his friend, seizing the advantage. Perhaps now was the moment to get him to go in. "Come, let's go in," he said gently, firmly.

But just at this moment they heard them coming up the road. It was twenty past ten. Giddy laughing, leisurely approaching. It was the leisureliness that was the coup.

They had been singing, *On the Town, Fancy Free,* and by now they were mockingly down to the bare rimes, "Spree," "you and me," and "wheeeee." Whee-he-he-heeeeee. Wendy sprinkled the tones through the night with her beautiful coloratura, and Mark hated his wife bitterly because she sang beautifully.

They appeared around the turn. To his surprise—both relief and disappointment—they were three, not two. He had been lying in wait for two. But with Wendy and Perry there was another sailor. Mark sprang at them from the shadows, his face ugly in the moonlight, and her giddy high-E became a cry of fright. He seized her by the shoulders and threw her to the side. "Get into the house," he said hoarsely. He had no voice. His rage was no longer spontaneous.

She stayed there a long moment by the road, waiting—it seemed—for Perry to protect her. Instead, the sailor drew back a step, and rapidly she crossed the field and disappeared in the house. The door slammed.

Mournfully Mark turned on Perry. (By now they both looked pathetic figures.) He took the two slow steps across the road and deliberately struck him, aiming the blow, but not in fury to destroy him but as a man deliberately picks a fight; he slapped him hard across the face. "Hey there, what goes on there?" said the buddy, and closed in and threw a punch that Mark blocked. But the doctor intervened with the authority that stops a thing short. He brushed Armisted away with his shoulder and

said curtly, "Go in," and he said to the other sailor, "Keep
out of it." Armisted lost his animus, his chest fell in depression, he looked hopelessly at his hands, the tears
started again into his eyes, and he reeled slowly across the
field and disappeared in the house. The door closed more
dully. Perry did nothing at all and the mark shone on his
face in the moonlight.

"Why did you let him get away with *that?*" demanded his
friend indignantly.

"I have no rights," said Perry surprisingly.

"But you said you were in love with her."

"Yes. Yes, but I don't mean to come across. You
know what I mean, God damn you. God damn that cold
fairy!" His anger flowed back in him and the color spread
all over his face. "I should've knocked his teeth down his
throat." Perry lived in the conviction that Wendy's husband was sexless and that that was why she came out.
Vaguely, somewhere, he knew that this was not the case.

He said, "Let's go," and walked brusquely away. His
buddy caught up. They went back down the road and
disappeared around the turn.

A few moments later, to the doctor's astonishment, they
were again singing, their voices fading in the distance.
He shrugged.

The door of the house opened its bright rectangle and
Armisted came out with a pail and crossed over to the
chicken house.

II.   DR. GROVES' POEM

As he walked back through the old locust-planted town,
the doctor saw that the tree trunks were rough and mas-
sive, their foliage black and delicate against the sky, the
houses wan in the moonlight: so he projected his own
personality. His thoughts had turned away from the disturbing scene he had witnessed, but he was disturbed by
the ring of his own heels on the pavement, as if a man
had no right to exist and go.

A couple passed him by, the man talking earnestly in a
low voice, the woman weeping. They passed, and the doctor halted and looked back after them. Then, as he

walked the few streets more to his home with its shingle,
Dr. Groves made the poem:

When the couple passed me on the walk
   and the woman was crying out her eyes,
the man continued in earnest talk.
   His tone was measured, his manner wise,

there was no doubt that he was right,
   but something was wrong, something was wrong,
as they drifted past me in the night,
   as I hurried along, hurried along.

III.

Wendy was blank, having sung the little child asleep.

She had been singing the *Coventry Carol* and the *Rag-
gle-Taggle Gypsies,* such songs as express good-bye and
separation. It was not that she was thinking of these
things—she was not thinking of anything—but they were
the songs that came to her to sing. Often she felt blank
and did not know what she was feeling, but her behavior
revealed it to others. Armisted was sensitive precisely to
these signs, more than was useful, for he addressed himself not to what she *was* feeling, *where* she was, but to
what she might be feeling if she felt it. She did not understand that what she did not feel nevertheless had an
effect on other people. And he, by knowing what she was
feeling when she did not, uncannily threatened her; she
was afraid of him, afraid of her unknown self. She was
afraid.

Hearing the songs she chose—but the child fell sweetly
asleep—he was clenched with alarm that she was going
to go away. What he did not notice and make much of
was the overt fact: his young wife was singing to their
child falling happily asleep.

"What are you thinking of?" he said; but he *knew* what
she was thinking of, that was just the trouble. (Often he
did, sometimes he didn't.)

"Nothing," she said. "I am not thinking of anything."

"Yes, you are thinking of something—" he said. She
was thinking of leaving.

"No, I'm not." She was not lying; she was not thinking of anything. She looked up at him with eyes brimful of reproach and fear. Demanded of, she agonizingly felt her mind, and it was blank. "Don't wake up the baby."

"Yes, don't wake up the baby," he said. This was real and they went into the other room.

"You sit there looking defeated," he said. "Why should you feel defeated?"

"Defeated? How am I defeated?" There had never been a battle.

"What's the matter now?" he cried. "Why are you looking at me reproachfully?"

"Nothing's the matter, dear. I don't feel reproach. Really I don't." She could hardly be heard.

"That's just it!" he almost shouted. "You won't give me the satisfaction. You spite me by talking in a low voice. You won't give me *anything*—neither demand nor reproach. I *know* that your mind is blank, you aren't thinking of anything. But *why* aren't you?—" He wanted to say, in his jealous fit, that she was thinking of Perry, and to have her say, yes, she was thinking of Perry, in order that he could cling to this and torture himself with it. But it was too humiliating for him to begin. "I don't believe you," he said.

She hung her head as if she had been struck a dull blow on the nape of the neck, and her eyes became wet. "Why do you bother with me if I am so worthless?" she asked. "If I don't give you anything at all and if you think that I am a liar. That's what I don't understand, why you keep at me if I make you so unhappy. Why you don't tell me to leave."

"Ah! that's what you want!" he cried, beside himself. "*I* am to take the responsibility. So you can go to Perry. But I won't give *you* the satisfaction!"

"That's a lie!" she cried, with flashing eyes. He had found the key to make her angry: she was "unjustly accused."

"You sit there thinking of Perry to rescue you," he tormented her, "defeated by me and thinking of him. Why don't you admit it?"

"No, I was not." She looked at him with disdain. But he did not feel humiliated; rather, pleased because she looked so bright and real when she was flushed and angry. He smiled.

"What are you laughing at?" she asked, stung.

"I was thinking of your question: why do I bother you, what do I see in you? I know the answer. Because you are brave. It's your bravery I love and it's your bravery I can't bear."

She was bewildered. "How am I brave?" She was beguiled because she knew that it was a great compliment but she did not understand him. She looked up, as she often did, like a small pupil in a classroom.

"You are brave because you won't give in. You are unhappy, unhappy here with me, but you stick out your jaw and clamp your teeth like grim death, you go blank and don't know what you're feeling at all—you will do anything and go to any lengths, but you won't be compelled. What's wrong with that?"

He said it with pleasure and with his better self that was not jealous. But she took it badly, to mean that he was giving her her freedom. What would she do with freedom? She became panicky. She felt he did not want her any more and this wounded her vanity.

Controlling her panic, and to control her panic, she said in a flat voice, "Yes, I am going to go away and leave here. Yes I am, I am, yes I am. You always put me in the wrong. Every day is the same." Everything she said was music, and this too turned into a grievous chant, "Yes I am, yes I am. You trap me, I don't trust you."

"No, you're not!" he said, and stood barring the door with his arms, as if he could stand there forever and keep her a prisoner. He was clenched, as when he first heard her singing the songs, but worse. Now she had said it. But his heart was bounding and hammering. For both of them the child in the other room did not seem to exist, although one could, if he listened, hear her breathing.

IV.

The courage, the kind of courage, that Mark ascribed to Wendy did perhaps belong to her; but certainly it was an image of his own character. He willed, and would not

resign. He willed to live satisfactorily, to make his life succeed as a whole, even though the conditions of our lives
do not seem to permit an organic success. He risked
chaos, he did not stop making his demand. His troubles
with his wife were of a piece with the rest of his existence;
he saw this and tried to generalize about himself; and he
became confused by principles, which are nothing but
thwarted deeds. He thought, and often spoke, like a so-
cial-psychologist; he suffered torment like a possessive
peasant; he was sexually open like a child; he aspired to
justification like his Calvinist ancestors. Each of these was
unlikely; together they were impossible. He clung to farming as a way of life, although in our society it was not a
way of life because there was no wilderness; it gave plenty
of small anxieties but no big challenge and no big satisfaction. He was successful at farming and that made
it all the worse. He knew too much to live the way he
did. He implacably willed his marriage to be reasonable
and worthwhile, but it wasn't. He was ashamed.

His shame was not that he was miserable, for this he
could have borne philosophically. But he was tormented
by an idea in which he unfortunately believed, namely
that unless a man is happy he cannot realize his powers,
and that therefore Mark Armisted was going to die
wasted. This abstract thought awakened in him an awful guilt, and he redoubled his strenuous efforts to be simply at ease.

He had the manliness of the old time, by which a man
suffers sleepless nights and headaches because of a contradiction between two propositions. And this behavior was
not obsessional with him, because if he sometimes happened to find his way out, or life provided it, he smiled
sweetly and slept.

Wendy watched him wrestling this way, when he did
not know that she was looking. He used to pace up and
down, up and down, and drum loudly on the tabletop with
his fingers. Then he would suddenly go out of the house.
At these times she loved him and felt for him. But by
timidity she neglected to make the simple advances to
him that would materially have alleviated his dilemma, by
introducing a new piece of evidence, a proof that "my
only world does not disregard me." Because his wife did not

help him in this simple way, *she* was his dilemma and he glowered at her with hatred. Feeling this hatred she shrank and could not make simple physical advances. When he saw this, he went out of the house.

He was right to be afraid that she was going to leave him, for harshness can, in the end, drive anybody away. But he was mistaken to fear that she would choose another man against him.

V.

When she came to the interview with Perry, Wendy was carrying a tooled leather purse that Mark had made for her.

The sailor did not notice it. He felt just fine; he had already, waiting for her, had three drinks. He was glad to see her, he did not notice that she was on edge. She became annoyed at his roseate cheer and pointedly she called his attention to the bag, for he had, a month ago, enthusiastically offered to make her one, among a number of other warm promises. "Mark," she said, "made it."

At that time she had carelessly let slip Perry's promise to make her such a bag, not realizing how hungrily Mark listened to every word. And the very next day, more mischievously than maliciously, Mark gave her the leather bag, "Here is the bag you wanted." He was proud of it because it was beautiful and as if commissioned. She was moved. "You see," said Mark, "if you only ask me for a thing. How else can I know what you want?" In this way he put her in the wrong and she went blank. "I didn't ask you," she said, and poisoned his pleasure.

With Perry, however, she was able spitefully to attack, and so she felt free and emptily happy. "You talked a lot," she said, "and didn't make the tooled leather bag. Mark said nothing and made it."

"I meant to do it when I said it," said the sailor cheerfully. He was immune to this kind of spite. He had a wonderful confidence that he had what all women desired— if they didn't, so much the worse for them!—and this harmless vanity made him so generous and outgoing that it was hard not to love him, unless you had to rely on him. He had the beautiful vanity that aims to please, and he did please. But the woman across from him was in despair, and he was slow to perceive it.

He picked up the bag and examined the workmanship with unfeigned admiration. "That's fine work. That's really fine. It's better than I could have made you."

"Thank you," she said drily.

"No, seriously. Look at the ends—" He turned the leather inside out to show her.

She was stifled. Here it was again. The two men were conspiring and she was worthless and had nothing to say. She did not know whether or not it was good workmanship. (*This* was why she could not make Mark feel that she appreciated the gift.) At the same moment she felt a powerful pang of lust and stealthily caressed the serge of the sailor's blouse with her fingertips. "Mark does everything well that he turns his hand to," she said stiffly, to conceal her emotion. "It's too bad that you—and he—that you can't talk to him like a younger brother. Maybe *he* could help you to find out what you want to do with yourself." To give herself a presence, she assumed the role of go-between.

The sailor drained his drink, leaned back, and ordered another. He said, "Mark seems to have all kinds of talents—except what a woman needs."

"What do you mean by that?" Wendy became rigid and went white. It was the first time that Perry had made a direct remark, or any remark, about her husband. Immediately she felt dirty and disloyal. She was in a frantic mood and her feelings, suffocation, lust, chill, degradation, succeeded one another pell-mell, and all were climactic.

He laughed, his laugh a little ugly.

With the precise clarity of an insane moment she saw him; that he considered her husband as a defeated rival, and that it was this that gave him his charm and address, which he would not dare against a looming father, sexually powerful. He assumed, he quickly assumed, he always assumed, that he was the victor—but there was never going to be any battle. She looked at him: he was a child. She looked at his childish uniform and felt sorry for him. In a flash she made sense of what had truly puzzled her, their submissiveness to their stupid officers. "I understand you only too well," she said with brutal contempt; "but if you imagine that Mark is not a healthy animal, you are very much mistaken. He doesn't satisfy me because I won't let myself be satisfied; but he satisfies himself, be sure of that. I'd be afraid to deny him. Also—I wouldn't want to." She was flushing deep red, the pulse pounding her temples. She had never before spoken this way to any one, nor used such words.

Perry was stung. "What in hell is it your business what I imagine!" he snapped. "*You* seem to imagine that it's all up to *you,* whether you will or whether you won't. What conceit you women have!" He hated women. He had sat up and suddenly he looked at her with horror, rallying to the defense of the other man's insulted manliness as well as his own. He was outraged by what she had said.

Everybody was against her. Her eyes began to roll wildly.

The young man's native courtesy made him hold back. And now that he noticed her, he began to be alarmed. With a wrench he rose above his hurt feelings and his indignation. "Look, Wendy—" he said; almost he said, "Look, mother—" For he held her in awe, she was the only sensible and mature woman he had ever intimately known and he did love her. She was in trouble. He took her hand. It was lifeless. "Do you know why I love you?"

"No, why?" she said listlessly. She didn't care.

"I love you because sometimes I was able to make you laugh, and you didn't seem ever to laugh and sing." Her face was frozen and her fingers twitching between his hands. "Darling," he pursued gently, "now why don't you and Mark—you and Mark—why don't you and Mark try—"

"That's enough!" she cut him short and stood up. "Put up or shut up. Will you or won't you go with me to Boston?"

Bewildered, he shook his head slowly from side to side, at a loss what to say, but of course saying it well enough by his dumb gesture.

She burst out laughing in her gay and thrilling artist's voice that both gathered force and became lighter as it soared, coloratura, with rolls and trills and scattering a random shower, but true at last to the leading tone and the tonic, and she said, "I shall have at last a place of my own, and come and go as I please. And take the opportunities I choose! To whom am I beholden? and what if I won't? No! no! not at all. But I shall go to Boston, where there is no difference between night and day."

And she flashed him a childlike smile and picked up her bag and left.

VI.   WESTOVER POND

There was a large pond where the country-folk went to bathe. The water was clear, the bottom was sandy, and the minnows came up to your white toes. There were black holes where the bass hid. A mighty willow leaned over the surface and was mirrored in the surface. The afternoon was still. Stiff-legged skippers walked on the tense water. In the silence, a trout leaped and fell like a bell.

In one angle stood the tiger lilies in August. That part was muddy and pond lilies snaked up from the bottom and lay on the surface. A frog dove from a lily pad, like a sob.

It was a large ordinary pond lovely beyond anything. The facing shore was a stony pasture, down to the water; your eyes followed it up to the blue sky, and to a tremendous towering cloud, whose reflection you could see silent in the water, so most of the water looked white. All these ordinary things were so strange. How do we people manage to live on among them?

Wendy came finally wandering by here, carrying her shoes, but the hem of her skirt was soaking wet. With her came clamor, because she was singing, imitating bird calls and the birds answering her sounded off, rousing one another, until the din was terrible and deafening like morning, that tramples on our awaking and rushes by. Pretty soon she went past, walking barefoot on the path, around the bay where the sedge was, out of earshot, and the birds shut up.

VII. BATHERS

About six o'clock the dirty farmers and tired women and three adolescents came down to wash and swim. They were raucous in a more vulgar and bearable way, calling out *our* calls. Without a pause as they came, the two boys kicked off their brogans and dropped their jeans and plunged headlong with a splash, hitting out for the center, two shining furrows shouting, "Ouch!" "Cold!" "It's fine!" The frogs dove down to the bottom. The girl made no effort to undress or go in; she was menstruating. She sat down on a rock and lit a cigarette.

The farmers and women disrobed and bathed more solemnly. An elderly man went into the water up to his knees, in the reddening sun. The sun had suddenly dropped another foot toward the horizon and there was a chill.

The boys climbed out, shaking themselves like dogs on everybody. An angry man said, "For Chrissake!" The boys dove back in. "Don't think I'll go in after all," said a matron complacently, half undressed. "Really?" said her friend, "how can you do that way? If I once come down I feel I just have a moral duty to go in and get wet. Brrr. Zip in, zip out." "That kind of consideration doesn't bother me a-tall!" said the other. "It's a remarkable way to live! it's a remarkable way to live!" said her friend in sincere admiration. The men were uncorking a gallon of wine grown by Italians in California; there was no local wine. Every little while a man or woman walked to the edge and dove or slipped in. The women tended to stand and soap themselves and then swim. Two of the men were strong swimmers and stroked away toward the far shore. The elderly man, without getting wet much beyond his knees, emerged and lit his pipe. He was Dr. Groves. Another man climbed out shivering and set to work making a fire (he was the angry man).

The sun tinged rosy the linen lying in untidy heaps. The orange adolescent boys, but none of the others, seemed to be bashful of their nakedness and tied rosy towels around their waists. Pouting in a mirror, the girl put on lipstick. From the long branch of the willow where I had climbed, overhanging the water, I watched with envy the rapid swimmers at the far shore, wishing that I were as strong and daring as they. In the opening of the clouds in the west was a moloch hearth of embers. Our fire began to crackle.

The gallon jug was going around, and most of the folks had put on clean clothes that they had brought.

"We should've brought supper, we could have it right here."

"Next time."

"No I couldn't, because of the kids."

All at once Mark Armisted was in the midst of them, carrying his little girl and bawling in a hoarse voice, "I separated the mother from the child." Because of his loud voice the child began to cry. From where I watched in the tree, he looked again like a man of the old days making open confession on the street corner. They crowded around him.

The complacent woman tried to take the crying baby from him. Mark clutched onto the baby, and must have hurt her, for she screamed. He seemed to believe that Wendy had run away to Boston.

Yet the scene was peaceful, as if becalmed. It was the few minutes of the onset of evening when the sun, touching the horizon, has ceased to cast long shadows. The space is like a painter's north light, but red and shining. It is homogeneous, breathing, quiet. The frantic man; his excited, sympathetic, and alarmed audience; and even the scream of the child did not importantly disturb the peaceful ending of the day. The birds sang in small bursts as they do at that time.

"She ran away," one fellow said to his friend, "with that sailor who come up from New London. He's in the submarines."

"Maybe she did. But he always seemed a decent sort to me."

From near the sedge came a sickening cry, from the throats of the adolescents who had gone off there to stone frogs. The strong swimmers, on their way back, cut sharply in that direction. Immediately—the time it took me to get out of the tree—the two men and the two boys broke through the brush carrying toward us the clothed

and drowned body of Wendy. They laid her down by the
fire at the feet of the doctor, and one of the men, snatching up his trousers on the run and awkwardly cramming
his feet into his shoes, went through the woods to get his
car. Mark Armisted stepped back from our circle with
the pained look of a man who has made an important
wrong inference and, as if a forfeit, he gave over to the
woman the baby who had suddenly fallen asleep.

Groves had rolled the body over onto a woolen shirt.
He used me to work her ribs and one of the kids to raise
her elbows. He (his metabolism) was a little too fast on
the count, and I kept slowing the pace. There was no
doubt he meant to pull her through. "Not so bad," he said,
"she jumped in not more than fifteen minutes ago."
"What? after we got here?" "*Because* we were here," he
said, "—and *two*—and—one—and—two."

I had plenty of time to observe our doctor as I mechanically swung. His face was defiant, as if to say, "This one
isn't going to die either." Mark hung over us, with an expression of simple concern. Pretty soon there was a fluttering and she began to breathe and take over on her
own.

"Oh good!" said Mrs. Erlanger. Groves stopped us.

The people cheered, or did not so much cheer as finally
expel their held breaths in a loud noise. But the menstruating girl burst into hysterical sobbing. Groves sat Wendy
up, and she looked about with wondering eyes, then closed
them wearily. "Whiskey," said the doctor. It was to hand.
"Will you shut that girl up!" he snapped ferociously toward the hysterical adolescent. The fire was roaring hot.
Mark said not a word, but smiled a very pure and un-
mixed smile, almost a grin.

Wendy downed a mouthful and coughed. She seemed
tired and she lay down again flat on her back and looked
up at the sky.

Then—to our universal astonishment—lying flat on her
back, she broke into song and sang the spacious *Clouds*
of Ned Rorem, which the composer has marked "in a
pale half-voice; infinitely slow, pale," and so she sang it:

> So effortlessly are we not given
> to move on earth as these in heaven

> clouds, nor without desire
> to tend whither the airs conspire.

> The clouds exaggerate and pile
> into heights of mile on mile.
> In the breathing of the universe
> they drift asunder and disperse.

There was the roar of the car and the fellow came back out of the woods.

"No! she's alive!"

"She's alive. Groves pulled her out."

"No! no! she's alive!"

This curious motto, "No!—she's alive!" seemed to take everybody's rescue-drunken fancy and people kept shouting it rowdily, as a way of exploding their suppressed excitement and perhaps to deafen the unearthly echo of the song.

"No! No! No!"

"She's alive all right!"

"Couldn't she swim?"

"Couldn't she *swim!* Wendy Armisted?! Are you out of your mind?"

"Stubborn."

"No! no! she's alive!"

VIII.

It was very dusky. The firelight shone on our faces.

The doctor was in a roaring anger, the outcome of his defiance. He did not work it up, as we say, but rather gradually opened the valve and let it roar, it was there always. "Oh, get out of my way!" he pushed a fellow, who would ordinarily have retaliated, but not now.

"What you so mad about, Doc?"

"What am I so mad about? All my life! these idiots! Do you think I enjoy it? Now see ye to it! see ye to it!" He seized the questioner by the shirt-front and pushed him again. Out of the way? *On* his way? "Yes she's alive!" he fairly shouted, "and what lesson shall *we* learn from this text?"

We formed a decent circle around him, to let him rant. Almost one expected him to begin by crossing himself in the name of the Father and of the Son and of the Holy Ghost, except that he was an atheist. "I'll read you the lesson. She's alive there because there wasn't a sufficient reason for her to die, it wasn't worth it. That's it. That's it. It takes a stronger justification to die—more shame than that! or failure! or such happiness lost that it's not worth living on again. *Where* do you have it? Where do you *see* it in this county?" He looked around at us with a terrible accusation. Into the eyes of each one. "Is your marriage so sacred? is your adultery so interesting? It's not easy for your writers to make heroes of the boys who die in the war, rather than fools."

He turned away in disgust.

"What do you mean it isn't worth it for Wendy to die?" asked a man offended. "What a thing to say!"

"I mean what I say. It's not interesting. It doesn't interest *me*."

"Oh, and are you the judge?"

"Who else?" he said recklessly.

He was speaking recklessly, not what he meant, yet it was not obscure to some of us what he meant: he meant to say that *he,* Dr. Emanuel Groves, found justification in keeping the other people alive, but he did not himself find a reason either to die *or* to live.

If you have a reason to live—answering the question, "What is the meaning of life?"—then you might have a reason to die, for example to defend your reason to live. And oh! if you are in that happy condition that you do not even need a reason, then you are in fact *making* a reason in your life, you are growing into something, and that fact will be obvious to every awestruck observer, and felt by you as faith. Are you in fact that happy?

As gradually as it flared, the doctor's anger speedily abated. He became habitually compassionate, his shoulders drooping to their habitual depression, and he said gently to Mark, "That's a sick woman you have there. Do you know?"

"Yes, I know," said Mark.

"*Do* you know?" The doctor looked at him searchingly. "Yes. Underneath I know it all the time, no matter how I seem to act up. I stop, for instance, when her eyes begin to roll. This is what I live with. Also—" he hesitated. The doctor waited. "I do *not* know. How to cope with it. My only world. Do you follow me? If I *knew* what was good for her, I would do it and gladly."

"I believe you," said the doctor.

IX.

Mark went and sat beside Wendy at the fire. She was awake and she sat up.

"How are you feeling?" he said.

"All right. I'm sleepy. Can we go home?—Will they let me go home?".

"Yes. Of course. Albie will drive us. Let's go." Neither offered to get up.

It was clear that the husband and wife were not going to refer to the incident any further.

"Where is the baby?"

"Asleep." He got up and brought the baby and she took it in her arms and touched the face lightly, with her fingertips.

Mark held back a moment, but then put his arm around Wendy. He waited, hoping against hope, that she would lean her head on his breast and perhaps weep. But she did not, no more than she ever had. But he was horribly tired and rested his own head on her shoulder, saying to himself, "I must not cry, it would probably be a bad note"; nevertheless, he at once began to shake with silent sobs. She petted him gently.

A LIFEGUARD

Two fat yellow ropes, across the sand into the surf,
marked off the area for the exclusive use of the Beach
Club, and the members had Tom, their own lifeguard, on
his perch. But the non-members, especially mothers with
small children, would set down on the sand pretty close
to the Club's ropes, where they could feel secure because Tom was near.

There was a certain amount of class-spiteful humor as
to whom, in case of a necessary choice, the lifeguard
would plunge in to save first, a member of the Club that
paid his wages or a drowning child outside the ropes. Inevitably, each time the talk recurred, somebody pointed
out that when the *Titanic* sank, "Women and Children
First!" meant women and children of the First Class. Because of a TV program, people in 1958 were astonishingly
informed about the sinking of the *Titanic* in 1912. But
everybody really assumed that, like anybody else, Tom
would do his best to save everybody, whether they paid
his wages or not.

He was a good lifeguard but on the conscientious side,
considering that people went swimming for fun and fun
has a factor of risk. He was studious among lifeguards,
a student of Oceanography at New York University,
a member of Dr. Neumann's team that measures the
waves. Tom could predict the tows and the swells, and
tell you how many hundred miles away the storm had
raged; and he had a keen intuition for the formation of
sea-pussies, those sudden serpentine eddies, a few yards
wide, that pull the strongest swimmer out to sea before
they loose him—which is all right if he's a strong swimmer and doesn't panic. Unfortunately, Tom believed the

obsessional proposition that an ounce of prevention is worth a pound of cure, and he blew his whistle too much. The members of the Club didn't like to be whistled at; those outside the ropes didn't pay much attention.

Shrill blew Tom's whistle.

The swimmer, a couple of hundred feet out, paid no attention.

"Oh, toin off dat whistle!" said a gentleman of the Club who had been reading *The Hairy Ape.*

The swimmer went his leisurely way, already in the fringe of a dangerous sea-pussy, an outsweeping tow.

Stepping into the surf churning about his knees, the guard blew a terrible blast and shouted, "Hey you! out there! come in out o' there!" He looked a fine human figure, our champion against the dangerous elements, his eyes sparkling with concentration, clothed head and shoulders in purpose, while up around his waist foamed the breakers. Some of the bathers outside the boundary began to shout at the swimmer who was also from outside the boundary. At last he heard them, and for a moment he faltered in his stroke and seemed in a panic, whether because of their shouting or because he felt himself in the grip of the strong sea. But he recovered, fought to a new course, and headed toward the shore.

Satisfied, Tom waded onto the beach and returned to his perch and his cigarette.

The swimmer, however, was not satisfied at all, at all. Still up to his knees in the water, he came over to the rope and barked, "Hey you! up there! you whistle at me?" He was a big shaggy fellow, with black tattoos, peevish because of something his mother did to his father long ago; because he had quit high school; because his car burned oil.

"Yes, I whistled at you," said Tom.

The other gripped onto the rope. "What in hell is your business, you whistle at me?"

This Tom did not judge worth a reply.

"You whistle at me I punch you in the nose! Why in hell you don't whistle over on that side o' the rope where they pay you?"

Tom came down to the water's edge. He darted back fastidiously like a sandpiper in order not to get his toes wet. He said courteously, "I whistled at you because you were in a sea-pussy."

"Sea-pussy!" cried the shaggy one. "Sea-pussy!" He appealed to one and all with a roar of rage, *"Sea-pussy!* you hear him?"

"Yes! you couldn't see it, but I could see it," said Tom, unconsciously quoting a sentence out of the ancient times, and it tolled in every heart like a bell.

It touched exactly the wrong note, of ignorance. "Listen to him! he whistles at me! I been swimming in this ocean before you was born, you—you college-boy."

Tom turned his back and walked away. By this time there was a small crowd of spectators.

"That fellow does look, Tom, like he could take care of himself," said one of the ladies of the Club, kindly.

Sudden anger seethed in the lifeguard's heart. Why was he wasting his summer? Whirling, he came down to the shaggy swimmer at the dividing rope. Frowning brow to brow, he stood to his knees in the surf. But when he burst out bitterly, his words were directed at them one and all. "If I *minded* my business, if I let somebody drown over there, *then* there'd be a hullabaloo, wouldn't there? *Never* hear the end of it. You make me sick." His speech came in gasps. They were now both in a passion.

"Yah! yah!" said the shaggy one.

"You shut up," said Tom. "So long as *I'm* in charge here, I'll give the orders. Any questions? F'Chrissake, how *else* could I do?"—he ended with a weak and piteous appeal.

Pitiful, for of course he was *not* in charge. He had no major premise. Nobody had given him any mandate whatever.

"Naturally if somebody was in trouble, you'd jump in —we know *that*," said a woman.

"When I patrol the shore, you won't even *begin* to get in trouble!" said the guard arrogantly and bitterly. He meant it and he was proud of it, and he hated the prudence that he was proud of.

"Maybe *that's* the trouble, Tom," said a gentleman of the Club, who was a physician. "The trouble with you, Tom, is that you forestall every emergency. Nobody will cooperate with anything before he's convinced that there *is* an emergency. You come through in an emergency and you're a hero, everybody's crazy for you. You act like a prudent man and prevent the emergency from arising, and everybody's sour on you because you're a worry-wart. Yes! and you're sour on yourself." The physician said this with extraordinary melancholy, his voice drowning in its own undertones, so that people looked at him in wonder. He was a physician.

But there was another elderly man, from the other side of the rope, not a member of the Club, and he was a famous Constitutional lawyer. "No, I beg to differ," he said in his rich voice. "People *have* to protect themselves from interference; how can they let themselves be pushed around? Consider the present difference of opinion. If the members of your Club there don't like the way the young man fulfills his reponsibility, let them turn him out! let them vote him out and fire him. But what recourse do *we* have, here on our side? *We* neither hire nor fire. Are we to submit without question? But the answer is obvious: we can go and set a hundred yards down the beach, out of the young man's surveillance. Nothing hinders. Now why don't you do that, madam? Yes, you, madam." He turned the question point-blank at a Mrs. Roche.

She blushed. "Why—you know—it's safer for the children, of course."

"Precisely!" said the lawyer, having scored his point. "What you people don't see is that you put *him* in an intolerable position. What warrant has he? He has no warrant, and nevertheless he has an obligation. Now really! let's face it! If you people want to avail yourself of Tom's services—and the facts speak for themselves—why else camp just here on all this magnificent beach? If you want him to be your agent, then you ought, however informally, to make a compact and constitute him as your seashore chieftain. I for one say, Hurrah for Tom! Three cheers for Tom!"

Swept by moderate enthusiasm—and also delighted by the play of ideas, which were not a dime a dozen at the seaside resort—nearly everybody sang out, "Hurrah! hurrah! hurrah!" Especially the mothers of small bathers frantically clapped their hands.

This proposal and the acclamation were intended, of

course, to mollify the angry lifeguard (as, for instance, they would have mollified me and made me blush and, like a fool, take on another duty without pay, except for a uselessly expensive piece of luggage tendered at the end of the season). On Tom they had the opposite effect. In the first place he thought he detected a note of mockery in what was really good-humored pomposity. The reasonable language of the jurist was a little over his head, and he was stung to fury. But more important, and no mistake, the proposal *was* a trap. For what *would* he get out of it? He had accepted this summer job in the sanguine hope that there would be pretty girls available at the Club —no objection if they also had money. But it hadn't worked out that way. There were no pretty girls at the Club. If a pretty girl visited, she passed him by. The matrons and the men who courted his attention didn't interest him. And meantime it seemed to him that, always a hundred yards away, up the beach, down the beach, anywhere but where he was chained to his post, there was a bevy of pretty girls, or a solitary girl who had surely smiled at him as she strolled past and out of reach.

The jurist had accurately sized up the social situation and proposed a practical remedy. But it was the physician who had vaguely and feelingly glimpsed the live, underlying causes that were not so easy to remedy. Namely, that Tom was hedged in by his duties, and that he hedged *himself* in, more than was necessary.

It was at this laden moment that Colonel Burke, the manager of the Club, came down to the shore to see what the fight was about and what the crowd and the cheering were about. From the outset his attitude was unsympathetic because he didn't like to see that crowd on both sides of the yellow boundary; he didn't like it at all. It was strictly not exclusive. "What goes on here?" he said in a peremptory tone.

"Oh I whistled some guy in," said Tom.

"He whistled at me!" said the shaggy man.

"I told *you* to shut up," said Tom.

"You tell me shut up!?" shouted the man.

"Shut up," said the Colonel. "What, was he drowning?"

"No, he wasn't drowning," said Tom drily. "No, he

wasn't drowning yet. There he is, ask him." His voice rose. "How in hell would I know whether he was going to drown? Use your head."

"He's not one of our people."

"No, he's not. What about it?"

"What's the matter with you, Tom, anyway? We're paying you a good salary. What in hell business is it of yours if this person—"

"That does it!" said Tom, and cut him off; almost as if to prevent him from saying something dreadful. "I quit!" he shouted. "You can take your lousy job and shove it!" With a snort he yanked the whistle with its elastic over his head, and childishly he slammed it down on the sand. He jostled his way through the crowd and jumped over the rope and kept going. Then awkwardly he had to return back across the rope and walk to his perch for his cigarettes and lighter. He was acutely conscious of how ludicrous this all was. He stalked off the second time with great dignity.

There it was. Now neither those in the enclosure nor those beyond had any lifeguard at all.

II.

By a couple of miles up the beach, the young man had gotten over his first mad and was breathing more calmly. All around there spread, sublimely, nothing; the sea, the sun, the fertile Void, from which spring the monsters of the deep. It was five o'clock.

"Hurrah for Tom!" Their shout rang in his soul. "I *quit!"* His shout rang in his soul.

After awhile both shouts faded and left him in silence, in the hiss and moan of the breakers.

He was out to the lonely dunes, for nobody walked out this far. Sometimes one of those odd hiking couples, man and wife, sixty years old, bent under their knapsacks, the man in shorts with knobby knees and she looking very sensible. But today there were not even the sandpipers.

The sun was small and red. Up near the dune was a magnificent writhing driftwood, a satiny gray stump and its roots, undermined long ago in Nova Scotia and carried here by ocean currents that Tom could have named. He stood and admired it and stroked it. On an impulse he picked up a great black sheet of wet seaweed with a lettuce-curl and tails, and he flung it wide around his shoulders like a cape. New clothes! He had *shed* his old purpose and duties; he took on, not another purpose, but loyalty. *To* the elements. He was no longer our humane guardian against them.

Calm, joy, and violence were his immediate rewards. He stripped off his human mask.

Or we could describe his state another way and say: that the very soul that is conscientious when the environment is other people, is *large* when the environment is only sea and sky.

However it was, as he sported there, it seemed to him absurd to be wearing swimming trunks and he stripped them off too. He hung them on a branching root like a tan weathered flag:

"MAN WAS HERE. 1959."

For the first time all summer, he himself ran down with a shout and dove through the breakers. The water stank with algae. Shaking the hair out of his eyes, he headed into the sun's spangles. West! West! He *played* with the sea-pussy. He whispered to her that her name was Evelyn. For a quarter of a mile he rode, as in triumph, the golden trail. Meditatively he headed back toward shore, swimming an old-fashioned Australian crawl. All in all, he had a good swim in the choppy water, and he came out of it much the happier.

Shrill blew the whistle, and the shore-jeep ploughing up the sand whined to a stop.

"*Hey you!* Come out o' there! What in hell do you think you're doin'?"

It was the constable on his round.

"Are you whistling at me?" said Tom innocently, but he could not imagine who else was there to be whistled at.

"The matter?! Nude! that's what's the matter. Indecent exposure! What d'ye think this is, nudists?"

"Indecent exposure?" said Tom, wondering, looking down at himself, surprised. "Indecent exposure to whom?"—But instead of protesting, he burst out laughing, loud and long, like the Olympians, a laughter that was not letting off tension, nor was it resignation. Tom's laugh was round and solid laughter at the absurdity of mortal beings. Fetching his trunks, he went docilely along back to the club to get his wallet, and then to pay his $25 fine at the county seat.

THE UNIVERSITY IN EXILE

I.

Some, exiled from all possible lands, lived on a boundary, a road or a river or a no-man's plain crossed by shots from both sides. Others were killed before starting out. There was no concern but train connections or missed connections, then long hikes; and "long" meant five hundred kilometers often undertaken, sometimes accomplished, by persons sixty years old. It seemed that the ones successful in heroic escapes now enjoyed renewed youth, restored health, freedom of perspective; this was partly because they were already a selected group, of those who had been secretly waiting for a chance to break with their habits, so that the general calamity was their release. Thousands were put to flight and shot because fleeing. A few were able to feel

> for wandering is it
> that the world is made so wide;

others committed suicide in moral or physical despair. Jailed, some were so naturalized to conventional opinions that they were ill with mere shame. Prior collusion with the rising powers sometimes proved to be the key to escape. Bribery or foresight or fortitude or ingenuity or callousness or friends or wealth or luck, or all of these together even when it seemed that they were incompatible in the same person, were the virtues of escape. Then, after all, the boat sank or the general conquest overtook the individual fugitive. At best, after the excitement of rapid motion had died down a little, there were bad memories, a gloomy present, and no prospects. One did not talk about the others or what one heard.

II.

The secret object of the dinner party in New York was to get Kaplan the jeweler to contribute five thousand dollars to the University in Exile.

When Niko Verein, the young poet, lecturer, and (already) editor, arrived, the maid Frau Luisa blushed, and her face lit up. She helped him with his coat.

"Isn't it Niko Verein, the poet?" she whispered to Mrs. Clyde.

"How did you know?"

"Often he came for dinner when I had my home in Prague. He doesn't recognize me."

Frau Luisa had been the wife of the chancellor of the ancient university. The husband was perhaps dead. But she, for the most part, was content in her new activity which she had intelligently and quickly mastered.

Inside, the conversation was not so much desultory as plain difficult. Almost everyone was haltingly trilingual, and the conversation, manfully launched on the greatest subjects, was foundering when it had to be carried on the English phrases that the Germans and Frenchmen knew in common. But Clyde, the host, was strong-minded enough to prevent them from separating into little groups and speaking the languages they knew. He boasted that in his house they learned English.

Under these conditions they were discussing world sociology.

They greeted Niko enthusiastically. What a relief! He represented the interests of all and he spoke all languages beautifully.

Professor Leinhardt despised him as the embodiment of official cultural extremism, heavily rewarded. Jarno couldn't bear any of these bourgeois, but Verein was the worst. To Mme. Chapelain, his mere vulgar presence was a thrust to the heart.

"Pardon, pardon, vous ne deviez pas m'attendre. Je viens de donner une causerie chez les aborigines de *Harlem!*" cried Niko, a bombshell. Everybody laughed.

"De *Harlem!*"

"Vat is Harlem?" asked Frau Doktor Becker.

"We are waiting for Didier," said M. Chapelain sourly.

Mme. Chapelain was anxious. "Où est-ce que ça peut être maintenant?" she asked, holding her watch, which she wore on the inside of her wrist, close to her eyes.

They explained to Doktor Becker what Harlem was, and she, too, had a chance to laugh.

Etienne Chapelain was bursting because he had a far-reaching thesis which, if he could expound it, would no doubt (this is the belief of every third party in an argument) end the sociological argument. If the German ideology, he wanted to say, were as factitious as claimed, would not the reality of human personality corrupt it from within, not in our generation of course? But he absolutely could not move his tongue. His tongue was paralyzed when he tried to express in English anything like an idea. Finally in despair he croaked, "Le luxe— le luxe corrompt, amollit."

"Ils ont insisté que Beethoven avait du sang noir," cried Niko; "they say Beethoven was a nigger." He often spoke in French and English concomitantly, rarely in German. Certainly this socially tactful gesture was a mark of unconscious alienation from and contempt for the German refugees. Herr Leinhardt was right to take offense. At the same time the causes of this alienation were worthy of pity. In Europe Niko had been a very important literary figure—but not among the best wits, as he was intelligent enough to perceive; he hadn't yet perceived that it was the same in America too. Meantime he was happy and violently active, much more so than ever before; except that he was nervous and had a hundred tics. His eyes popped, looking for someone who was never there.

When he spoke German it was to quote from Goethe, which at home he would never have dared to do. His more sophisticated tone had not necessarily been better, and Niko's present conversation and even attitude were really immeasurably improved by association with those noble saws; except that it was all spoiled when he passed himself off as the spokesman of the deathless culture.

Speedily the sociological argument degenerated to

what was in the headlines, especially since all the linguists had just spelled out these words to themselves.

"Ze Grand Mufti even is now an Ahryan," said Professor Leinhardt.

He was ashamed. He and M. Chapelain looked at each other with dumb sympathy. The linguistic difficulty was stultifying; they felt that they not only seemed but were becoming stupid. At the same time, here was a problem in wild mental acrobatics: to use only the vocabulary and ideas of the news reports and yet, by irony or by being contradictious, to avoid idiocy, or at least to indicate that one's self was not an idiot.

The net result was that the Americans thought they were complete idiots.

Meyer Kaplan was a Russian Jew who was a great joker.

"This Hess—you should poddon the expression—" he now began. He was, he always said, the first to invent this classic joke about the notorious Hess.

Mrs. Kaplan squealed with joy. (Meyer had invented the joke on the way upstairs and was only waiting his opportunity.) Mme. Chapelain could not, of course, catch the joke, but she recognized Mr. Kaplan's type and she paled with disgust.

None of the foreigners, even Niko, could catch the joke. Clyde chuckled deeply.

"You could never explain it!" choked Mrs. K.

"It's quite stupid; it would take too long to explain it," said Clyde apologetically. The Americans nevertheless couldn't resist laughing on—at the others—while the refugees wore strained smiles.

But Niko brought them all to a pause by appreciatively observing: "A long explanation takes the humor from a joke."

The doorbell rang.

"Didi!" said Madame, with a sigh of relief.

It was Didi. When he came in, hatless and coatless, he was still muttering to himself, "For-mi-dable!" Anyone could have told at a glance, from his color and disarray, that he had been necking. "For-mi-dable!" he whispered.

"Madam, dinner is served," said Frau Luisa.

Didi, who was nineteen, gulped his cocktail and poured

another which he took to the table. "C'est formidable."

He was seated opposite the Frau Doktor.

To explain why he was so late, he rapidly told a story, in French, about going through a traffic light and then diving in and out of alleys, like a taxi, to escape a police car. He lent verisimilitude to this by explosions of laughter. In his anxiety, he was betrayed into the pathetic error by which, to conceal the crime present to our consciences, we confess to another which is worse in the minds of the audience.

"A police car!" cried his mother, terrified.

Fortunately the word was at once seized upon by everybody else.

"How apsurd!" said the Professor. "In America ze police car is a peculiar color; everybody *knows* it is a police car! Ze—how do you say—ze verbrecher sees it and away he runs!"

"Don't worry, they have his license number," said Clyde, beginning to be angry, so that, a bad host, he cast terror into the hearts of Monsieur and Madame. He could not help burning when these people criticized American institutions.

"Same in ze hotel!" cried the Professor. "Nobody hass —how do you say—an identification. Why could I not sign *any* name?"

Clyde became red to the ears when he heard the refugee from the system of tyranny advocating the fingerprinting of non-aliens.

"In America," he said, restraining himself, "we have the principle that a man is innocent until he is proved guilty. This is Anglo-Saxon law."

"Ah so! it iss very interesting to study ze comparative law of different peoples."

"The policeman is there to appeal to if a crime is committed; it is not his business to ferret out crimes."

Great! great! thought Jarno. He suffocated when he heard this bourgeois discuss legal formalities. But the academic was even deadlier.

"Niko," exclaimed the hostess tactfully, "tell us about your lecture to the aborigines de Harlem."

"My land," said Mrs. Kaplan, "how did Beethoven turn out to be a Negro?"

"Zere iss no such zing ass black Blut" said the Professor.

Helping himself to the wild lamb, Niko, munching, prepared to narrate the story with high spirit when once he would have his fork free to wave in the air.

Frau Luisa, the maid, slowed up the service, to hear as much of the story as possible.

Didi meantime had relapsed into his trance. "Formidable!" he said mechanically. Whereas in French he was bashful and tongue-tied and could not make love, in English, which he hardly knew, he allowed himself to say anything; and his success was simply astounding! It seemed that the English words retained their primary meanings and the compliments were clever (it was clever of him to be able to phrase them). Besides—

Absently chewing, he began to remember that he had once before experienced a similar freedom of language, when he was a little boy and first went out. It was perhaps not a matter of language, but being away from home. . . .

M. Etienne Chapelain likewise felt that when he tried to speak he was again becoming a child, but with the opposite effect: inadequate to the situation, abashed by his father's authority. For the second time in his life he began to hear, now interiorly, the word Syntax, that made him tremble.

"The climate of New York is O. K. for the boys!" said Mme. Chapelain. "Didi has grown four centimeters. For me it's not so good." She had no appetite. She was puzzled whether the meat was pork, veal, or horse. It was lamb, soaked for three days in buttermilk.

Leinhardt was thinking, as he methodically chewed: "The meat is excellent. And, after all, this small talk—is not so stupid. I am no longer in the habit of considering everyday topics philosophically. But the kind of knowledge people have of these topics is not altogether erroneous, especially if you take everything into account psychoanalytically. It's really very interesting."

Niko began his story about Harlem. Luisa was hovering in admiration, half turned toward the pantry.

He glanced at her sharply.

It seemed that someone had asked him, "What about Beethoven's race?" They didn't understand, he explained;

what he was trying to show was just that race made *no* difference. "Beethoven was a Negro!" the old man shouted.

Luisa hurried away, to return, as soon as possible, with the broccoli.

Niko leaned forward and whispered to Mrs. Clyde: "The maid isn't colored, is she?"

"No," said the hostess.

"Ah," sighed Niko, smiling happily, relieved.

"This I never heard, did you?" he asked. "The theory is that the Van in van Beethoven makes him Dutch and his father was in slave trade."

"What? through the *mother?* It's ridiculous," said Clyde.

"There was Dumas."

"Ah, Dumas. Yes, Dumas. Everybody knows Dumas père. But this other I never heard. Does it seem likely I shouldn't even have heard of it?"

"Now you hear it," said the Professor drily. "Every-zing you muss hear for ze first time."

"Also Pushkin," said Kaplan.

"Pushkin?"

"Pushkin—zis is famous," said the Professor.

"But how were there Negroes in Russia?"

"They came as servants to Catherine the Great, isn't it so, Professor? Don't you remember in the paintings there is a little pickaninny with a turban?"

Luisa laughed resonantly, as in the old days, when she, too, had her house and these very people came to dinner.

Kaplan could not swallow, and the tears flooded his eyes.

"I am thinking of my brother Max," he said; "I can just see his face."

Aha! Mrs. Kaplan and the Clydes exchanged glances across the table. Clyde looked at his watch. They were getting toward the moment of the business.

"Was there an accident?" said Jarno disdainfully.

"First he was in Berlin. We are jewelers," said Kaplan in such a tone that the other conversation stopped. "Max couldn't understand anything. From way back my father said he was a shlemihl, I should take care of him.

"So I said, 'Max, go to Vienna.' So I set him up a little business in Vienna. So no sooner was it all ready to open, with a neon sign—I wouldn't say much, twenty feet high —than I said, 'Max, go to Prague.'—"

As soon as the familiar joke pattern established itself, the others—not to be caught short this time—immediately began to laugh in anticipation. Mme. Chapelain could hardly contain her indignation at the tastelessness of telling such a joke.

"In Prague there was not even time to choose a good spot. 'Max,' I said, 'there's nothing here; you had better go to Brussels.' "

The Professor guffawed. Clyde was puzzled, what was funny?

"Brussels was a jewelry center," Kaplan doggedly continued, "and here maybe we could do a little something. But I said, 'Max, pack up and go to Paris.'—"

The others leaned forward for the dénouement.

"And I forgot to tell him to leave Paris!" said Meyer Kaplan in bitter self-reproach.

It was a mad success. Something everybody could understand. The Professor clapped his hands. "He forgot to tell him to leave Paris!" echoed Niko. And even Jarno was forced to smile. Indeed, when Jarno perceived the full malice of the story—told in such company—after the others were subsiding, he laughed out loud.

In a desperate attempt to restore the society to the level that she was accustomed to, or at least to make it clear what that level was, Mme. Chapelain said: "The story is like that what Mme. de Sévigné wrote to Mme. de Grignan concerning the death of Turenne. He was galloping away when St. Hilaire called him back to the fatal spot, like to say: 'Monsieur, arrêtez-vous un peu, car c'est ici que vous devez être tué.' Le coup de canon vint donc. . . . 'Sir, stop a moment, because it's here you must be killed.' "

Mrs. Clyde rang, and they went inside for coffee.

"German Jews!" hissed Kaplan.

His teeth were chattering so violently that he could not clench the lump of sugar in them.

"Fine ladies and gents, nobody has tsures but you. To you my tsures is a joke. Oh, the donations that in mem-

ory of Max I *won't* give you! In the earth I should lie before I give a *cent* to a German charity. This minute I
make out five thousand *not* to you!"—

With trembling fingers he opened a check book and
wrote a check to the Hartsdale Military Academy.

"When you hear that I give it to goyim you'll burst a
blood vessel! Max Kaplan Salle d'Armes!

"To *my* charities," Meyer said between his teeth; it was
not a new resentment; the bitterness of this charitable
rivalry was of old, "to *my* charities you don't contribute;
but *I* should feel myself *honored* to help found the University in Exile! Naturally, a Litvak, you're doing me a
favor. 'He forgot to tell him to leave Paris'—ha! ha! . . .
Maxileh."

He tore up the check he had just written and made
out the sum to the Sholom Orphans and Old Folks; for
though angry, he was not completely demented.

By the wonderful law of opposites, the reflections of
Jarno, as he slowly stirred his coffee, were not far from
those of Meyer Kaplan.

Jarno had been a Spartacist; he was in America
because there was a price on his head. More recently he
had embraced the opinions of the Pole Machajski, according to which the class of the intelligentsia is even
deadlier than the capitalists, because they are willing to
make a revolution to become the new exploiters. Now,
here were these professors, journalists, technicians
(Chapelain was a chemist) temporarily lost out, yet still
struggling in the new environment, plotting a return home
not only to privilege but to power. Jarno was an anti-
Semite not on principle but statistically—he had an especial hatred for physicians and surgeons. As he looked
narrowly at these persons who could afford to escape,
with their bribes and professional connections, their affi-
davits and visas, he found it not hard to think of the
others who could not afford to escape death. He knew,
likewise, the principles by which the American Department of State admitted certain types, rejected other types.

Niko Verein, though not a Jew, was precisely the type
of vermin to whose annihilation Jarno looked forward.
If he allowed himself to come to such a dinner party, it
was in the spirit of an apprentice exterminator. But he

was beginning to fear that the end was not to be in his generation.

Niko was dog-tired; his jaw sagged, and he looked like what he was, no longer one of the Young Poets. So, sometimes for a moment he slipped from his role, for which he had only hatred.

But it was impossible; there was too much to do, that is, to save from being *completely undone*. (Such an effort of conservation is not very grateful; it requires infinite pains for an admittedly finite object—which soon enough becomes an object of disgust. Nevertheless!—) Here was M. Etienne Chapelain, for reasons that we know, deriding the syntax of the English language; a single demitasse brûlot had been enough to throw him off his balance. Niko pulled himself to his feet and advanced with a waving demitasse spoon.

Monsieur said: *"He—was given—a book*: 'book,' if you please, is accusatif, in the construction passive. Voilà, accusatif! Tiens, Didi—" he turned to the boy to whom he had never taught syntax or anything else, "On lui a donne un livre: *He—was given—a book!* Ha!"

"What is this accusatif?" asked Clyde, worried.

"In English we say Objective," said Mrs. Clyde.

"Oh, Objective! Direct Object—Indirect Object—"

"We explain 'book' as a Retained Object—un objectif retenu."

"Retenu!" screamed Monsieur at the top of his lungs. *"Objectif retenu!* oh, oh."

"Etienne," cautioned Mme. Chapelain.

"When they squeal *yy* I could cheerfully step on them," thought Clyde. "These squeal, the others growl. If they don't like it—"

Against his deepest, and perhaps his best, inclinations, Niko yet again raised his voice to harmonize western culture against barbarism. "You are judging English by the rules of Latin grammar, M. Chapelain. Still, you are partly right; English is less logical than French but belongs more to the people. We must remember that each language has its own genius; there is living room for all. French is rational and Cartesian; English is irrational but infinitely flexible and Shakespearian." As he said this, poor Niko felt a pang between the eyes. Back home he would not have stooped to this level of the gymnasium.

"What's irrational about it?" said Clyde. "He was given a book—it means, someone gave him a book."

Like a faithful soldier who, wounded and thirsty, and maybe dying, and on a field where at best he is fighting a rearguard action, still briskly salutes, Niko drew back his lips from his fangs in an amiable smile. "It has the rationality of an organism," he said, describing with his hands the shape of a plant.

Professor Leinhardt looked at him. But Niko was the more heroic.

It was 9:30. On the dot.

The outer doorbell rang.

"Here he is!" cried Nora Kaplan excitedly and sailed out.

Meyer was asleep with his fountain pen clutched in his fist.

Nora returned arm in arm with Max, who was smiling radiantly though his other forearm was in a cast.

"Max!" cried Mrs. Clyde, who had casually met him in Berlin and of course did not recognize him, but she had arranged the surprise of the evening.

"Shh!" said Niko warningly; he grasped the situation in a flash. "We mustn't wake him up—the shock, the pleasure, the heart—How *are* you?" he said warmly to Max, shaking his hand.

"After so many evasions, we must avoid a malchance," said Monsieur.

"How did you hurt your arm?" asked Didi.

Jarno took command. "Let Max wait inside. His wife will wake him. Then we tell him to prepare for a surprise."

Startled by the quiet, the sleeper awoke.

"Moish!" he said.

"Meyer!" said Max.

"My little brother—" Kaplan exclaimed several times, embracing him. "You hurt your hand," he said reproachfully.

The radiant, perfect satisfaction of this reunion was such that M. Etienne Chapelain was reminded of the wonderful promissory verse of Virgil,

Forsan et haec olim meminisse iuvabit.

Overcome with emotion, he said to his wife, "Emma, peut-être qu'un jour le souvenir même de ces choses sera agréable! N'est-ce pas, Emma?"

Jarno sat down and relaxed into his contemplative dissatisfaction.

"Peut-être qu'un jour—" whispered Monsieur. "Maybe that a day—" he dutifully translated.

Kaplan now saw that their laughter, far from being contemptuous, had been a sign of the most intimate kind of sympathy. His ideas underwent a revolution. He wrote out an additional check and gave it on the sly to Leinhardt. "But not a word," he cautioned. "Take it, use it."

"Zees is wonderful!" said Leinhardt, "seven zousand dollars!"

"Max!" Meyer called out to his brother, "you have just donated a professor and his assistant to the University in Exile."

"—le souvenir même de ces choses," said Monsieur to himself.

When they left, Mme. Chapelain burst into tears. "Je connaissais Picasso—I used to know Picasso. We'd have dinner at Leo Stein's, then do our duty as the claque for Jean Cocteau's latest clarinetist. When poor Rilke was alive and came to Paris, he rang us on the telephone; am I lying? We didn't discuss whether the spirit of the French language was Cartesian! But even Niko didn't seem then what he now is—you remember he used to sit on the floor? But if you now drop a hint of these things and implore a little response, he pretends that all that never existed.

"And *instead!*" sobbed Mme. Chapelain, "we have dinner with a stockbroker whose name is *Clyde,* whose wife learned pleasant manners from a young ladies' finishing school. She flashes her teeth. We hear the jokes of Mr. Kaplan; and his brother, the itinerant jeweler, arrives *with his arm in a plaster cast!* Mr. Meyer Kaplan, mind you, is now asleep in the company. And our little Niko, the same, declares: 'the shock, the pleasure, the heart'!— *this* I shall never forget as long as I live."

But M. Chapelain, who was still entranced by the promissory hexameter, said: "Ne pleurs pas, Emma—don't cry, Emma. It is true that now we have come to spend the evenings with these bankers; after all, what did you expect in coming to America? But we also, I am afraid, had our dear habits; even Rainer Maria Rilke was a habit. It is possible that now, because of this horrible shock, we may come to meet these other persons *anew,* on the level of their humanity. If we were still *there* (*là-bas*) you could not have spent such four hours without contractation of the skin and quickly putting on your hat; the changed circumstances have made the meetings at least tolerable, or at least unavoidable. This is a sign, my dear, that there is more in us, and in them, than ever you suspected. What follows? two things: the idea of ourselves was in part conventional, no? and there is still something to be found out."

M. Didier Chapelain said to himself: "C'est formidable! Wait till tomorrow!"

New York
1941

THE OLD KNIGHT

※   "Chivalry is pride aspiring to beauty."
                              —HUIZINGA

I.

Nothing comes from nothing. Every thing is all of a piece, but the folk won't take causes with effects. Avoiding facts, they dream up phantoms. That too is all of a piece! But who can make his way in this thick second-growth forest? I cannot work it, I am beat.

I was once a man of promise. The folk who knew me clung to me, wasted my time, hindered my gait; yet I waited for them, patient and instructive, because I tend to be a teacher. On the whole, they were not ungrateful; they would willingly have given me gifts, except that, in the nature of the case, they, having little, had little of interest to give me.

Alas! The one superlative gift that they did have to give, namely to take me as I am and let me act out my doom among them, this they refused me. For (I have been told) I frighten people. My doggish way of life, my rude but harmless manners, offend and immobilize. Out of their own banalities, the folk fitted interpretations to me, and then they fearfully protected themselves against their own projections. What! Did they imagine that I would take them by surprise according to their *expectations?*

Then it came to an open quarrel. Naturally I worsted them, for I at least had an idea and they had nothing at all. Nevertheless they then said, "*Admitted* that you are better informed and have proved yourself by achieving such and such; still we maintain our opinion!" And they fell silent.

That made me wild. I felt that I was being choked. Towering with anger, very unlike my usual patient self, I roared, "Who do you think you are? Get out of my sight before I rub you the wrong way and teach you respect for evidence." And indeed they were frightened and hid.

II.

But I could not let it be that way, for I am more needful of my folk than they are of me. I cannot live solitary; and my very nobility compelled me. Let me explain this, for it seems not to be widely understood these days. Suppose the folk are working at something, and I see that it is badly done; then I *cannot* not lend them my hand and heart and help. If I can and they cannot, then I must: noblesse oblige. For otherwise the job would be badly done, servilely thought, timidly effected, remaining to me as a reproach and awakening dismay in my artist heart.

"All right, you hateful little brothers!" I said to myself with spiteful lips, "I know you do not want me butting in—" "Yes! Who asked you?" they heartily agreed. "But I will nevertheless lend you my hand, noblesse oblige."

This was not a gracious attitude and it made them resentful, and especially since they could not refuse me for I was in the right. I was resentful and they were resentful and one word again led to another, and our voices rang sparks. This time I was pleased; this time there promised a bang-up fight.

I drew a line in the sand between us. "Ha! Now you have something to say!" I said with thrilling contempt. "Come! Cross that line and let *me* have a look!"

In their number was a youth, a good-looking young Welshman, who looked about at his elders in astonishment at their hesitation. He could not brook my haughty insulting tone and he rushed across the line drawn in the sand.

"Now you are on my side!" I cried with a ring of joy at the childish joke.

III.

Yet so it was. For, having crossed the line, in utter embarrassment the youth knew that I was in the right, and his raised right dropped powerless to his side. He blushed for shame.

At this moment I was smitten with love for the daring youth, more fatal than I had ever felt for a woman. To me it seemed that he was the perfect Knight, destined to achievement, and I knew myself for what I was, a wretched failure. Our eyes met, we both flinched, and in confusion we turned aside and went opposite ways.

This meeting of ours was touched by immortality, by, as Jean said, the mortal boredom of immortality. There was no clash. How could there be a clash? When our eyes met for an instant, we saw in each other's eyes the mortal boredom of immortality, and we retired in confusion.

IV.

Then I was sad and weary, feeling my age, and I would willingly, knowing me for the fool I was, have slipped unnoticed among my folk to be one of them. But they were so superstitious; in what language was I supposed to converse with them?

These people recognize excellence, they *are* touched by a stroke of power; but they will not attribute it to a natural cause, and therefore they cannot *foster* excellence. I used to show them a poet's lovely poem in which every common word came alive; yet I could not make them understand that the poet of it must therefore have had a different integrity of speech than they were used to; they still wanted him to guard his speech and speak with mental reservation as they did. They admired the skill and devotion of a teacher who had remarkably reawakened a defeated boy and taught him boldness toward the girls; but they would not allow that that teacher was in love with that boy. And I myself, I wore out my heart reaching for the community that was in fact amongst us; and for it I got nothing but abuse as an irresponsible utopian. After a while I was at a loss, I was beat.

Sometimes I have been touched by the tolerance and courage with which people put up with me, for I am often merciless and stinging. Especially when I smile my bland and happy smile of the justified; oh, when I smile that way—"we happy elect"—I can see by their twitching fingers, their narrowed glance, the tight corners of their lips, they would like to stone me. Instead, gathering up their cattle and children they withdraw into hiding behind their walls.

To some of them I seemed to be a kind of dragon, marauding, grinning, flaming in my nether parts and tongue.

V.

Well, I came no more and I think they missed me. Poor folk, it was not gay among them; they did not have much conversation to share. Without me, they became waspish to one another instead of to me. And why did *I* no longer come with my challenge? marauding. With my affront? Flaming in my nether parts and tongue. With my patience? Didn't I have something new to offend them with? And more courage to drain from my heart hour by hour in insistent love that was not asked for? I began to receive invitations to lecture at the university to "stir things up," because the youth were becoming too conformist. This is the fate of an old knight!

"So," I said, "I am their clown, an entertainment for them. Thank you." This was how I now interpreted my life, and I withdrew in my pride.

My mind was closed until further notice. My will was clenched until further notice.

(God take care of me, until further notice.)

I was really preposterous. I began to live by points of honor; like the porcupine, I let no one come near me; neither did I venture forth.

A point of honor is a principle of a man's integrity

that he insists on when he no longer has to fight for his integrity. But I was secure in my integrity. (What among the meager satisfactions that this world has to offer could tempt a man away from the satisfaction of his integrity?) I was insisting on points of honor as if I wanted to make *them* recognize my integrity! Poor lonesome man that I was. It was preposterous, I was stripped to the naked pride.

My mind was closed until further notice. I believed that I was an alien, not in my native land. Having no world to converse in, I felt myself becoming stupid by the week. I could no longer remember names.

You might have seen me then, holding my will clenched and the courage slowly draining drop by drop from my fingers; and the tears also already starting in my eyes. And you would have said, "God take care of him, for he is not going to take care of himself."

VI.

But God sent his bright angel Love to rescue me from dying, in order that I could grow old with honor among the folk. This was how it happened.

I was going in my pride and scorn and with death in my heart, and once again I saw the young Welshman, sitting by himself at a table in the tavern, rolling dice from a cup, and marking down the score. That beautiful and gifted youth, destined for achievement, broodingly rolling dice from a cup and marking down the score. When he saw me pass, he flashed me a look of reproach.

I flushed with anger; what did *he* have to reproach me with? Him, at least, I had never "corrupted", as they said, nor indeed had anything to do with him except the exchange of a single answering glance in the heat of a quarrel that came to nothing. But his look was a look of disappointment in me, and I was stung. I came back to where he was sitting, and I said:

VII.

"Boy, stop rolling those dice a minute, and marking down the score, and I'll tell you the history of chivalry and of the beasts that prowl on the plain." Then he looked up and said, "Tell me."

"Long ago," I began, "when St. George and Hercules came by here marauding and slew monsters, it is likely that the wild beasts were really dangerous. It was necessary to purge the forest of dragons to make the world habitable for the folk.

"Later, there was a noble knight demented who used to ride here; his name was Don Quixote and he battled against terrible enemies. But these enemies, we are told, were nightmares of his own imagination, and his battles were like dreams. The simple folk ran no risk from him if they kept out of the way of his frenzy, and they had in him a subject of much innocent merriment.

"But now, boy, do you know what is the case on this smiling plain traversed by gentle streams? It is again peopled by Monsters, by Dragons, by Subtle Snares—by the Horned Dilemma and the Vicious Circle—but these exist only in the imagination of the folk themselves, for people seem generally to have become quite demented, worse than the Don. Everywhere they look, they see threats. Yes, and it's a lucky man who, riding freely here, is not himself mistaken for one of these non-existent Giants or Magic Pitfalls, and cunning intentions attributed to him which, if he had them, would long ago have made his fortune. Everywhere are to be seen Basilisks—except in fact to a candid gaze.

"It is because the folk have trained themselves to believe that what exists does not exist, that now they have come to believe that what does not exist exists.

"Alas! here now comes a young knight who would like to perform a serviceable exploit. It is you. What is your amazement to find that you cannot employ the obvious natural means, direct action, releasing desire, or using words to say what is the case! To act at all among these folk, you must become involved in the same phantasmagoria as they. Oh, but it is confused and thick in this second-growth forest!

"Yet woe to you, boy, if for a moment you imagine that these fictions exist and you try to tilt at them! At once the courage will be drained from your heart. But there is a mystical gesture that I am going to teach you, in order that it may not be forgotten in the world. Use it when the occasion arises. Wave your right hand in front of your eyes, in mock despair, so, and say 'Oof!' This is what a man does when the madness becomes too thick. For it is too thick."

I paused, but the young man listened on, waiting for me to continue, since I had not yet finished. I hung my head, and I said: "All right, let me tell you further about the history of the knights. Painful for me to tell! painful for me to tell! Among the demented folk there is again a cult of knights demented—yes, who might have done a useful deed if they had not lost their wits. These knights have a blazon with the motto Alienation, saying that they are 'alien' from the folk and do not live in their native land. But they are preposterous. (I say it with shame): for they are taking the fantasies of the folk as if such things existed, as if such fictional non-things were real facts of our native land. But nothing comes from nothing, man. To the degree that our society exists, it exists not by fictions but by natural powers; by plenty of endurance; by bread and wine and fortitude in adversity. Our land is the same for the knight and the folk. What kind of man is it who feels that *he* is alienated because somebody else is having a bad dream? Is he a Knight?" So describing myself, I was deeply ashamed.

"No no!" I cried, "now is the time to use the little gesture, and do not forget to say, 'Oof!' "

VIII.

The young man listened to me with bent head, no longer looking at me, but his ears were hungry, so that I knew my words were imprinted on his soul.

"Why are you ashamed?" he said at last. "You are not one of those useless knights."

"Am I not?" I said. "Deluded about my role, and stalking in my pride like a flamingo."

"Oh, your points of honor!" He laughed briefly. "But they are simply that you are vain and people have hurt your feelings." He saw it with the surgical eye of youth, that judges without pity and does not hold it against us. "You are not one of those knights because you have in fact done useful and famous deeds."

"I?" I said in astonishment. It did not seem to me that I had achieved anything of significance, and I knew very well how I was a failure.

"Oh yes, oh yes," he insisted; and he named, ticking them off on his fingers such and such exploits that I had indeed performed and forgotten. I could have bawled, to hear that they lingered in somebody's memory. He told me something that I had done in Chicago before even he was born, and a word I spoke at a college that no longer exists.

Then I fell to my knees and prayed, "Creator Spirit, come. You have saved me from death by sending your bright angel Love, in order that I may seasonably grow old among my folk with honor. Thank you, for you continue to reward me for deeds that I all unconsciously did, by the way, when I believed that I was solely bent with all my efforts toward some other goal."

IX.

Thenceforth we rode together, young Davy and I; except that I do not really ride, but *he* rode and had his adventures that I am too old for, whilst I mainly sat, here and there, and exchanged thoughts and gossip.

Davy kept his blazon hidden. But I carried a shield with my blazon public for all mankind to see: and it is a Winter Sun, that shines bright but does not shed much warmth.

THE FIRST ADVENTURE:
THE THREE YOUNG WOMEN BEWITCHED

Now there were three young women who lived together in an apartment and daily went to business. Their names

were Leah, Clotilde, and Hermione, and they were under
a deep spell. When Davy began to go to dinner there, he
saw that they ate little of the food and were wasting away;
and Leah, the oldest of them, who had a small child, was
losing her eyesight.

Continually they talked of their future and their ambi-
tions. Clotilde wanted to be a dancer and move with
abandon to the music, but she worked at modeling
dresses and felt constrained and embarrassed in the stiff
postures she had to assume. Hermione, however, thought
that it would be wonderful to show herself as a statue
and model dresses, but she worked as a typist in an office
where nobody ever came. And easy-going Leah wanted
only to keep house and take care of her small son, waiting for her husband to return from the Pacific, but in fact
she worked as a bookkeeper far into the night.

They talked with bright eyes of the future, but they
complained bitterly of the hazards of their jobs day by
day. Keeping slim to model the dresses, Clotilde complained that she was losing the strength of her dancing
legs. Hermione said that in that lonely office bending over
the machine, she was beginning to feel like an inconspicuous mouse. And Leah fretted about not seeing her
little son, who stayed the week with her mother-in-law.

"The worst of it," said Leah, whose husband was a
sailor, "is that my husband doesn't know my eyes are going bad because of the job, and I'm afraid to write him
that I'm wearing glasses because maybe he won't love
me."

Listening to them, Davy looked from one to another in
amazement, which, however, did not hinder him from
eating his lamb-chops with good appetite.

"But why don't you go at it more directly?" he
said finally. "You, Clotilde, I'm sure you have talent; if
you want to dance, why don't you tie up with some dance-
company and dance?"

"Oh I couldn't do that," she said. "It doesn't pay
enough. What I want is to get some money so I can study
seriously."

"Are you saving any money?"

"No. In my job you have to spend a lot on clothes and putting up a front."

"My trouble is just the opposite," said Hermione, laughing joylessly at the humor of it. "If I made as much money as Clotilde I'd feel wicked. The way they brought me up, I feel I'm only worth my keep. My daddy told me to be quiet as a mouse; so I guess I'm being a good girl after all."

Obviously these young ladies were enchanted. They were under a spell. Davy waved his right hand in front of his eyes and said, "Oof."

—"What shall I do for these people, old friend?" he asked me soberly, as if confident in my wisdom. "Whatever I say, they talk themselves out of it. Their theory is that in order to do what they want to do, they have to find a means to the end which to be sure does not lead to the end but contradicts it. How can I handle that?"

But I would not answer this question. "What do *you* want to do, young man?" I asked. "Why do you go there?"

"Why do you think? I'm hot for the young one, Clotilde, and I'd like to fuck her once or twice before we go our way."

"Why do you tell *me* this?" I asked. And at once the light broke on the young Knight, that he too was not going the easy Way, and was thereby worsening the tangle.

That very night he went more directly at it and slept with Clotilde, with the remarkable result that she resolved forever to glide and bound about to music; and before the week was out she had tied up with a dance-company and was dancing. And Hermione, who wanted to exhibit herself and therefore hid herself in a lonely office in a deformed posture, when she saw that her friend was a bad girl she easily applied for her job and got it. But she prudently used the money to pay the rent and groceries, so that Leah could quit her job and bring home her little son, and throw away her glasses.

I quoted to Davy the maxim of Franz: that there are problems that we could never get by were it not for an operation of nature. And thus in glory ended the First Adventure.

THE SECOND ADVENTURE: THE CLOISTER OF THE
ELITE OF THE BELIEVERS IN MAGIC

We came to a great University where old friends of
mine did their research and made programs for the nation; and I thought it would be salutary if the young
Knight became acquainted here in this pleasant square
shaded by maples. There was a time when I too was a
scholar, and I have a robe with slashed sleeves and the
silk shining brightly through.

"Perhaps these scientists of society," I said, "are really
physicians and can teach you to follow close after nature." But I was rather dubious because in their dress and
manners my friends looked, not like naturalists, but like
small financiers.

In fact the maple-shaded square proved to be the cloister of the elite of the believers in magic. The professors
believed in the miracle that our social world continues to
exist, and can even be reformed, without a chain of proximate causes, nor the initiation of a new chain of proximate causes. Rather, they relied on an abracadabra of
words and votes and cash, and they believed in the powerful influence of the invocation of Names and Roles.
They did not much consider the laborer confronting his
machine, and how a man takes leave of his heart in the
morning to go to work; nor even, these latter days, did
they follow the harried folk into the market. But the
Names formed a great system of Names and so our society stayed in being; and there was no loophole in the
system for the direct action of men.

Naturally, in their personal dealings with one another,
my friends had become expert at avoiding contact. For
instance, one would write in the journals, "What can Professor B. possibly mean by thus and so?" But he would
not think of knocking on his door and asking him. They
had invented the categories of Private Life and Professional Life; and with regard to the folk, they spoke of the
Primary Environment and the Secondary Environment.
Having taken leave of the connection of their hearts
and their hands, they easily came to take leave of their
senses. Yet maybe they were not so demented after all,

for they went about the campus merrily whistling the new *Foundation Song* that was all the rage:

> "My bulb won't light for microgrants,
> Needs megabucks to make it shine!"

Davy drew me aside under the arcade and said, "Old friend, I am puzzled. You tell me your friends are scholars and earnest scientists, but they talk and behave like small financiers and the world they refer to does not seem to be the world in which I go. Am I such a poor observer?"

"No, it is they who are superstitious. But partly they are right. For the folk themselves believe that they act according to these Names and Roles; and if you give them a questionnaire to find out what they are about, they will answer it as if the questionnaire made sense. The science of Names fits the subject-matter of the Names. These Names are therefore magical; they invoke the reality."

"Ah, but will it come? will it come?" asked the young Knight, like Hotspur.

"No, it does not come," I said. "But one gets plenty of money for research."

Davy shrugged and began to draw heavily on the excellent sherry, for we had repaired to Professor M.'s office.

"No no, listen to this—" I said. Professor M. was telling Professor N. to put on the tea.

"How?" asked Professor N.

"Just plug in the kettle and let it come to a boil."

Davy smiled and took another swig and soon he was pretty lively. We were talking about the Brink of War and it was a serious conversation, to which my young friend was adding nothing very coherent.

"It is astonishing, and refreshing," said M. to me sotto voce, "to see a young American so personally disturbed by a political situation."

"He's Welsh."

"Ah, so. That explains it. They are very unstable."

"I think he's getting drunk," I said drily.

"Really? I've never seen a man drunk," said Professor M., who was a psychologist.

"You told me," cried Professor N. testily from the other room, "to let the water come to a boil. But how does one know when the water comes to a boil?"

At this, Davy came to his senses with a little click.

THE THIRD ADVENTURE: A DRAGON

Now when a man had graduated from the University and was a Doctor of the Double Dementia—trained not to see the things that exist, and to believe in the things that do not exist—then he was qualified as a teacher for the children and the adolescents.

"Let us stop a while at my old School," I suggested, "where the kids are famous for their beauty and intelligence."

"Is it again manned by old friends of yours?" said the young Welshman disrespectfully; and when I shamefully admitted that it was—for I too had been a teacher—he said, "Giddap! I'll meet you later."

But I can't help it: it is something in me—a need to be liked, not to lose touch—that makes me obsessionally seek out my old friends and try to repeat the situation that was. They, however, sometimes don't see it that way at all, at all, and they become stiff when I appear.

To my delight I saw that at least the boys and girls of my old school were taking their endogamic sexual pleasures as of yore; and that a warmth of affection glowed in their loyalty to one another and to their school (alas for them! the cold world would never be so paradisal).

"But it *is* distracting to formal studies," I said sympathetically to my former colleagues, for I knew what a teacher was up against. "The trick is to go along with the fun. Maybe you can use something like this—" and from my trunk I produced a little Latin primer that I had prepared, stories of rapine and dirty jokes, not hard to collect among the classical authors, charming to translate accurately at the age of 14.

I saw in their eyes that I should be lucky to get out of there half alive.

"There are no such goings-on as you mention."

"What! what?" I took it for granted that they were demented; nevertheless I was surprised. "Ah, perhaps you're wet blankets. When one of you appears, the lovers disengage, the boys put their hands in their own pockets, and there is a lull in the conversation. Believe me, you're missing something. If you'd sit down and share a caress, soon they'd no longer notice your presence—an experience also not without its pathos."

"We're not fools," said my former colleagues, "we know what goes on. But it's quite another thing to recognize its existence and regularize these aberrations. If we behave as if no such things existed, they'll pass away and not hinder the normal adjustment."

"Hinder normal adjustment!" I cried; "they are now in paradise and you want it to pass away." I was surprisingly vehement, but they had touched the spring that opens my box. "Do you *mean* to strengthen the illusion they already have that there is a secret satisfaction that they'll learn about later, if they bide their time, if they bide *your* time. But you have no such secret and there is no such secret! You non-teachers! you retarders! you say that you know what goes on, but I doubt that you remember what goes on. What gayety and mutuality, emulation of the possible, pasture of the soul: and all this under the most useful sign in the heavens, acting out desire. Under this sign a man goes *steadily*, with increasing power, to victory. Are you resentful of it? Resentful people aren't teachers? Aren't you ashamed to envy the exploits of boys? . . . But when you refuse to see what exists, then indeed you begin to see what does not exist, and you say 'hinder a normal adjustment.'"

For what they believed was this: that the lads and lasses were racing without circumspection in a field full of pitfalls, quicksands, bear-traps. That there was a narrow path one had to follow to arrive at the goal. And that there was a nightmare dragon marauding, flaming in his nether parts and tongue, ready to destroy whoever fell on the slippery road. Yet the fact is that it's a rough field where every smart kid can jump and tumble and get up again; and Eros is ever serviceable in harness to pull you out when you get stuck in the mud.

So they thought, and so I thought. But they were ominously silent. I persisted, as I do: "Tell me, is it logical to do what you do?" I asked. "To assure the goal you cramp their speed all along the way, instead of encouraging them to try everything out all along the way. Answer me! I challenge you! In what other part of education do you reason the same way?"

But they did not answer because they had run away. They were in hiding. A teacher stuck out his head—and I could see that *I* was the dragon.

Suddenly I was on the alert—for there was at that school a beautiful and gifted boy, and he was broodingly rolling dice and marking down the score. (You see, I am subject to obsessional repetitions.) "Which of you," I cried indignantly, "is responsible for neglecting him during the years he has been here, and he has come to this?"

For answer they began to throw stones at me, and I was lucky to get out of it alive.

Then, as I staggered away hurt, I spoke out my Complaint and said: "Give me air! air! But no matter, let me die quick before I again breathe the same air as these persons. For I have heard deep reasons that came to me in love and service, called the rationalizations of base motives. Please! do these persons imagine that ideas that meet the test of need, and cast light, and make possible patient service, that such are conjured up for a man's convenience? Or do they think love-poems are written as tactics? Well, from now on my mind is open to all comers. There is no nonsense so abject but I am ready to entertain it—if certain persons I could name are generally esteemed as educators."

THE FOURTH ADVENTURE: THE BLAZON

But meantime, pursuing his adventures elsewhere than among my friends, and getting more gratification along the way, my young knight too ended up in a ditch beside the road. He was thus able to confirm the formula that Life is Simple but Hard. Life is not complicated, as my friends imagined; it is not easy, as no one is fool enough to imagine; but it is simple and hard.

And while he was lying there, more dead than alive, there passed by two petty bourgeois; their names were Emulation and Timidity.

"So young," said one to the other, "and already on the skids." He clicked his tongue against his teeth.

"This is the fellow," said the other, "who has been under an evil influence." And he whispered something in his friend's ear.

The other agreed that this was indeed Balinese. "Let's get out of here," he said, "before a policeman comes and we have to appear as witnesses."

(In this way it is possible to die unattended in New York City or along the roadsides of northern New Jersey.)

"Well," said one, "he must pay the penalty."

"Yes," said the other, "the wages of sin is death."

When the first said "pay the penalty," Davy's right eye opened wide. And when the other said "the wages of sin," then his other eye opened too, and he leaped to his feet and seized them by the lapels of their coats and began to knock their heads together. "You dogs!" he shouted at them, half between sleep and waking, "how dare you speak of me in such a language of exchange and hire? I know you for what you are by the words you use, petty bourgeois! . . . Do *you* think I would deny that my own doing has led me, and must still lead me, to disaster? In the present instance, I confess, I was a little sanguine and imprudent, but even at the best the end of desire is death, and the suppression of desire is death . . . No! This bond, this *bondage,* of cause and effect, this chain of consequences, is what I glory in and give *thanks* for—" He was panting and gasping, but each has his own way of praying. "This is nature, that reveals herself to me. When I see the consequences and trace them to their causes, then I know what I am. Say that the Scorpion stings itself to death, and I'll honor you."

And like the emperor in the play, he ripped open his shirt-front and revealed his proud blazon: It was the Scorpion deadly-ringed, and under it the motto, Character Is Destiny.

That was a gloomy emblem of Davy's, I grant you, but wasn't it better to carry his trouble along the open road than to sit rolling the dice with himself and marking down the score?—until, God willing, we come upon a physician with as much love as I have for him, and more wisdom.

THE FIFTH ADVENTURE: THE KNIGHT BERSERK

But I heard the roars and dolorous shrieks of outraged nature, Davy roaring and the people shrieking, and I broke into a run. Yet I knew it was too late, for the young knight had gone beserk, having ripped open his shirt-front and revealed the Scorpion deadly-ringed. It is not with impunity that we invoke the magic of a man's true Name, and God knows what would occur if we could say the ineffable Name itself (but it is my *faith* that the grass would then grow on the hills!). My youth was standing there among wounded people—the shopkeepers, a woman, an officer of the law (He sprang down from a tree above; he must have been a leopard.)—his face and hands were bloody. Our rage is limitless but luckily we go unarmed; otherwise many would be dead, they are sometimes so outrageous. I looked, and at him, with round eyes, and he said:

"I heard a child screaming with pain, and I could no longer bear it, so I killed these two the causes of his hunger. And then I heard the child screaming with grief, and the mother was there so I killed her. Then I heard the child screaming with rage, and the soldier came and I killed him."

"Listen closely, Davy. Is the child now still?"

"I cannot hear him screaming now."

"My son! my son! I don't doubt that the child was screaming with hunger and grief and rage. Likely he is screaming still though you cannot hear him. But you have made a mistake; it is not these persons you meant at all: *they* are not responsible, they are dumb agents of impersonal forces. Take them as persons one by one, and each one of them is also the child screaming. You are a murderer."

"So?" said Davy, standing there ugly with his bloody hands. "And let me give *you* some news about the facts of life, you who are always in the right. In me was rage and grief. How shall I let out this rage that is making my life sour? for rage was given us to destroy what thwarts and insults us. Shall I murder some big and impersonal force? *Where* is he, so I may bash his face? But *these* I have been able to strike at." He began to bawl.

"Now you are crying. What is grief?"

"Grief is for loss. I can now cry because it is some particular thing that I have lost."

"What have you lost?"

"I have lost your love, that is why I am crying. I see that you think I am ugly."

"No," I said dully. "Simply, I am responsible for you and it is heavy. Is it so that the folk must put up with their knights? Let us get away and hide in the hills, for the first snow is already on the ground."

THE SIXTH ADVENTURE: A MOUNTAIN CONVENT

Over the winter, we nursed him back to health, in a religious house in the mountains. And one day I came on him sitting in the pale sunshine, and I said: "Why are you so quiet, Davy? whose medal are you wearing? And where is the golden scorpion, your ill-luck charm?" (For a young knight will often wear an ill-luck charm, to remind him that the evils that befall him belong to his nature, till he is confirmed in his integrity.)

"I'm in love," he said. "The medal is a superstitious medal that Joanna gave me. See, it is St. Christopher. And, do you know?"

"What must I know?"

"Strange! Although she believes in these absurd ancient allegories, she has never even heard of the folk-tales of the demented people of this world. She loves me almost as I am? must I not love her for that?"

"What do you say! she hasn't heard of them! is the girl an imbecile?"

"She was brought up in the convent, on the mountain. The sisters here have taught her nothing, either false or true, except hunting, music, and the saints' lives. Now she has met a man—she was a virgin, but very lustful, once it occured to her—and she does not take alarm at the hobgoblins; she fails completely to see the things that do not exist. We make love by the side of the road. Oh, very lusty. Shall I have a child with this wicked innocent?"

"Wait till she finds out more about you!" I warned him prudently. "Wait till the others have told her that you speak the truth just in order that they may not take you seriously, and that when you love something it is in order to harm it; wait until she is persuaded that strong ideas are rationalizations."

"Not at all!" he said cheerfully. "They've already got to work on her. But when they whispered—"

"Yes—"

"I had already told her all that. And when they attributed to you the subtility and malice which, if you had them, would long ago have made your fortune—"

"Yes—"

"Why, she said to them, for she is keen, 'You poor folk! All this resentment and superstition is nothing but hidden love and loyalty that you cannot help but have for the honor and freedom of these knights. Why are you so indirect, and make yourselves miserable? Can't you go directly? Is life so hard? But he tells me, what I haven't yet noticed, that life is hard, though simple. I've always found it easy.' "

"Let her have your child, the fool, and she'll find that it's hard."

—I spoke spitefully. But the tears started into my eyes, and they are in my eyes now also when I am writing about it. For I too once met and loved and married and had a child with a dear lady whose blue eyes likewise did not see the things that do not exist and she loved me almost as I am. Many times I compared her with Saint Harmony my patroness; and she was the theme of many of the songs I used to sing:

But although, or because, we were not demented like the others, we lost our wits in our own way. We made what was simple complicated, and even harder than was necessary. And the end of it was meaningless words and the deeds of fools and the disquiet of our daughter.

THE SEVENTH ADVENTURE: THE BLACK KNIGHT

And now it was April and time to set forth on my last adventure, to seek out the terrible Black Knight in the grove, whose reputation was so fearful that nobody ever

went that way any more. Indeed, it seemed to be a gratuitous act to come so far to harass a roaring bully in an out-
of-the-way place, whom the world simply avoided, rather
than to let him grow old raving till he died. But it is
knightly to perform a gratuitous act, and about this
Black Knight I had a theory and I was driven by curiosity
to corroborate it or die for my mistake.

"Why do you say it is *your* adventure?" said Davy angrily. He was healthy with his love, flushed with the onset of spring. I, although I was not yet an old man, was an
old knight; and to me it was only another spring passing
me by. "It's up to you to choose the adventures, for you
know best; but to fight this champion, I am younger and
stronger."

"If you had not tried to kill the four," I said, "I should
have trusted your strength for this. As it is, I must do it
with my own hand. Don't ask me further."

Naturally this wasn't satisfactory, and he came along
feeling in my bad grace; yet he soon, being sexually happy,
began to whistle with the birds who were busy building
their nests.

"I'll tell you about the Black Knight," I said. "He
keeps prowling alone in his little forest bellowing his challenge. He is mad for all-comers to seek him out and give
battle. No one comes."

"Why should they?" said Davy. He enjoyed this.

"Yes, he's ridiculous. Do you know? I'm sorry for that
knight. How lonely he must be! Especially since he is
so fearsome. Just his voice, heard from afar, keeps everybody away; and his aspect is so threatening, so they
say, that no one can confront him."

Davy looked at me oddly; I was not that kind of champion, why was I going soberly to my doom?

But *my* theory, that I did not explain to him, was that
the Black Knight was not bellowing a challenge at all, but
was calling out, "Come and rescue me!" But his voice and
manner were so terrifying that people took to their heels
instead. How did I know this? Ah, how did I know this?

I have known persons who are hard to help; but what
kind of help is it that cannot cope also with the fact that
the person is hard to help?

So conversing, we came to the grove. And sure enough,

at once—as if he were listening for footsteps—we heard a voice like a nearby thunderclap. Davy blanched and paused, but I am not frightened of noises, for I throw them back by childishly imitating them: if an engine goes Bang! I shout out Bang! and now he growled and I growled.

He appeared, bellowing; and indeed, Davy could not abide his look but broke out in a sweat and fell back among the oaks; he did not take to his heels, of course, for he would not leave me. The Black Knight loomed bigger than the Gorilla, and he was armored in what looked like cast iron, rusty and blistered, like an old stove, with a magnificent gray plume nodding across his visor. His bellow was, for sure, inarticulate; if he meant to be saying, "Rescue me!" you would never know it; and perhaps he was stretching forth his arms in invitation, but he looked very like a fierce bear. I was not frightened at all, for I was armored with compassion, and from my belt I took a heavy axe that I had chosen, and I held it firmly in my right hand as I came forward.

Davy was looking at me with such admiration that the grove and the clearing became like a stage and a play, and the cawing crows like the bassoons of the orchestra.

"Softly," I said to myself, "this is for the surgeon's hand, gentle and firm," and I hefted the axe. It was for this moment that I was unwilling to trust the youth, who might have murdered him.

The Black Knight simply stood there as I closed, and I swung. The clang of it was the B below middle-C, as you might hit a bell and crack it: its name is Liberty. I struck him deftly in the middle of the brow and, in two halves, his iron shell fell apart, revealing, and outstepped the Green Knight of April. He was pale, he had yellow hair, and a suit of apple green; he could not find his voice, but his eyes spoke his gratitude.

THE JOKE

Crossing the 181st Street Bridge after a friendly game on the first floor of a house on University Avenue, Mr. Taylor was in high humor, for he and his wife had ended the evening with a small slam in hearts, redoubled.

"Do you want to hear a funny joke?" he said, unaccountably lapsing into a phrase, "funny joke," that he had not used for thirty-five years. And this was his initial mistake, for we must not revive memories of the time when we were seven and eight.

Mrs. Taylor, who was in a temper, for good reasons that we need not go into, did not answer.

"Well, it seems," he said, hurrying on uninvited to destruction, "in 1492 Columbus and his ships anchored off the island of San Domingo, and there were two Indians on the shore. So Columbus took out a megaphone and yelled: 'Hey there, are you the Indians?' And they yelled: 'Yes, are you Columbus?' And when he yelled, 'Yes,' they turned and waved to the Indians who were hiding in the bushes: 'C'mon out boys—we're discovered!' . . . Ha! Ha! Ha! Ha! Ha!" Mr. Taylor laughed at his joke.

But since Mrs. Taylor, who was cross, did not join him, his laughter rang out alone among their footfalls on the deserted bridge. For it was half-past two of the silent night, when many things can be done with a common understanding that there will be no scandal.

"What's funny?" she said. "I can't see any joke. He did discover America in 1492, didn't he?"

"Yes, but how did he know that they were the Indians? Ha! Ha! Ha!"

"He was *looking* for India. He set sail to find a Western route to India, didn't he?"

"Yes—but how did they know they were the Indians,

I mean? How did they know that *his* name was Columbus? Ha!"

"I can't see the joke," said Mrs. Taylor.

"How did they know they were *discovered?* What a
thing to say: 'C'mon out, boys, we're discovered!' "

But at this, laying such stress, such undue stress, on the
word *discovered,* Mr. Taylor started, and paled somewhat, as if someone had called his name, or tapped him
on the shoulder.

"Frankly, I can't see it," said Mrs. Taylor. "It was bound
to happen, wasn't it? They couldn't expect to remain there
in isolation forever, on the other side of the ocean; somebody was bound to find them out sooner or later. Why
shouldn't they say, 'Well at last, comrades, we're found
out,' or whatever they said: 'C'mon out, we're discovered'?"

". . . to find them out—sooner or later . . ." mur-
mured Mr. Taylor, as if in a trance, and stopped walking.

"Well?"

"Look at that launch all lit up, coming up the river,"
faltered Mr. Taylor, to cover his confusion, and account
for stopping short. He moved against the rail of the bridge,
where the waters of the Harlem River could be seen
swirling below; and he took out his handkerchief and
mopped his brow. A street lamp patiently glowed on the
secluded pavement under High Bridge. On Ogden Avenue
a little white dog trotted after me, looking for a home.

"It's not a launch, but a tugboat. It's not going up the
river, but down," said Mrs. Taylor.

Once more they started on their way. "About that
joke," he said. "Can't you see it's stupid, for them to think
of being discovered? Nobody ever thinks, himself, of being *discovered.* He's *there,* he's known; *he's* the one who
does the discovering. Let me explain it."

In this way, Mr. Taylor persisted in his self-destruction,
or at least in the destruction of an elaborate framework
of safety, which amounts to the same thing. At this time,
had he dropped the whole matter of Columbus and the
silly Indians, Mrs. Taylor would not have been the one
to remind him. But to stop, once he had started, was, of
course, what he could not do.

"Who ever said the Indians were stupid?" said Mrs. Taylor. "Why shouldn't they think of the possibility of being found out, some day. It could happen to us, too, couldn't it? Supposing some explorer today—"

"*Where,* where could he come from?" cried Mr. Taylor.

"Supposing he came from the planet Mars, and he saw us, right on this bridge, and called out, or tapped you on the shoulder."

With an awful shudder, and a haggard look on his face, Mr. Taylor turned sharply around to the right, away from Mrs. Taylor, to see if there was anyone behind.

"There's no one there, beau. We haven't been found out yet," said Mrs. Taylor.

"Is that so!" said Mr. Taylor angrily. "A lot you know about it."

"What now? Another riddle? One of your jokes that nobody can understand?"

"It was a *simple* joke!" screamed Mr. Taylor. "The joke's on *you,* for being such a FOOL—" he bellowed at his wife. "WHY DID I EVER MARRY SUCH A FOOL?" he roared at the top of his lungs, so that there was a remote echo from the wooded cliff in High Bridge Park.

"Murray!" said Mrs. Taylor, perplexed.

"Can't you understand this simple joke?" he insisted petulantly. He was about to begin to whimper, and Mrs. Taylor might have noticed, if they had not just passed a lamppost and entered a zone of darkness, that there were tears welling in his eyes. To bring these coursing down his cheeks required but the words he now spoke:

"Those Indians—standing on the shore—when suddenly the three sails, the three ships, appeared above the horizon: how could they possibly have foretold that the captain's name was Columbus, as if they had read it in Merrill's 4A History Book, on page sixteen in boldface type, opposite a full page picture that I can no longer visualize?" (At this, the tears coursed down his cheeks.) "Maybe you're right," he faltered; "if they had truly understood their situation, they ought to have seen that they were on the verge of being found out. And if they had gone into it more deeply, they might even have seen that it would be a Genoese captain who would come—for the commerce of Genoa bred daring mariners."

"Murray, you're crying!" said Mrs. Taylor, as they finally came into the illumination of the next lamp.

"What you said—that they couldn't remain there in isolation forever, on the other side of the ocean—makes me cry."

"No one is on the bridge. Not even a streetcar."

"When you have to explain it, almost any joke is likely to make you cry."

"It's not my fault, I hope," said Mrs. Taylor.

"If only I could recollect the picture on page seventeen. I think it was Columbus kneeling before Ferdinand and Isabella."

"Are you sure you're not ill?"

"I'll be able to stop in less than a minute," said Mr. Taylor in a woeful voice.

"Here, sit down on the bench," she said—for they had come to a stone bench built into the pier at the middle of the bridge; and he sat down heavily, defeated—but the fact was that he looked fifteen years younger than he had before. The lamp above him on the right, not far from his head, drew his profile in a sharp line on the pavement. At the end of the bridge sounded the distant rumble of a trolley car, causing a tremor to run through the entire structure, from end to end. The water tower of the High Bridge reservoir stood against the night sky. And in a doorway on Amsterdam Avenue, two adolescents who had spent the small hours in vicious practices, lit their cigarettes.

Of a sudden, Mrs. Taylor saw the point of the joke about Columbus and the redskins; and now she too burst into a fit of laughter. "Ha! Ha! Ha! Ha! Ha!" she gasped.

"It's a good one," she said gaily: " 'C'mon comrades, we're discovered!' "

She could not contain her laughing; and there she stood laughing, and he sat crying.

New York City
1935

IDDINGS CLARK

> ※ Lo! on every visage a Black Veil!
> —HAWTHORNE

I.

In the assembly room of the Northport High School they were celebrating the day before Christmas. The children filled the seats, and a crowd of parents the rear, and many graduates—some of whom were parents and some collegians home on vacation. The greatest hilarity and yet decorum prevailed, as always (so that many held that "the best part of the holiday season is the High School celebration"). This year was given a pageant of the Nativity, only half reverent, for at intervals a great burlesque Santa Claus rolled in, did tumblesaults, and so forth, while two end-men bandied jokes. All this was invented and directed by Mr. Iddings Clark, M.A., a teacher of English, a mind spirited and original, with modern notions of Art (considering the community); and these masques have since been collected and printed. He was also in charge of the singing. To see him on the platform, waving his arms, lifted everybody to enthusiasm; ordinarily a shy, almost reserved man, on such occasions he was red with pleasure and crowned with joy. Recent students of his, home from college, crowded beneath him to the platform. The song rang through the hall:

> "Jingle bells! jingle bells!
> Jingle all the way!"

—when suddenly, in the midst of a note, the conductor fainted away and fell from the platform on his face. A cry of horror rang through the hall. The young men who had been at his feet now bore him up; they laid him on the platform and loosened his collar—he was pale—and dashed a glass of water in his face. His eyes fluttered open and he came to. "It's nothing," he said. "I see you all clearly. I am happy having my friends around me. Everything is exactly as it was."

The fact is that at the moment he was about to faint—perhaps because the blood rushed from his head, or because the electric light faltered, or for some other reason—at that moment he beheld over everything a cast of darkness. He saw on each face a veil. It was the Black Veil in the harrowing story of Hawthorne, from which I have taken the motto for this story. At one instant all faces were lit up—the lights overhead ablaze and the falling snow outside—and all printed with an indulgent smile at the well-known song; the next instant, though their mouths were open wide, the sinister shadow was everywhere apparent! A teacher of literature, Iddings Clark was only too well acquainted with Hawthorne's unnatural romance; twice a year for eight years he had read through with his classes the tale of the Minister's Black Veil. But although each time he came to that awful outburst "Why do you tremble at me alone? tremble also at each other!" he was so moved that the sweat appeared on his brow, he hardly thought that it would come to this. The next instant he fainted away.

He sank in the dead faint and the light came and went. Then there was no more light and his soul was profoundly torn—accompanied by trembling and shaking in all his limbs, so that the students among whom he had fallen felt the body quiver in their hands. Thus quietened, he began to rise again through the zones of light, and he had a dream: that he was walking on Hooker Street in the snow and he saw, with a sense of appalling loneliness, that all the passers-by wore half-masks like highwaymen; but he entered the school and stark naked stood before his class. With a cry, he awoke.

II.

That night, Christmas Eve, Iddings Clark went to the home of Otto, an instructor in chemistry, to trim the tree for his five-year-old daughter. To spend the night thus had become a custom. "Yet soon," said Otto, "she will be beyond the age for Christmas trees."

"I am all right," said the English teacher in a strained voice. "Anyway, there is a compensation for everything! Emerson was correct."

He was famous as a decorator of trees. For here also— as in the clever masques he composed—sparkled fancy and originality, in the dramatic contrast of white lights and the deep boughs, not without a touch of wild wit, such as a jack-in-the-box in the heart of it. People dropped in at the house where he had decorated the tree.

"The tree is strange tonight, Iddings!" cried the chemist. "It looks almost sinister; you can't mean to leave it so. The tinsel, the silver globes, the dolls, and candy canes are crowded down in one corner, pell-mell, without beauty or order. The rest of the tree is black. Why have you cut out a little recess in the dark boughs, and there put, so lonely, the silver star that is supposed to ride brightly at the top? And around it four upright candles, above, below, on the left, and on the right, so rigidly?"

"This much order from the riot."

"But the star itself is not balanced; it leans to one side. . . . Why did you arrange the candles in a cross? It doesn't fit Christmas."

"They are four soldiers."

Frau Otto looked attentively at the young man and said, "You are feverish."

"I've been neglecting a cold; it's nothing. Perhaps you could give me an aspirin tablet."

She dosed him with two, and a cup of hot milk to wash them down. "You can't go out now in a sweat," she said. "We must put you up overnight."

"Oh!"

"We'll sit up just a few minutes."

At the opportunity to stay and talk the English teacher

was pleased. He smiled and started to talk about himself, saying, "I remember when I was a boy, in Boston, and at night I used to walk on Washington Street, among the bright lights, and look in the faces of all the people! Dr. Otto, did *you* ever do anything like that? I mean, not necessarily in Boston . . ." He went on in the same vein. After a few moments, Frau Otto rose and excused herself—though indeed there was nothing scandalous that he had to say.

"You're strange, Iddings!" said Otto, thinking of the uncanny tree, which, he felt, would frighten his child. "Maybe I ought to call the doctor."

"A different person exactly!" said Clark. "I don't apologize for talking about myself because nothing is more important than that we understand one another."

"I understand you less and less."

Soon it was past midnight. The chemist was disturbed about his daughter, that a rude fright was in store for her when she saw the Christmas tree. He speculated on the possibility of putting his guest to bed and then stealing down to redecorate it. He could not foresee that this tree would be the merriest his daughter ever had; for throughout the morning, her newly gotten toys—dolls, a house and furniture, a mechanical fire-engine—all lying neglected, she kept climbing a chair to right the lopsided star and then, dancing for joy, knocked it awry again with paper balls aimed from across the room.

In the afternoon, several visitors, teachers, dropped in at Dr. Otto's—Messrs. Bell and Flint; Dr. Croydon, the dean; and Miss Cohalan, the registrar. Iddings Clark continued in the same nervously intimate strain; his sleep had been only moderately feverish, enough to generate almost pleasant dreams—and these he now proceeded to expound in minute detail.

Otto took Dean Croydon aside. "He's not well. I tried to keep him in bed but he won't stay."

"What is his temperature?"

"Normal."

"You see," cried Clark, "there is nothing we're not capable of!"

"Nothing is more false!" said the Dean sharply. "We think ourselves creatures of any chance fancy, not as we really are—just as, brutally frank with rage, we tell our friends what we think of them in a rage, not what we really think."

The situation rapidly became strained. Each of the friends cast his eyes upon the ground to avoid looking at the others; only Iddings himself eagerly sought them out with his eyes.

"When all know too much, all are ashamed," thought Otto.

"It's lucky he's taken ill during the holidays; he'll be better by the start of school," thought Dean Croydon.

III.

On New Year's Day, which fell on a Tuesday, Iddings Clark was scheduled to deliver the annual Hooker Lecture on Literature, in the auditorium of the High School. And this year an extraordinary audience had gathered, for not only was Clark always a treat as a lecturer, but everyone remembered the dramatic incident that had befallen him the week before, his dead faint in the midst of the singing. Many children, as well as the grown-ups, came to stare at him in curiosity; the ushers were given orders to shunt those boys not with their parents up into the balcony—and there they sat, staring down, their lips pressed against the shiny rail.

Dean Croydon introduced the speaker as their "beloved friend who occasioned so much anxiety on the day before Christmas, but who has since quite recovered." The subject of the lecture was "The Incentives of Poetry."

When the English teacher stepped to the front, however, he seemed the opposite of quite recovered—thin, white, with somber eyes. Everywhere there was a leaning forward to see him better. He said in a strained voice, "I had intended to speak of poetry as objects and forms, and of the excitement of *inventing* something: for there is a pleasure in creating a new structure, or in elaborating a living plot, as if a man were Prometheus. But instead I shall speak of it as communication, and why it is that one person talks to another.

"But talking to you," he cried suddenly, "is like talking to a wall!"

As he spoke the pink color mounted in his face, and his dark eyes burned. He made no gestures, but with white-knuckled fingers gripped the edges of the lectern, and his voice came forth over his hands. " 'Come alive, Galatea!' cried that famous sculptor, 'that I may talk to you!' and he kissed a statue not yet free of the formless rock. What a pity that centuries of history could not create a human friend for him!"

People looked at one another.

"Poets speak clearly," said the lecturer, "sometimes with exact symbols but sometimes literally. It is amazing how often they say literally what they mean. It's easier to interpret it as tropes, as fiction. As irony! he can't mean that! he's *joking*.

"I myself as a reader have felt summoned to the rescue, at least to offer handshake, if I cannot provide what is really called for. But in such cases, I have noticed, the poet was always conveniently dead. In criticism, we read the facts more literally from long ago.

"And what if he has *just* died? Aren't you ashamed that you let him exist like that?

"Needless to say, one does not have to be a poet to cry out very clearly and be unheard. Your silent neighbor is standing there with a tell-tale face; you continue your conversation as if it were not so."

"Our friend Iddings," whispered Miss Cohalan, seated behind the speaker, "is likely to go out of bounds, don't you think?"

"I have not heard more moving eloquence," said the Dean sharply. One would not have expected him to say this.

Thumbing through the volume on the lectern, Iddings began to bombard them with quotations from Baudelaire. "Ah!" he cried, as if struck—

> "Et le printemps et la verdure
>   ont tant humilié mon cœur
>   que j'ai puni sur une fleur
>   l'insolence de la nature—

'the springtime and green humiliated me so, I took out on a flower the insolence of nature.'

" 'J'ai plus de souvenirs que si j'avais mille ans'— 'I have more memories than if I were a thousand years old!' "

In the balcony the children began a whispered debate.

"He says he is a thousand years old!"

"No. He says it was as if he was a thousand years old."

"Mr. Clark is a *thousand years old!*"

"Quiet!" said the usher.

The afternoon growing late, the snow outside falling thicker—the hall became dim. Yet all, straining their eyes in the dusk, thought that they saw the speaker clearly.

"It's a common experience," he said, "young people in love are unable, even if they try, to keep from talking about the person.

"But when they are *out of love,* still wounded, hopelessly hunting around in every direction for sympathy— then they *still* talk (making all ashamed)."

Suddenly—just as he had begun, and as he continued —he stopped. His voice no longer came in separate gusts across his white-knuckled hands. But the faint light that seemed to play on him on the platform persisted.

They began to clap and abruptly found themselves in pitch darkness. The applause grew loud. There was a hubbub of people trying to put on coats and galoshes in the dark. At last the lights came ablaze. Blinded, the people took this opportunity to add to the infectious applause, but the speaker had slipped away during the darkness.

"Would the young man have us go around confessing each other?"

"No. It is only that we read poetry more sympathetically."

" 'Come alive, Galatea! cried that famous sculptor.' He said that well."

"How pale he looked at the beginning!"

"I thought that he was going to keel over again."

"How was he at the end?"

"You couldn't tell, it was so dark."

IV.

The next day, it was a Wednesday, school reconvened.
The snow lay deep on the ground, but the sun shone
brightly; it reflected from the snow and sky and poured
into the large-windowed classrooms. At nine o'clock,
flushed and damp from a snowfight, the boys and girls
came trooping in.

Out of his little cubicle off the English lecture room,
Mr. Clark stepped to face his class: he was stark naked
except for his spectacles and a Whittier in his right hand.

With cries of fright the young people fled up the aisle
and through the doors they had just entered; before the
period-gong had finished sounding, the classroom was
emptied—except of one small girl who sat spellbound in
the front row, and a boy who stopped near the door on
his way out.

"I'll tell Dean Croydon," he said, and left.

Now Rea, the small girl, and the teacher of English
were left alone, facing each other, she seated behind a
desk, he standing naked beside his table.

"Why don't you run off with the others, child?" said
Iddings.

"I'm hot and tired with playing; I'd rather stay here for
the class."

"They have an unexpected holiday out of me."

"Won't there be a class, Mr. Clark?"

"The assignment was *Snowbound,* by Whittier."

"I read it," said the girl.

"It's not a great poem. What the devil prompted him
to write it?"

She stared at him closely, from head to foot, and said,
"Is it true, what they say, Mr. Clark, that you are a thousand years old?"

"Heavens, no."

"They say that you said you was a thousand years old,
and I see that in some places you're grown all over
with hair."

"I am 31," he said, smiling.

"I'm 13, just the opposite," said Rea. She kept looking up into his face.

"What's your name, girl?" he said sharply, "my glasses are sweated over and I can't see you clearly."

"Rea."

"Rea! that's a strange name. It means the guilty one. Rea. Is there any of the boys you love?"

"Donald Worcester."

"Come here, child," he said in a tight voice. "Have you told him that you love him?"

"I wrote on the school wall with chalk," she cried; 'REA LOVES DONALD W.' Just as if somebody else wrote it."

She rose from her bench and came beside the teacher.

"That's clever!" he said. "I wonder what he'll do."

At this—as if for no reason—she burst into sobs. The door in the rear opened, and in came the Dean with a posse of instructors summoned from their classes for this extraordinary occasion. With a cry of fright the girl fled across the bars of sunlight out of the room.

"She's crying. What did you do to her?" asked the Dean.

"I did not!"

"Iddings! what's the meaning of this?"

"It's the story of Hawthorne's, *The Minister's Black Veil.*"

"I don't remember. It's many years since I read Hawthorne," said the Dean.

"I at least shan't wear a black veil!" exclaimed Iddings Clark exaltedly, and a wave of color swept over him, from his feet to his forehead.

The Dean took off his coat and flung it round the shoulders of his trembling friend.

"This is serious; this is awful, Iddings Clark," he said. "We won't hear the end of it. Where are your clothes? Get dressed. It's *my* fault; I knew it was coming. At least we'll try to hush the matter up. It won't come before the School Board. But how can I answer for the consequences?"

New York City
1933

FIGHTS

I.   A STATUE OF STRENGTH AND WEAKNESS

I

This allegorical sculpture consists of two figures, Strength and Weakness, represented by a man and a woman. Strength is constraining her on her back, mostly by his mass and weight rather than his power, his knee in her belly, his legs pinning her knees; and his two hands are grasping her wrists, keeping her arms wide and helpless. On the face of Strength is a look of intense perplexity.

The meaning of his perplexity is that Strength does not want to exert force on Weakness, yet she is intent on hurting him, wants to hit him. On his left shoulder and the right side of his back, he is marked with bleeding scratches that she inflicted before he pinned her.

Being powerful, Strength wants not to force but to rule. But this puts him in difficulty when his power is challenged by the violence of Weakness. The difficulty is expressed by the perplexity on his face, but even more tellingly by the strain of his muscles far beyond what is needed to hold her down, as if he hoped to subdue her merely by forced *inaction,* while at the same time not transmitting his hurtful power to her but constraining it within himself. The real struggle is the knot of his own muscles. If the stone could speak, he would be saying, "Do you give up?"—when she will not give up.

But Weakness, on the contrary, wants to strike and be struck just in order to have her own nature be proved; what she wants is not to be ruled but to be defeated. Therefore on her face is a look of exultant wilfulness and guile; she is waiting her chance. So it is Strength who bears the marks of wounds and effort, whereas Weakness is happy and untouched. This is a triumph of the artist who thereby, in expressing her nature, can avoid portraying any ugliness of deficiency.

So these two remain fixed, by his perplexity and her wilfulness; and it is this static moment that the sculptor has seized on for his composition.

2.

But it is not only in this moment of spurious external struggle that Strength is characterized by the conflict among his own powers. The artist has seized on the present struggle to show obvious signs of this interior conflict, a knot of muscles, a frown. But by these he calls attention to other features of the figure of Strength that are *not* involved in the unequal external struggle but express the *habitual* constraint that characterizes him. Thus, the habit-formed lines of his face express the day to day perplexity of withholding his full powers in order not to do damage in the world as it is. The modeling of his ankles and toes has a nervous alertness whose meaning is deep just because in the present struggle he has no need of it, for it is clear that by the weight of his knee and shoulders alone, resting in her belly and pinning her arms, he is easily able to hold her down. By these details we are shown the Strength of all his life, as it acts in this particular conflict but abides in him in every case.

Seen so, his posture is almost that of a dancer rather than a wrestler. There is something fastidious and almost effeminate, in the way he doles out his force in accordance with the just measure of an idea rather than the vigor of an instinct. Except that he seems to be saying, "It's not yet time!" to loose his forces. And we are overwhelmed by the pathos of waste, for when will it ever be the time?

What is here presented to us, we realize in a flash, is an effigy of Fear! Certainly not fear of something in front, but self-fear. What *crime* is it he sees inside him, that keeps him from striking, perhaps from striking *again?* Did he once strike?

So it is not far-fetched that helpless Weakness will not give up now. For she is in danger. And this gives a *dark* sense to that look of baffled perplexity on the face of Strength.

We see, now, why the artist has shown us the woman untouched. In this allegorical art where the outward shows the inward, she is not wounded nor contorted by guilt. Her wilfulness is innocence. Her hair is widespread on the ground; her lips and eyes are wide; there is here nothing guarded. She is willing to scatter her resources, even to blows given and received. She is screaming, in stone.

In such a moment, before the perpetration of a crime, the sculptor has fixed these two forever.

3.

It is odd. The stone figures seem to be in motion!

Is not Strength in the very act of bringing down his great head and shoulders in a kiss? and she of relaxing to this kiss? His hands, we see, are *slipping* from her wrists to cover her hands palm to palm; and his knee is sliding to rest touching her knee. This is why he is withholding his weight: it is with the considerateness of a lover, for it is not yet time to lie full weight. It will be time when their excitement is intense enough to transmute force and pain into pleasure. What we took to be a fastidiousness in his posture is nothing but the indefiniteness of beginning to change position. The perplexity on his face is his passing from one thought to another; one would say that he has just noticed that she is no longer resisting.

The artist has seized on a kind of *lapse* between strong contraries in order to get the static moment for sulpture, and thereby he seems to have dissolved the fixity of sculpture into motion; for the eye cannot rest in this presented moment.

It is a natural transition. For it is not with impunity that, body to body, they have paralyzed their own strongest purposes. They are unprepared for the feeling that wells up.

Only love can dissolve the thunderous block of place in which Strength has imprisoned himself. Only gentle Violence can assuage the crime to which he is paralyzed to commit himself.

The sculptor has chosen the moment when the lovers are confused, lost. Yet—not like the melting loves of Rodin—they are quite disengaged from the formless rock.

Now notice how the artist has given to Strength, and to the breasts of the woman, the beginning of erection. In this there is nothing far-fetched; it would often occur in persons wrestling.

II. A PAGE OF SKETCHES OF FIGHTS

HOT FIGHTERS

These two fighters have one mind, to cut each other down. They are going about it hot, doing as much immediate damage as possible, neither one defending himself. Yet they do not much feel their hurt because each is thinking only of destroying the other. Hurt is a blast blowing up the fire. Stung, they hit harder.

They do not frustrate each other. It is even conceivable that both could succeed: for instance, if it is a boxing match, the one might knock out the other and be standing over him with glassy eyes, but when the referee counts four, he himself falls down unconscious.

Each is not much aware of his own body, nor that his legs are braced against the ground. The blows he throws are attracted by, created by, the face to be demolished, and he does not hear his hissing breaths nor feel how his punches have bounded up from the center of the earth. But the impact is glowing loud with joy.

Neither has the aim to inflict damage, but simply to destroy. So naturally they inflict a lot of hurt and damage until, according to their unequal power and skill and luck, one of them is no longer able to carry on his single-minded aim. He is surprised when he is no longer busy cutting the other down. He was not counting on any other activity. His damaged body has suddenly become a huge thing. And the object before him is fading away, out of reach. A fist looms and hits him—this time he is immensely aware of its slow coming—and he falls.

Looming over him, the face of the victor only momentarily flashes the look of achievement, for it is at once crossed by trying to remember his ulterior purpose in the fight. So the one lies with a look of surprise in his anguish, and the other in his success has a wandering mind.

A COLD FIGHTER

This time, with the fighter single-minded to destroy is matched a man who is prudently defending himself against being hurt, biding his time till he can coldly smash and cut his opponent down. This man is not single-minded for he is afraid of hurt and death, but he controls his fear by will.

Soon the anger in the fight is streaked with hatred. Perhaps, just as he defends his body with his guard, the cold and deliberate fighter is warding off feeling hurt by taking relish in smashing the other towards his finish. He wants to *damage* him, it is part of his plan. And he is conscious of throwing every blow.

But suppose that for a moment (or for good) he himself is badly hurt and loses control of the fight, while the other still keeps coming single-mindedly to get him. He is in confusion and may be gripped by panicky fear, not knowing what to do and unable to rally spontaneously. For, centered in himself, he has *not* simply been conveying his punches coming up from the center of the earth through his heels across his back to their impact, and now he is out of touch. He crouches as small as he can behind his guard, while the aggressor rains blows on that not impregnable fortress.

But communing with himself behind his guard, he recovers control, he raises his head, and he resumes with a more steely will, like an ax. And finally he has put together enough damaging blows to cut his opponent down, like a tree. Then he stands over him, breathing heavily, safe, clenching and unclenching his fists, beginning to mutter— till at last his passion rises to the surface and he is shaking with rage.

HEADS OF VICTORS

A boy who has fought single-mindedly only to destroy his opponent, and then afterwards his wandering mind finally realizes that he has won: he is grinning and waving his hands in rapturous appreciation of himself, and shouting, "Ma! I won! I won!"

Another boy who fought single-mindedly, but fighting is the only thing in the world that he does honorably and naively, so afterwards his face at once narrows again to the settled suspicious leer of a conceited gutter rat.

Another boy, a deliberate and skillful killer who has maintained all through the fight an impassive countenance; but now he is swept by uncontrollable fear and you can hear the loud clicking of his teeth.

A COWARD

A coward, whose blind terror of hurt or death—or simply of the fact that the other is angry with him—has paralyzed his arms so that he can neither strike a blow nor even lift his guard to protect himself. The other slugs him.

His only recourse is to fall down and be passive, screaming in pain even before he is hurt. But this is not a defense, for the other simply mauls and kicks him like a sack. This beating is not cruel so long as the aim is single-minded to destroy him rather than to hurt or damage him. It is ugly when, as a worthless hoodlum might beat a cowardly homosexual, he is vindictively punishing him and taking satisfaction in that; or both are taking satisfaction in that.

But the radical evil in cowardice is that the coward, unable to stand up for himself, has nevertheless adventured into this situation where he has to fight. Doing so, he has not respected, he has violated, his own animal terror, his timorous nature. A man like that should be circumspect.

But it happens that just when he is being beaten up, he may suddenly no longer be paralyzed. In a flash he single-mindedly accepts his terror and, jumping up by surprise, he takes to his heels. He is likely to get away, for his fright is stronger than the killer's will.

Then the tables are turned. The coward is a coward no longer, but simply a weaker but swifter man. He taunts and jeers at his enemy from a safe distance and makes him look like a fool.

A MAN FORCED INTO A FIGHT

Yet it is a melancholy but common thing in the world
(and makes for a melancholy world) that while the one
fighter is for some reason single-mindedly bent on destroying a man, that man does not want this fight; he
does not believe in it, he does not think that it is worth
the hurt and damage involved. He has been forced into
it, and it happens that he cannot quit the field.

Even though he guards himself skillfully, he continues
to be hurt and damaged. He fights poorly because he
does not mean it, to destroy or even hurt the aggressor,
but he wants to establish some different relation with him
which is incompatible with fighting with him, but which
the other will not allow him to establish.

Hurt, he is not stung but made sick. Naturally, doing
something that seems to him senseless, he is awkward.
It is evident that he is pulling his punches, so that he looks
disdainful, too proud to fight or too superior to fight; indeed, he *is* disdainful; except that he is bewildered what
to do and he is wincing because he is badly hurt. But even
worse, if he happens for a moment to be stung and comes
back fighting strong, he is at once paralyzed by prudence,
knowing that any damage he now inflicts he will later
have to remedy.

So even a strong, wise, brave, and benevolent man is
often cut to pieces in this world by the passionate inten-
sity of weakness and ignorance. Somehow he cannot draw
on the strength he has. (How then does he "have" it?)

He is felled and on his face are hurt feelings at having
been misunderstood. The glee on the face of the victor
standing over him fades to its usual spiteful stupidity.

ARJUNA

Is the just man, then, powerless? No, for here finally is a
fight—if it can be called so—where though the one fighter
is single-mindedly in error bent on destroying a superior
man, the superior man is going about his duty and is *in-
cidentally* cutting him down like an executioner. Like an

executioner, continually drawing on the power that is in patience, wisdom, compassion, and the joy of life.

This hero is no warrior. He is fastidiously afraid of being hurt, for he has an affectionate love for his body. But he draws courage, as Socrates said, from his idea. The superior man is not fighting in *this* fight (perhaps in some different fight in which he is in agony at midnight, for he is not too proud to fight), nevertheless his fist is a hammer from which the other reels back stunned. And though the inferior man rallies viciously, the right is like an impersonal sledgehammer and fells him.

It was not the hero's wish to degrade his opponent who was so fanatically throwing away his life in despair, unable to prevail against the future of the nature of things; but inevitably the poor wretch takes his defeat as an insult and expires purple with rage, as ignorant in death as he was in life.

The victor is Arjuna, to whom evil does not cling as water does not cling to the shining lotus. He is standing in his chariot with Krishna the charioteer, and they sound their whelks named Fivefold and God-Given.

HEADS OF BEATEN MEN

The head of a man who has fought single-mindedly in error, and still in death he imagines that he was worsted by a trick. There is unbelief in his glazed eyes.

The head of another man with closed eyes, smiling, enlightened in death by the precious knowledge that he no longer has to try.

THE DETECTIVE STORY

I.

Long ago when I had fallen out of love, I decided to write a detective story, and this was to be the plot of it:

A detective is assigned to the solution of a number of crimes which bear the mark of one criminal. As he pursues his investigations he feels that more and more closely he can understand, and sympathize with, the mind of this criminal; this gives him an increasing insight into the crimes. "No one can solve a crime," he declares, "unless first he puts himself in the criminal's place." And at last, at the last crime, he discovers himself committing it; he, the criminal, has been pursuing himself all along.

Fired by this interesting idea I set to work and soon had written many pages. I called the detective Mr. Fort George after the neighborhood in which I happened to live. "Soon at this rate I shall be at the end!" But this very self-gratulation—which was the last I would enjoy in this work—tempted me to reread what I had written. Here began my troubles.

What I had written was very nice, but not worthy of my fine plot. For all at once I came to see my idea not as a simple detective story but as a detective epic, a narrative of crime detection in its most general form, the philosophy, indeed, of detective stories. But who was I, and how was I fitted, to undertake such an enterprise? I had as yet committed no crimes, I had no experience of the police and no knowledge of criminology.

I began to do research. Even while I was hard at work on a little crime, I struck up an acquaintance with the corner policeman. He lent me his blackjack and playfully imprisoned my wrists in handcuffs. I loitered in the station house and played poker. I planned and executed a complicated robbery of the Great Bear Butcher Shop and got thirty-two dollars, which I later returned through the Post Office. I read Ferri and Lombroso and the celebrated Essay of Beccaria.

All this was not done in a day. To execute the robbery alone, as I planned it, I had to seduce and then train an idiot-boy to knock down a blind old hag at the one moment when, every morning, she passed in front of the butcher shop, so that in the confusion I could rifle the cash register. A thing like that took seven or eight weeks. But always I had the burning confidence that finally I would be able to return to my story. While I was doing everything else, the idea of my story shone bright above it all, like a lamp that lighted the other things but was itself constantly before my eyes.

To my dismay I found myself farther afield. I could no longer unify my material. I now found myself in the perplexity of a problem of style. Where previously my plan had been adequate but only my experience limited, now the result of my researches, my material—the Irish humor of the police station, the fear and trembling of the crime, the odd statistics that I learned from the anthropometric school—all these refused to be collapsed into a story. I took the matter this way and that way, by a hundred different handles, and wrote a first sentence but could not write the second sentence. As soon as I put down a word, a world of experience was excluded forever; and, of course, the harder I tried, the more thronging memories came into my mind unwilling to be omitted. That lamp of mine illumined so much that I could hardly raise my eyes from the ground and had but a distant and hazy image of it itself.

I turned to the experts in this kind of unity, to the creators of Sherlock Holmes and Arsène Lupin, to Gaboriau, Poe, and Wilkie Collins, and even to dozens of modern small fry. I read two hundred episodes of Nick Carter, gathering the only complete collection in New York— which I have since sold at a small profit. In two years I read 1,712 detective stories. In the end a positive physical loathing overcame me; I could not conceive of myself

adding to the detective literature of the Western world.
In despair I wrote the following two verses of an epic
poem:

> Of those who look with sidelong sight
> at the blue police with gloves of white—

and this effort killed the idea forever.

II.

In this crisis, suddenly—for every transformation in this
curious history caught me by surprise, though I can only
too well account for each one—my problem presented to
me a different face, because I was desperate and, what is
equally true, because the foreknowledge of this very
change made me turn away from what I had been doing
up to now. "The trouble is," I now thought, "that I have
not conceived of my plot profoundly. Up to now the con-
ception has been superficial, on the level of a detective
story or a realistic sociological description; but obviously
the profound story here is the case of a Dual Personality
rediscovering his ego."

I immediately saw that my story of the detective who
pursues himself from crime to crime was nothing but the
self-analysis of a split personality disturbed by the irruption into his life of a number of alien symbols and com-
pulsive acts (those are the "crimes"); spurred on by a
need that becomes ever more acute and passionate, he
achieves reintegration by discovering the truth about himself! That is, a simple clinical case, but what ancient literature! for it was half Dr. Jekyll and Mr. Hyde but also
half Oedipus the King who with growing horror hastens
on to discover that he is the man who slew his father at
the three-forked road. A dual personality by ignorance,
the bedfellow of Jocasta was two persons, her husband
and her son, but one of them came to confront the other:
the cunning Oedipus who solved the mystery of the
Sphinx, engaged on his second piece of detective work.

My new plot. But what was to be the cause of the hero's initial loss of half of himself? Sophocles did not find
it necessary to explain why a finite man should be in

ignorance and come to grief; but I, fired with enthusiasm by my new and remarkable plot, was determined to explain this too. Once more I began my studies, more soberly perhaps than before, but with undiminished energy, just as if I had gained a second wind. I no longer hoped to dash off my work in a month, once I could get started, but the idea of at least starting burned before me like a lamp.

I read about the multiple personalities of Miss Sally Beauchamp, as described by Dr. Prince; Dr. Rivers on shellshock; and here and there in Freud. The phenomena of hypnosis and somnambulism occupied my attention, and the twin sister of somnambulism, the act of falling in love.

Ah! "Why do I want to write a novel at all, and why have I invented this particular plot?" I asked myself; for where previously, writing a detective story, I had been obliged to leave my desk to fraternize with policemen and execute a robbery on a butcher shop, I now naturally turned inward and began to question my own motives.

"It was when I had just fallen out of love that I began to write this novel. Was it because I was afraid that I should have nothing to fill my time that I turned to an exciting and fantastic occupation, not realizing how deeply I should soon become involved, but inwardly knowing it very well? It is not by chance that this business has come to fill my time day and night. Or on the contrary was it the very prospect of undertaking a novel —but not the novel I was then thinking of—a prospect not yet born in me but operative all the same, that made me fall out of love, so that my love was dead before I knew it, and before ever I invented the reasons, such as they were, that allowed me consciously to fall out of love? If indeed I did fall out of love? and this novel is not just a screen, a stratagem to distract my attention.—What is the plot of my novel? It is the story of a man who thinks that he has fallen out of love; but he is troubled by the irruption into his present of experiences which he no longer recognizes, for they were organized under the forgotten signs of his ancient love. Disturbed, anxious, soon panicky, he hastens on from clue to clue, until he finds that he is still in love . . ."

At this I began to tremble, at the thought that perhaps, after so many years, a certain face would return in nightmares as she used. But my dreams were far less suggestible than my waking, and no face reappeared; for I had fallen out of love. Instead, I proceeded with the greater assiduity to study for my novel; for it kept seeming to me that very shortly I should start to write again, although now, looking back, I see that every step was taking me farther afield.

You cannot understand the criminal, Fort George had declared, unless you put yourself in his place. This was the first guiding principle. Now I added to it a second: The first step in detective work is a self-analysis, an inquiry into the mind of the detective himself. Who is he? what are his motives? For if this is not known, how can he put himself in the place of the criminal?

Thus the new self-analytical frame of mind that I brought to my novel became the plot itself, the psychology of my empirical ego. I changed the name of my hero and called him Paul, my own empirical name.

It was during this period of my life that I married and, so to speak, settled down. (I became a kind of anarchist and committed some public crimes.) All this, as I then thought, was merely a means to an end: to satisfy myself, in order to hasten on to my novel—which all the while was becoming a dim memory.

I bought a home in Brooklyn and the years passed slowly by.

III.

Despite my hard work and new humility, one morning I awoke to discover that my story had changed itself again. I could not recognize what I had been working on. When I thought of it, that old story of me seemed a worthless object to waste so much time on. What sort of fellow must I have been to be absorbed in such a thing? The only serious study, I now saw, worthy of engaging a man's attention, was the following problem in logic: how is it possible for any proposition to be adequate to its truth?

Not the case of a detective tracking a criminal in order

to convict himself; nor of a split personality feverishly seeking out himself; but of how the minds of all of us try somehow to understand those objects given to us (these were the "crimes").

But this effort of the mind seems futile, for the mind is only rational, and all things are infected with irrationality, given to us in an arbitrary way. The contradictions multiply and the investigation becomes more and more desperate.

When this transformation of my plot into a problem occurred, I was not in a state of disgust, as I had been previous to the prior transformation; nor did I now become joyful and enthusiastic. I realized that I was not the master of this transformation, but as if looking on, with fascination.

I saw by what process my psychological novel turned into a problem of logic. For how was it possible for my detective, by looking into his own consciousness—on the maxim, to analyze himself—to find himself there? If he was there, how could he be looking from outside? How was he to know that what he found there, the strange memories and impulses, was really himself? How does a person know, in general, that when he has found something it is what he was looking for? Only by having a criterion (so I decided at that time!). Thus Paul's search for himself became the search for a criterion of the adequacy of subject and object in general; and there was no longer any use in calling him by my empirical name.

My detective was to have a third maxim. First he saw that in order to understand the criminal it was necessary to put himself in his place. (A strange thing for a detective to think of! obviously it was only he who had committed the crime who would ever have thought of it.) Secondly he discovered that even before that he must find himself out. (A peculiar inference! obviously it was only he whose personality was split, etc.) Now he realized that the foremost thing is to have a criterion of adequacy, otherwise how is one ever to know that he has indeed found himself out. (A curious dilemma!—it would occur only to a man living haphazardly.)

I read the *Theætetus* of Plato and Aristotle *On the Soul*; and what St. Thomas Aquinas had to say, and the

Discourse on Method. I noticed, as I came to the later writers, that the search of the subject for its object was becoming more desperate; until, in the *Phenomenology* of Hegel, I was face to face with a detective novel like my own, a hundred years old. I read the *Appearance* of F. H. Bradley and was persuaded that it was impossible in principle, when once the subject and the object have been split asunder, ever to bring them together again.

I began to feel that my novel would never be written after all, it was impossible in principle. Heretofore I had been buoyed up, if not always by enthusiasm, at least by the sober conviction that the longer and harder I worked, the more substance I would give to my novel, as an animal long gestated is most perfectly formed. Now, whichever way I turned I saw that there was no use in proceeding further. For if the subject were different from the object, how could it know it? and if the subject were the same as the object, how could it know it?

Occupied with this conveniently endless perplexity, which I soon saw lurking under a thousand different disguises, so that even the most simple thing was a fatal paradox, I do not know how much time passed during which I did not sit down to work on my novel. (And these were the years, of course, during which I divorced my wife and did not bother to live anywhere and made no use of anything I knew.)

Very thoughtful, I read over some of what I had written long ago, and for the first time several passages became clear to me. I saw, for instance, why I had said that my great detective, Caspar Fort George, would never convict anyone except on circumstantial evidence; for how was his mind to come to grips with the actual crime?

His methods—I had written at that time—were pure. He never experimented, tortured the facts; never laid traps for the criminal, nor an ambush to nab him in the act; never extorted a confession by the third degree. His attitude was passive: let the facts come, do nothing to force the issue.

This seemed unreasonable. Why should one not expedite matters by entering actively into those "facts" and making them talk? He used to say, "I refuse to infect the object with myself . . . I have never gone to work on a hunch. Just because I should myself have committed such and such a crime (this is the hunch), shall I convict somebody else on my manufactured evidence?" Again, "My mind is nothing but a schematism, a framework of classes into which fall the clues—till they form a legible pattern."

"What sort of classes?" asked Hepzibah.

"M. is a such and such, of such and such a physical and emotional type, in such and such a stress of circumstances. This pistol is a such and such; this bullet-wound is a such and such—

"In this way I will contrive an enormous fabrication and never come to the criminal."

"Is not such evidence merely circumstantial evidence?" she objected. "The conclusion based on it is only probable."

"Right! if I were a *judge* I should never convict on this evidence."

So long ago! How far I had drifted from this original story. These fragments coming to light after many years and changed by the weathering (for in the beginning I could never have understood what I then wrote so lightly: "My mind is a framework" and "never come to the individual")—these surviving fragments made the ruin more ancient than if there were no trace left, just as the broken drums of marble columns, transformed by the weathering of years, perhaps sprouting weeds from the dirt in a crack,

> à chaque printemps, vainement éloquente,
> au chapiteau brisé verdit une autre acanthe,

says Hérédia—vegetation from the newest season—make Greece and Rome more distant. I no longer thought, as once I had, "What a pity I did not hasten on when I was able and finish my story in one flourish!" for I understood that if I stopped at the end of Chapter Two it was that something was amiss, and all my efforts subsequently were predestined by a contradiction from the first. Either in the plot or in myself—at first it appeared only as a difficulty of style—and I vainly tried to remedy it by research, introspection, point of view. Until finally the root of my error is laid bare. I could not come to grips with things.

IV.

Now I have come to understand this novel. This is the plot of it;

There is a man who, still young, determines to convince himself of his freedom and power by making something, for instance, a story. After years of trying he finds that, being as he is, he is powerless to accomplish anything at all. He cannot give existence to any whole thing, for where is the existence to come from? The work dies in his hands. Far from being able to give existence to something outside himself, he learns that he cannot maintain even his own life. On every side he is beset by questions that he cannot answer, and he finally cries out at the very edge of despair, "Where, where, where shall I put my next step?" But in this crisis by the grace of God he is no longer cut off from his Creator, and is assigned to his proper place.

Was this, then, the story that had kept appearing to me in variations, like Proteus, god of the ocean, but perhaps now I have caught him in a net? In the guise of a detective who is able to solve the series of crimes only when he is himself the criminal; of the split personality who finds (let us say) that one of his symptoms is what he really wants; and so forth. It is not by his own efforts that the split personality is made whole, or that mind and object are one with each other. Help comes—if of course it does—from elsewhere.

It is not to write a novel, I think, that I have been brought on this lifelong tour, as it were, among many provinces and kingdoms; but to be made aware of the true condition that I am in. For each time, faced with a question that cannot be answered and cannot be ignored, unable to cope with a simple problem of style—I imagined that by retreating to a new vantage ground I would then have firm footing and could return to resolve every difficulty. So I retreated from my desk to the company of the corner policeman, and from there to myself, and from there to the theory of error. But I found the vantage ground itself give way beneath me; and indeed, if it was solid ground that I wanted, I would better have lingered on with the corner policeman! But the realization of my true condition could only, it seems, be effected by a painful retreat, struggling at every step. Without fighting a losing fight, I could not, it seems, come to the realization of the true perplexity of my condition, as it is said: Seek and ye shall find. (That is, in my case, precisely that "you shan't find.") If I had not in the first place fallen out of love I should never have entered on this way.

I read the Book of Job and the Epistles of St. Paul. And it seemed to me that apart from the critical writings of Kant and Maimonides the books of philosophy were love stories. That insistent book that keeps posing a question, the *Commentary on the Epistle to the Romans* by Karl Barth; and *The Castle*, by Franz Kafka, a Jew like myself. I saw how many men by many different highroads stumbled into a dead end.

Some get to the point, I am told, by brilliant successes, as it says in *Paradise Lost*:

> —greedily they plucked
> the fruitage fair to sight . . .
> instead of fruit
> chew'd bitter ashes which the offended taste
> with spattering noise rejected.

Others by a string of failures (for with some people nothing seems to succeed, even the most expected probabilities),

> Oft they assayed,
> hunger and thirst constraining; drugg'd as oft,
> with hatefullest disrelish writhed their jaws,
> with soot and cinders filled.

After a while the meaning of a string of failures becomes clear enough. And still others, like myself, by continued efforts, more or less ambiguous, neither successful nor failing, but tempting one further.

Now, it seems, I could put myself to write any kind of incoherent paradox, for I am no longer troubled by a problem of logic. On the other hand, this novel of mine could be a kind of *Odyssey*, the story of a sailor trying to return home; except that Ulysses knows there is an Ithaca, for he was born there, but we at the end of the story find that it is precisely this that we do not know.

It may be granted that I, too, shall one day be shown where and what I ought properly to work at, and what is to be the end of it. But I know, and this is a fourth maxim that I have discovered, that by myself I shall never be able to find this out. And now I understand, or hope I do, that whereas from my side I cannot go on with this work, I need not despair but only wait, or I need only despair and wait.

New York City
1934-1935

VIC McMAHON

While our soft-lighted bus flew through the gathering darkness, I could not help regarding with admiration the driver, whose name was Vic McMahon. He was the shepherd of the passengers. Confident and easy—our lives were in good hands—the passengers readjusted their seats to the reclining position, prepared for a night of travel. Our lights pierced the darkness; we were borne swiftly onward.

But not too swiftly. When we came to a railroad crossing, Vic McMahon brought us to a dead stop, in accordance with state law, and half-opened the door so he could hear any danger coming. And we rode on.

Reliable, obedient to the law, the guardian of the passengers bore us onward toward St. Louis at forty-eight miles an hour. There was comfort in this steady progress through the starless night! one of the passengers was already asleep. A nervous comfort.

As we rounded a curve, our headlights illumined a great poster depicting a small boy and girl menaced by a motorcar, and with the legend: *"Please! They Cannot Be Replaced."* Paid for by the Highway Commission of the Commonwealth of Iowa. This recognition of danger by the Commonwealth gave us, inside the soft-lighted bus, safe in the hands of careful Vic McMahon, a *thrill* of ease!

Vic was engaged in talk with another driver, named Sheeler, who happened to be a passenger; he spoke over his shoulder, never taking his eyes from the hurrying road; and the conversation was about a new license required in Wisconsin. Drivers were obliged to go to Madison for a medical examination.

"I had a certificate from a private doctor," said Vic, "but it was no use."

"Stiff exam?" said Ed Sheeler.

"Right down to the bones! Blood test, ears. They hit you on the knee with the little hammer."

"Did you jump?"

We came to a railroad-crossing and Vic brought the bus to a dead stop. Here there was a sign

STOP   LOOK   LISTEN

In obedience also to the last of these, he half-opened the door. Then on we drove.

"Yes, sure I jumped," said Vic McMahon. "There's a new law so they won't give you a license now unless you're 5 foot 7 and weigh 160 pounds." He himself looked to be 6 feet and weighed about 200.

Half a dozen persons in the bus were now sleeping, covered with their overcoats, so steadily and quietly we were flying along at 48 miles. Vic dimmed the inside lights.

Again there loomed that sign of the two children, this time with the legend: *"Please! Their Lives Are In Your Hands"*—paid for by the Highway Commission of the Commonwealth of Iowa. And this time I could see that the little boy and girl were hand in hand; the boy was older; and they were on their way to school, menaced by a black motorcar.

And almost immediately, at the next bend, as if the roadside was afire among the bushes, flamed a sign consisting of hundreds of tiny mirrors reflecting our head-lights, and they spelled out in dancing glory the words

TAKE TIME TO BE SAFE

But we were safe! borne thru the black night enclosed in our self-contained and dimly-lighted vehicle at forty-eight miles per hour. Poised on faintly joggling seats, more than half a dozen of the passengers were already asleep, covered by overcoats; and the rest of us—all save Vic McMahon—were hovering in that imaginary world between waking and sleep. In the brief space fitfully illumined by our searchlights as we rounded a bend, nothing was revealed but the solicitude of the Commonwealth of Iowa. No one could escape in any direction the sentiment of cautious comfort.

Vic McMahon, licensed at Madison, more than 160 pounds, and quick to jump when tapped on the knee with a little hammer, our lives are in your hands; *please!* we cannot be replaced. . . .

Half-fallen asleep, I imagined that I was piloting an airplane for the loyalists in the Spanish Civil War, returning to a time of hotter lust. It was the aftermath of a brief battle—the poisonous machine-gun rattle was still echoing in my ears, a faint noise in our bus the occasion of it. Now I couldn't bring the plane down; we hovered in one place, high over the earth; till at last I gave up the effort and was content to remain aloft. Whereat, waking a little, I smiled to feel myself pleasantly poised on the faintly joggling seat, covered with my overcoat. Yes! both I in the bus and I in the dream were content to be, as Keats was when he read the tale of Chaucer, kept "in so sweet a place"—

> I that do ever feel athirst for glory
> could at this moment be content to lie
> meekly upon the grass, as those whose sobbings
> are heard of none beside the mournful robins.

The fact was that this long ride on a bus was my *interval*—between an existence, such as it was, in the East, and a new existence, such as it would be, in the West; so that I was *well* disposed, I think, to enjoy by day the quiet variety of traveling through the countryside, and by night the security of the enclosing blackness, half asleep, in the hands of Vic McMahon.

There was a *rare* social peace among the passengers of

our dimly-lighted bus, our self-contained world,—every desire arrested. The recognition of danger by the Highway Commission of the Commonwealth of Iowa, confessed in dancing reflectors and in colored posters, was realistic, it added to our peace.

Wildly swerving, our bus skidded onto the soft shoulder of the road, but with a wrench of the wheel Vic McMahon brought us back onto the concrete highway.

"Oh no, stay a little longer, Ronny!" said the lady from Des Moines distinctly, out of her dream.

"Steady!" said Ed Sheeler under his breath.

How had it happened? A sudden maneuver of our driver to avoid the lights of a car coming toward us; but one saw clearly, if he happened to be looking, that there was no reason for the maneuver. This little error was a sign that our Vic McMahon did not have the situation well in hand, not, at least, the *whole* situation.

"No! stay a little longer, Ronny!" Those were the very words spoken by the dreaming woman of Des Moines.

"Victory!" was the word, out of our common dream.

We were flying thru the night, devouring the hurrying highway at forty-eight miles per hour.

We slowed down for a railroad crossing and came to a dead stop. The driver half-opened the door to listen. Then on we rode.

Almost immediately after this pause, we again slowed down and, pulling to the side of the road, came to a dead stop.

Vic McMahon opened the door and got out.

"Now what's the matter?" said a gentleman in back.

"It's where he lives," said Ed Sheeler. Looking out, one could see a house among the trees, with one window lit. "He always stops here to kiss his wife goodnight."

"Very nice; when do we get to St. Louis?"

"Oh for heaven's sake!" I said.

"I hope he doesn't take time off for something else!" joked an old stick from under his overcoat.

"He has two kids," said Ed Sheeler, "boy an' girl. You'll see. They come out in bathrobes to see him off and then they go to bed."

There rose a woman's piercing shriek, followed by a thunderous pistol-shot in the silent night.

"In the name of the Father, of the Son, and of the Holy Ghost—" said Ed Sheeler.

The wailing of the children was heard, rising to loud outcries.

The sleepers slept. But we others stared at each other in consternation and climbed out onto the road. At this moment rose the moon, disclosing the landscape.

And here was Vic McMahon carrying a white-garbed woman in his arms; her face was bloody and demolished; his face was pathetically distorted. He had lost his cap. The wailing children in bathrobes took up their stand on his right.

"She is my wife—" were all the words that Vic McMahon could say.

Another passenger climbed down and took his place amongst us, and so we tended to spread out in three quarters of a circle in front of Vic McMahon.

And there was a rare pause there then among us. The children stilled their voices. The moon scattered its honest light on all. I believe that there was no one of us (save perhaps the children) who would have wished to end this rest-period forever. It was so still after the nervous joggling of the bus. All were relieved to be standing on their feet, rather than reclining, so the blood could circulate in its customary way. Also there was in the proportioning of these circumstances a loosening of the soul, so flowed the tears. All were relaxed of flying thru the darkness at forty-eight miles an hour, brought instead to a formal way of standing, so the tears flowed easily down the cheeks of Vic McMahon and others. God! as easily as tears flowed down his cheeks, may the words of my mouth and the meditations of my heart be acceptable.

Chicago
January 1937

THE COMPLAINT OF
RICHARD SAVAGE

※　—"charioted by Bacchus and his pards"

FOR GEORGE

I.

"Don't give it a 2nd thought," said I. "After a certain
number of drinks you begin to have the thinks even *before* the one you're thinking. Let's call that certain number of drinks *n*. The n + 1 drink gives you the T — 1 think.
The n + 7 drink gives you the T — 7 think."

I was beginning to be animated and friendly, but the
feeling was already passing over into fright. The hand I
was reaching out to touch her ass was freezing and was
about to push her away. Next moment I made an angry
fist; I jammed it into my pocket in order not to see it.
Sometimes, especially if I fell into a rage, my hand was
my hand; other times I did not recognize it, it was none
of mine.

Nobody knew me at this place (where I did not know
myself). So long as I remained anonymous, I did not need
to tell my lamentable story. As for me, I am ready to take
up with anybody that will—I don't ask who *they* are. I
suppose I have no standards; from whom should I have
gotten standards? The question is how, living this way, I
haven't come fatally to grief? The answer is simple.

The answer is simple! Those who are willing to befriend
me are only the noblest and the best. I ask for what nobody can give, and I am surly (you will find) when I am
frustrated. I offer to give what nobody can safely take, and

I am stubborn and persistent in dealing it out. Whoever can put up with me is doomed to greatness! Am I a flatterer? Yes. I flatter you by assuming that the impossible is still possible. Naturally an ordinary person becomes anxious. . . .

Now she was looking in fright at the fingers twitching in space between us; she imagined I was going to pick her pocket. I regarded the hand curiously: did it intend to steal? and what did it intend to steal? My embarrassment gave way to anger and I angrily anticipated her and exclaimed: "You sit there so offish, very well contained in your skin. My compliments—" The thought that I remembered at the $n + 7$ drink was this: that our lives are the give-and-take of an organism and its environment; and around this thought there played a promissory glory; it seemed to me to be a means of persuasion. "My compliments to you and your touchable skin," I said; "but the case is that no such thing *exists* as an animal in its own skin. If it weren't for the gravity and the ground holding you up, you couldn't be sitting there on your ass. It's the weight of the atmosphere all the way from the moon that's shoving that drink down your throat. May I buy you another? allow me. Hey, cap—"

But as happens always, the force of my persuasion at once worked on myself and plunged me into deep gloom before ever I could reach a conclusion advantageous to us both. (Whatever the truth is, it makes me sad. It is truth that makes me sad.) I felt desolate. But *she* wasn't moved at all.

"I beg your pardon," she said.

I remember that I was breathing deeply, invaded by the air and mixing in the air; then suddenly I rose in power, and *what were all these things to me?* (T — 8)

II.

Next thing I remember: there was a small dead end square. The cars and trucks were roaring past, but no engines came into that cloister except a small green roadster parked under a quarter inch of dust. Here the boys and girls of 8 to 12 were playing a square ball-game and screaming and shrieking, or sometimes calling out to one another the encouraging words: "No matter how closely you contrive your folly roaring to hell, there are dead ends of quiet around the periphery. And time has always its fringe of present actuality, as it goes over the edge."

For these children were making up the actuality as they went along. In their style, playing our funny quick New York ball-game: neat throws with English bounces and sharp smashes aimed at a precise opening between. Yet next moment the ball was swallowed by the fielder without a trace. The hitter was off in a flash—in an instant stopped; and the nonchalance fell on his shoulders like a cape.

I had staggered by here drunk, finding it hard to keep in touch with the present actuality. If I broke into panic flight to escape, I was stopped short by the riptide of wheels across my toes. If then, willingly enough, I swayed from side to side in serene contemplation of such a sea of billows surging around my knees, I fell head foremost into a field of broken stones. Some one kept changing the environment. It was no advantage at all toward my happiness to initiate the locomotions of desire, for some one kept changing the environment.

But I turned to confront my huge slumber overwhelming towards me, and with a sigh of pleasure I staggered and fell into this dead-end safe haven. I was on the children's ball field and the last thing I heard as I rolled on my side and slept was their groans. "Jesus, he's on the field!"

In this way I became 3rd base. They made up ground rules relating to me, and my left foot was 3rd base. Unlike me, those children were adept at the actuality. Surely they pierced the meaning of the couplet of Jenye:

> "As I cross the river
> it is the bridge that is flowing under my feet."

As for me, to be 3rd base was to get more than one wild kick when the runner failed to cut the corner in his desperate dash for home. Home!

Such kicks make no difference to me! For still beyond the curtain of the present, and again the present, and again the present, there exists the deviating Way.

"Great Tao is a ship adrift!"

(Indeed it is by a misunderstanding that the thousands line the shore and wave their flags when I come into port. For it was not I that was doing the steering.)

I courteously waited until the last inning to awake. A pair of blue jeans was standing with his foot pressed against my outcast foot. I sat up. I saw that the enclosure of red brick was about 36 feet square. The sun of May late afternoon was blazing in the windows of the eastern side, but I could not interpret the signals. The girls and boys came and formed a semi-circle in front of me, to urge me to get the hell out of the way.

But *their* way was not necessarily the Way. "Oof, what a dream!" I said, following my own bent not theirs. I passed my hand across my face and found reality a little clearer on the other side.

"Whadje dream, mister?" asked the kid who had been standing on 3rd base and was therefore more intimate with me than the others.

"I dreamt that a leopard was chasing me and he caught me and ate me up."

"Jeez! what did *you* do?"

"I tasted good."

"Oh, that was Christian of you!"

It was a dream of poverty and need, such as we might well dream whose mothers often told us not to waste anything. (My own mother, to be sure, set me a more exacting task.) And yet there is no need; the nature of things, nature, is momently pouring forth its bounty; but we can hardly believe it. Suspicious, we do not take it; and grudging, we do not give it out.

III.

When I stood up, they drew back, by a law of the organism/environment field that I have frequently observed. (I have observed nothing else.) While I lay there, a base, I was a domesticated nightmare, like the stone head from Easter Island that they show on the top floor of the Museum of Natural History. But when I rose to my feet I was the terrible Bacchus, looming unpredictably in the circumscribed space.

It was they, not I, who were trapped in the actuality. I was the trap. At that moment I could by persuasion or violence—and these are the same, for one cannot help but hypnotically identify oneself with superior force—I could have led them after me in a train and over the edge, as the Pied Piper opened the hole in the mountainside.

My head was swimming and my senses were dark. It did not seem to me questionable to wreak vengeance on the children for my indignities. But I dismissed this thought for another time, when it would return in less convenient circumstances.

Instead I turned my wrath against myself and so began my usual complaint, reverting, as I recovered my wits, to the thought T — 7. "As I stand in front of you girls and boys," I began.

When it was evident that I was after all only a loquacious drunkard, the young ones took courage and listened to me awhile with apprehensive smiles of contempt. One forward girl waved her hands in the air and conducted me like an orchestra.

"As I stand here," I said, "my weight goes right down to the center o' the earth. I don't support myself. Did you ever think o' that? But if they keep taking away my environment, how can I stand?"

At this, I swayed more than a little and staggered, but I didn't fall flat on my face. "That's just a slip!" I said. "The earth is there good enough, solid rock, right down to the middle." I stamped my foot and proved it.

Slowly I shook my head from side to side. I was a boxer badly hurt. This lasted half a minute that I said nothing, for I was staggered by the force of the truth that struck me.

"What's the matter, mister, you going to be sick?" said the forward girl, and stopped conducting.

"It's only the human beings who don't know how to give and take," I said. "You kids don't realize it yet, but you'll learn." The next moment I was moved to song, and now I really began to sing, in a strong baritone,

> "Aaaall of me!
> Why not take aaall of me?—"

But now that I was really singing, the girl was no longer conducting, and nobody joined in the song that had been popular before their time. I had frightened them when I stamped on the ground with my hoof, and then lapsed into a silence awful in my own ears. The impact of my stamping in fact did go right down to the center, and it was as if they were waiting for the re-echoing earthquake.

My head was clear. I saw them all, the scene of rose, black, and white, like a photograph of long ago.

My more intimate friend was regarding me judiciously. "You know, mister," he said, "what you say is all a lot o' bullshit."

"What's wrong with bullshit!" I roared, for I cannot brook contradiction. "If you fuck a bull, naturally! What else can you expect?"

There was something menacing in my aspect, for they cried out in fright and fled from the mouth of the cul-de-sac into the heedless traffic. My friend hid in the abandoned roadster, that was of course stripped of its wheels, its windshield, its engine.

This made me hopping mad. It was again, *in parvo,* just what I was griping about in the big things. But there was no little and no big, it was the identical law of the organism/environment field. Namely, as soon as the going gets rough, *they* give up the actuality, my actuality, the one and only actuality that I have; and around me there spreads a vacuum.

Since I was hopping in any case, on my left foot, I took off my right shoe and threw it in a rage at the impassive wall. I was dancing about in choliambs, "lame iambics," putting my other foot down on every fifth beat, ᵕ′ ᵕ′ ᵕ′ ᵕ′′ᵕ.

IV.

After a while I turned to go.

"Here, you'll need this," said the boy, appearing from the dusty green roadster and handing me my shoe.

"I see you didn't run away with the others," I said.

"Naw, I didn't. Are you still a little drunk?" he said curiously, for I was trying to put the one shoe on the other one. It was as if he asked, "Do you still have a little environment, or are you finally only an animal contained in your skin?"

I saw that he intended to pan-handle me. I was pleased with the acumen with which he sized me up for an easy mark who still had a couple of dollars. He had orange hair —gray eyes—a faded sweater: it was impossible to take him in as a single whole, the colors fled apart. His style was brisk, but his voice came from the realm where there is no direction because there is no likelihood.

He was reviewing in his mind which of many unattainable things he would grant himself.

"Gimme—Mister," he began, "could you gimme— could you contribute half a buck to the Floyd Lewis Air-Rifle Fund? Half a buck and then we finish up the drive, we're over the top! I'd make you out a raffle-ticket, but between you and I they're phoney, and anyhow I left 'em home. But I gotta get that rifle, 'cause this way—just like you said—I'm left out o' everything an' I'm ashamed an' disgraced in front o' all my contemporaries. But if you gimme the dough," he went on breathlessly, "God bless you. I'll pray to Mary muvver of God to bless you an' all the saints an' St. Cecily because you sing and dance."

"Yes," I said.

"*Will* ye?" he cried, astonished but not unbelieving.

The tears had started into my eyes when I said "Yes," and now they were rolling down my cheeks.

"Whaddye cryin' about?" said Floyd. "You don't need to feel sorry on *my* account. I don't need the fuckin gun that bad," he said angrily. "Whaddye take me for! a beggar?" He was beginning to beat about for a means of nullifying my help, "All the same I could use that air-rifle," he said, beginning to hop.

"What could you use it for?"

"To shoot out the lamps, o' course."

I forced the coin into his hand, and the tears rolled down my face.

"Jeez, keep your lousy money!" he shouted, beside himself. "D'ye think I takes money from a drunk that's so stingy he's cryin' when he gives it away?"

"Listen, peanut," I said, "I'm not crying because *you* need anything, I assure you. People don't cry for other people, they cry for themselves, you'll find that out when you get older. I'm crying because you happen to need something and ask for it and *I* happen to be able to give it to you. That's why I'm crying."

"F' Crissake, that's a hell of a reason. You're drunk." He saw the coin in his hand and he flung it on the ground. " 'Ts no good to me. There ain't no Floyd Lewis Air-Rifle Fund, an' there ain't no raffle-tickets even if they're phoney."

Naturally we were not, he and I, among those who ask for what we need and could possibly get. (But it is not for *this* reason that we don't get it.)

"O Mary, whaddye *bawlin'* for?" he cried in consternation.

I seized him grimly by the scruff of the neck and he cried out in pain. "How much is the air-rifle?" I asked sternly.

"There ain't no air-rifle, either," he whimpered.

I tightened my grip on his neck. "*Where* is the store?" I said. I was not crying now; my tears had dried up in hot wrath, which is the nearest I ever come to compassion. Damn him! He *got* his air-rifle in spite of himself screaming with fright and lust.

He ran out of the store as if I was the devil.

V.

I understand that I am greedy; no doubt of it, I want more than is good for me or than I can digest. Having been starved, afraid of starving—I desperately clutch at the present—and drive it away. I can't help it: when I walk the streets and see the possibilities of joy, that are in fact impossibilities, I am *not* reconciled to the niggardliness of my fortune. I understand that I am niggardly to myself, too. I often prevent myself from taking what is reasonably offered, I am disappointed even beforehand (the while I clutch at something else and try to squeeze water from a stone). All right then, but why don't they *help* me, and more *insistently* make me their reasonable offer? "A person like you, disappointed beforehand, is hard to help." What a thing for her to say! to be offering help and say that help is being offered, when in fact she does not help *me,* in the way that *I* can be helped? What kind of help is that, that I can circumvent?

My name is Richard Savage. I am the son of that unnatural mother who cast me off to begin with and has, inexplicably vindictive, hounded me ever since. The story is by now well known, how she deprived me, who had nothing, of even that which I had, opportunity. Everybody knows it; there is no use for me to repeat my complaint, what I remember and what I fail to remember; but I find myself complaining it nevertheless. She cast me off, I say, as I—as I cast off that shoe—I confess I am beside myself. Hopping—

Oh forget my mother! no matter about my mother! For I see that all of us, not only I, are treated like stepchildren of nature. Nobody gets what he needs. And if you make the mistake of asking directly for what you need, ha, you'll find that *you're* the one that's moved, nobody else, and you'll wish you hadn't mentioned it because the truth is too hard to take. *My* life-story is no worse than the rest, only more obvious, more spectacular, so nobody can deny the truth. (Yet surely there is a misunderstanding, for indeed we are not the stepchildren of nature but her children and rightful heirs.)

Inevitably I have an unresponsive wife. Being as I am, what other wife would I cleave to? I give her my hand, my want—oh, she is unmoved by this. She does not push me away, but she lies there in sullen silence. And what is the result of banging myself against a flank that does not respond? Instead of being jovially proud of my powers—such as they are! such as they are!—I am made to feel inferior. Inferior? to whom? for what? You may well ask.

And so I burst into tears when I say the word "Yes." Crying not because the urchin asked me for something he could not get; but on the contrary, that he asked for something that, as it happened, he *could* get. For an instant my mother had relented. Relented! And all at once I caught a glimpse of lost paradise and the tears started into my eyes. But it is paradise lost—I am forty years old —crying for myself.

Bawling because it was *I*—notice! please! look at me!— it was I who was graciously extending the bounty of nature. Oh, this is a role I play with grace, with delicacy, to the manor born! I play it like a baboon. The boy was screaming when I gave him a gift.

Naturally this is all spite. I understand this. Frustrated, I complain in order to make you unhappy too. But what's wrong with spite? It is the last resource of us powerless who cannot fight back any more, but we can vent our spite. Of course spite doesn't accomplish anything, but it is a way we have of remaining alive, of not simply succumbing. You who are not spiteful in this world have long ago given up in despair; I say it spitefully.

VI.

When I was trapped, tired and bored,
I sent my shadowself abroad:
    went down the street and boldly had
    the simple joy I was afraid

to take—that even easily
the world might have given me.
    And he returned and was glad
    and stood beside where I sat sad.

"Why do you come back?" I said
"and not abandon me for dead
    with this body that I cannot use?"
    But so it was, and so it is.

VII.

I keep telling my story for spite in order to watch your faces fall and take the joy out of your lives too.

But you aren't even suckers for it and you stubbornly won't listen to me—you make as if I didn't exist—and so this too has become part of my story.

Maybe it's finally the most essential part: that you won't even listen to me. Then the question is this: if you'd listen and I had *this* satisfaction, would I let up on the rest of my vindictiveness—granted my vindictiveness is justified, you'd have to grant me that—let up and agree to

do a stroke of useful work to add to the general welfare?
But there is no way of testing this question either.

Why you should listen to me when I mean only to cause
you pain, is beyond me.

Because I will it, and you won't. If you all weren't so
damned stubborn, I wouldn't persist. Agh, so much for
that!—

"So much for that! Now for these Irish wars," as Dick
the Second said.

VIII.

My shadowself came back and found me at McHale's
Tavern, which is in a way my other home, on Eighth Avenue at 26th Street. Here there were as always the three
primordial elements of gayety: music, bright lights, and
liquor.

Music! think of it a moment: how the skillful corporation of the musicians, trained one generation to another
from the remotest antiquity, are still making for us jaunty
music on savage instruments, and Persian instruments,
and Italian instruments;

and Lights! think how these illuminations, boxes of
fire in the transparency, have been continually elaborated
by the generations of Prometheus to brighten our spirits
and let us see;

and how the brewers, experienced, experimenting always new fruits and ferments, coctions and distillations,
fix in this bottle the happy result sometimes achieved by
chance;

to think that these age-old quintessences of human wit
should have combined to no more merry hour than this,
at this dismal McHale's Tavern! The identical elements
of excitement! and this is the result! How is it possible?
how did it come to pass? There was from the beginning,
surely, a crack in our golden goblet, and the joy ran out.

"All right! I *have* thought of it!" said I to myself. "And
supposing it is just as you say, what must I conclude?"

"What do you mean?" I said. "You must conclude that
it is all very discouraging."

"Good. I grant you that it is discouraging. What then?"

"What then? What do you mean, What then?"

"I mean, you demonstrate that we are in a dreadful way, and then what follows?"

I fell silent. There was a pause. In this pause I was aware of how it was there, of the tinkling notes and the sparkling little pictures in the glasses, the apple-jack in my mouth, and so forth and so forth.

"Don't you see," I said gently, "you cannot conclude where you do, for you must *still* confront the present actuality passing over into the next."

I said it gently, changing my tone toward myself. For ordinarily we intellectuals are too hard on ourselves; we demand too much, more than we expect of anybody else. We have keen memories and we keep a strict accounting.

I hung my head. After a moment I looked up and said, "To the extent that *my* long face conduces to the fog along this bar, I'll wash it off and beat my feet and sing."

A VISIT TO CHARTRES

I.

I did want to go and see the Cathedral of Chartres, though with the dispiritment with which I want anything these days. I did want to; the proof is that I was not two days in France but I and my companion were driving the road to Chartres.

When we were a few kilometers past Ablis—and still I had no hot eagerness to arrive—I chanced to lift my eyes to the horizon, across the long rolling green plain. Far off, ghostly in the haze, were the well-known unlike towers of the Cathedral of Chartres, beyond the horizon, half an inch high, hovering in the haze. I, to my surprise, turned pale and flushed, and my heart was pounding.

But we sped on our way (Route 188) and when next the Cathedral flashed into view, she was clear to see and a neat size like a picture, she was "pretty as a picture" and very like a picture of the Cathedral of Chartres. It was a remarkable illusion, for there was the Cathedral of Chartres but there was no town of Chartres. I could not help smiling at how cunningly and skillfully that building put herself on display.

I had been now moved and charmed and alas! (I knew myself) these feelings—these feelings plus my usual effortful and earnest aesthetic and sociological reflections—would be the height of my joy in the Cathedral of Chartres. I felt I had had it, and I might just as well turn around right then and go away.

But a car drives on and when next I saw her—we were nearly in Chartres—now only the upper parts of the building on the hilltop were visible, girt and obstructed by her clustering houses. "Naturally, it is the Cathedral of the *town*—," I thought; I was already embarked on my usual effortful aesthetic and sociological reflections. There was a very ugly warehouse in the foreground, in the wrong century, in the wrong color, and hogging the view. "They really should take that one out of the way," I said to my companion in my usual helpful manner.

In Chartres, the Cathedral on her hill was lost from view. We took a wrong turning and we were out of the town. We circled back. We had to ask our way, and go up an improbable hill, and through a back alley. But this also was in the nature of the case (everything that is is in the nature of the case), for any community-square of those times would be enclosed and not directly approachable.

Sure enough! There, up the little alley, *was* the Cathedral of Chartres, on the square.

The square was not commodious enough, of course. Of course.

II.

Of course I was content with my immediate cursory inspection of the Cathedral of Chartres, for it was the Cathedral of Chartres and I am not a fool. I was far from disappointed. I was a little bit surprised. I had expected the surface to be more austere, but the worn, worn texture, was like a precious stone.

Yes, I walked about her and again and again she forced from me a smirk of satisfaction and a grunt of approval. The great transept portico, and the older tower. I was glad, I was satisfied, that I had not turned around and gone away without coming to see the Cathedral of Chartres.

I went inside to see if there was something amiss, but there was nothing amiss. The chairs and the electric lights were easy to think away. A few of the windows were missing. At the transept, if you looked into the choir, the big round columns were manly and lovely. How big and manly! If you went around the apse and looked back behind you, you would not be displeased. And when you stood on the stage and looked into the nave, then the auditorium was dark and the high rose shone, not brightly, close in your eyes.

There was no sun that day and the color was not gorgeous, but you could easily see that the color would be gorgeous at the hour that it would be gorgeous. I am uninstructed, I could not read the hundreds of pictures in the windows, but I had no doubt at all that, if I could, they'd be surprisingly appropriate and profoundly thought-provoking to a careful aesthetic and sociological reflection. I was content enough as it was, to the degree that I am content with anything these days.

Nevertheless, I kept looking curiously up at the small gallery. Couldn't I get up there? And how could I get up there? to whom did one appeal? I am childish and I like to climb around on these buildings. There were many sightseers, but nobody was up there.

III.

I weep easily when there is something beautiful—especially if there is no way to get closer by clambering on. (Thwarted, I weep instead of getting angry.) And by now my tiny smiles and grunts had given way to a few tiny gleams of tears. These tears were certainly tears for paradise lost, for when something is beautiful it is a reminder of paradise lost. But also—I am beginning to understand it —they were tears of hurt feelings. My feelings are hurt because they have left me out. This beautiful world, and my life is not so beautiful: they have left me out. Why has He left me out? Am I not as loyal a son as the next? I *am* a loyal son! But no doubt He is a loving father, only He does not understand me and He treats me in a way that is *not* really good for me; it has gone on too long. Skip it.

Skip it. Today at the Cathedral of Chartres there was some kind of festival preparing. A large company of nuns and several troops of cub-scouts. Priests began to light the candles at the table and shoo us nosybodies into the aisle. And certainly there was going to be a bishop. I had come on the right day to see my lovely in use! I didn't much care what it was about—although, of course!

I know! if I made more effort to read the pictures and inform myself about the day's ceremony, I'd be richly rewarded. But I am tired.

I was shooed into the aisle and, being in the aisle, I came by the door to the bell-tower, and there I saw posted the solemn warning:

WARNING
Ministry of Fine Arts

VISITORS TO THE UPPER PARTS OF THE MONUMENT
WILL PROCEED AT THEIR OWN RISK.
THE MINISTRY CANNOT BE RESPONSIBLE IN CASE
OF ACCIDENT.

Good! so it *was* possible to go aloft. That was for me. Something to do, to clamber. At once I entered at the narrow door and I began, two steps at a time, the circular ascent. By a hundred steps I was out of breath. It was dark.

IV.

I began to be afraid. Let me explain about myself. I am an exceptionally fearful person but not timid. I mean, I don't hold back, I commit myself rapidly, often too rapidly, to a risk that happens to suggest itself; not blindly, as if I didn't know it was a risk, but as if thoughtlessly, as if I didn't care about consequences. Then very soon I become afraid and, usually for no adequate reason, almost panicky. But I don't panic, I don't run away. (Although I *can* run away, if there's a real danger.)

However it was, now, climbing a public stairway, I became terribly afraid. It was that I was out of breath. On these circular stairs in the dark, where hundreds of thousands have ascended and descended in the dark, I was almost in a panic. My thought was that I would never get to the top. There were maybe 300 steps, I did not know how many there were, I could not calm myself to calculate how many there must be—but my heart would fail and I would die in that lonely tower lost forever, where hundreds of thousands had climbed before me for a thousand years, and God grant as many will follow me after! I climbed on.

At this moment, when I was almost in panic for nothing, there did occur something that was terrifying and I backed against the stone wall in terror. For right next to me, nay inside the dark spiral, sounded a mighty noise. I backed against the wall astonished. I clung to the wall and the stone wall was trembling. My hair stood up on my scalp.

It was the bell. The counter-stroke struck.

With a cry I leapt up the last steps and under the sky. I clung to the balustrade.

The square and the town fell away beneath me and I reeled. And all of the bells leaped into clangorous and joyous life.

They clanged around me, whichever way I turned. Deafening and delightful, till I held my hands over my ears for mercy. I was happy for the first time in a long time.

They say there are two things that frighten a child, loud noises and the fear of falling. I was frightened and I was certainly like a child. But it wasn't noises but the glorious clangor of bells that is almost noise; and I was not falling, but could safely see the far view from the tower of the Cathedral of Chartres.

Over the bass of the big bells, the small bells began their shrieking scales. My eyes leapt near and far.

(The Cathedral square below was too small.)

I clambered about the roof, not unlike a tiny baby who plays not with the grown-ups, but on them. For she was like *La Géante* of Baudelaire:

"Parcourir à loisir ses magnifiques formes!
   ramper sur le versant de ses genoux énormes!"

—"to roam at my leisure on her magnificent shapes, and to clamber on the slope of her enormous knees."

V.

There was a gentleman there with his five-year-old boy.

"N'a-t-il pas peur?" I asked.

"Mais non, il n'a pas peur."

The small boy was confidently holding papa's hand, without clinging to it or clutching it.

I never had a human father, and I loved this gentleman and his brave boy.

Tiny below, the police were clearing the square. The shrieking scales ceased. The thunderous peals were abating.

Hurriedly I came down from the tower to see the service. And this time I took care to count the steps, in order to know at least one thing accurately in this world, but I lost count.

VI.

The church that I emerged in was alive. In use.

Or it was that I had been touched in the body, as when somebody touches you intimately or slaps you across the face (it comes to the same thing), and from then on the situation is alive. Because I had been panicky in the narrow place, I emerged in the great nave trembling.

I didn't know what it was about, but surely it was a happy occasion and a joyous service, for each response of the choir succeeded in a brighter mode and a merrier rhythm. With vehement enthusiasm first the bishop and then the boys flung out their incense before them. The smoke was piercing sharp to the nostrils.

It was a short service. The procession of the nuns and the boy scouts was beginning to form. The chant of the choir was loud and allegro.

The chanting was not excellent, but good enough. The organ took it up with a roar.

Naturally I pressed closer. *Naturally* my mouth was hanging open.

God pity me! My expectation was extreme.

Nay, I see that He does not misunderstand me, His loyal boy. Simply that He can't, He doesn't have the material. *He* is in pain too.

For—what? Was it possible? Weren't all those people going to sing? Weren't they going to shout out and sing? All those several hundred nuns and troops of crystal-throated boy scouts? And the bishop creeping along under his palanquin? What on earth else were they good for? They marched awkwardly past and did not open their mouths.

Some persons were throwing flowers, in the silence.

They didn't ring the bells.

VII.

I began to be angry. My disappointment was deep. I was angry with my best, my indignant, anger that surges only when I have been a little happy and I see the world as it is. I was contemptuous of those dummies as they filed out in their well-behaved rows, during the festival of flowers, with never a peep out of them, even though the occasion and the place and the congregation had prepared for this moment the bellow of a thousand untrained voices singing the appropriate words, and also bells.

"What?" I asked myself coldly, "and didn't they *know* the appropriate words? Why not? Surely *I* don't know them, or I'd sing out if I was the only one." I am not timid to bear witness in such cases.

Or I put it this way: "If they didn't know the words—if you don't know the words, you dummies, and *therefore* are struck dumb, why don't you ask somebody to prepare you the words? There are three poets right here in France; or even me, for instance, though I am a stranger—" I am not unskilled at finding words for such occasions.

Or—God pity us! "If you don't even realize that at this moment there *ought* to be social words and a climax of song and bells, then by what right, how do you dare, to be marching in a procession from my Cathedral of Chartres?

"God damn them all!" I said. Such prayers in my mouth are simply statements of how it is, they do not imply any ill wish. It is a way I have of saying that these, who should have broken into heaven, were effectually in hell; and I —I who had been trembling with hope for us all—was firm with rage, because I am in purgatory living here with these people.

> Saved! as I have faith
> and probable proof,
>   but O God, am I weary
>   of living in Purgatory,
>
> in pain and fire, tedious
> waiting for the Voice
>   of love that summons
>   and the voice that responds.

Perhaps I expect too much. That's what they tell me, that I expect too much. Do I expect too much? *What* do I expect? That at the just moment we people should come across. Is this much? Such things have happened.

I stood there in the Cathedral, feeling strong emotions. Coursing through me, also, was a current of vitality. I was astonished and pleased at myself that I did not burst into tears. I had no hurt feelings. I was secure in my anger, for in the end in these matters I do know better, ignorant though I am.

They had filed past me and the floor was strewn with the petals of peonies. Oh Lord, what a waste!

VIII.

Softly.

Softly. A little patience. For look at my darling, how patiently *she* houses us, native fools and tourists. She comes across and gives herself, with nothing amiss. She is still so much there that our later errors are easy to think away. She thereby gives an honest poet also the occasion to vent his anger without hurt feelings. That's a great gift she gives, my darling. (That's a great gift thee gives me, darling.) I'm grateful for this beauty that has led me to present anger instead of as usual to the gleam of tears for paradise lost. This beauty that has led me to smiles, for by damn! isn't she lovely? Now that the bishop has crept out of the way under his idiotic palanquin.

I mean, it's not necessary to make allowances for the Cathedral of Chartres; *isn't* she lovely?

IX.

I went outside where my companion was waiting for me in the car. He set the motor going. "I'm sorry I've been so long," I said, "I'll be back in just a minute—" and I wandered as if aimlessly away, though I had a plan.

I wandered down the alley on the south, ostentatiously examining how the square tower of the Cathedral of Chartres mounts into its octagonal spire, something I had already examined to my satisfaction, but I was embarrassed and secretive for what I was about, and there were still a few loiterers. They left.

Swiftly I leapt up three or four steps of the portico, to where there was a fine little block in the limestone wall, to kiss, a good adequate sample of that worn and tender rock, to touch lightly and kiss.

Shyly I kissed the dumb stone with a little peck of a kiss. I was thinking, in a swift whisper, "There, I love thee; thee'll see. I'll come back often when there's more opportunity. Thee'll see how I am, faithful, whatever they say and think; once I'm in love I never change. (I'll write thee a poem when I'm away, no?) I seem to be so sour and hard to please always, and it's true enough; but I do love thee, thee is so lovely. Also so practical. It rarely goes together. Darling, good-bye. I'm sorry about the others."

I went back to the car and climbed in. He started the motor.

There was no denying it, the Cathedral square was not adequate for a good view of the Cathedral.

My companion said, "Well, did you find out what the procession was about?"

"Solstice. They celebrate it as a Fête of Flowers."

"Yes, they were throwing a lot of flowers."

I thought then, as I still think, if He is in pain too, my father, I ought to put on a bright face, to make Him more easy.

Yet here I am, cramped, oppressed, and uneasy almost to anguish because the Cathedral of Chartres' square is too small. Or alternatively—if the houses of the town of Chartres would cluster closer up to their Cathedral, and do without the square altogether. Creator Spirit, wouldn't either way do well for the Cathedral of Chartres? So I turn it and ask myself. I am absurd; my face is drawn with pain all day for what I cannot remedy.

A PRAYER FOR DEW

"And the offering of Judah and Jerusalem shall be a delight unto the Lord, as in days of old, as in ancient years."

With this ending of the great Standing-prayer, the congregation sat down.

It was Passover and a springtime shower was washing the windows of the synagogue, with prolonged rumblings of thunder and many flashes of lightning. It was dark and the electric lights had been turned on—by the Negro janitor (in accordance with the injunction, "On the first day shall be a holy convocation, ye [Jews] shall do no servile work").

Moonfaced Rabbi Horn stood up in front of the closed curtain of the Ark, adjusted his substantial sleeves, and said: "We come now to the most beautiful prayer of the day, *Tefilas Tal*, the Prayer for Dew. This prayer is said before the open Ark; it comes from the heart of springtime. What could man do without the rain? The rain falls in order to fill the rivers, and the rivers flow into the seas and lakes in order to evaporate into clouds. Who will give me fifteen dollars for the honor of opening the Ark for *Tal*, for *P'shichas Tal*, opening the Ark for *Tal*? What am I bid? Do I hear anybody bid fifteen dollars?"

"Four dollars for my son, in memory of my husband Isaac Podolnik," called Mrs. Podolnik from the women's gallery.

"Six dollars!" said Mr. Brody with a quiet smile.

The Rabbi and the President, who wore a silk hat, looked up at the widow Podolnik.

"Just what," I turned round to my friend Leo, sitting behind me with his white-shawled father, "is the *mitzvah* of a bid made in honor of somebody when it doesn't win the auction?" I was at that time a member of the skeptical fraternity.

"Seven dollars!" called a voice in the rear.

"Seven dollars is bid back here," said the beadle, hastening to the spot.

"What's the name please?" asked the Rabbi tending his large ear, that was like a handle to the moon.

"Thumim."

"Berman! Mr. Berman bids seven dollars."

"Seven-*fifty*," said Brody quietly.

"Seven-*fifty* is bid for the opening of the Holy Ark for the springtime Prayer for Dew," said Rabbi Horn.

Meantime the rain, not prayed for yet, thudded against the windows and on the skylight. The water could be heard busily flowing down the runnels and the drainpipes, a "pleasant noise of waters." A burst of lightning silhouetted the old men near the window with their fringes over their heads, and brightly illuminated the silk fringes.

"*Eight*-fifty!" said Mr. Thumim.

"Mr. Berman bids eight-fifty," said the Rabbi.

"Eight-seventy-five," said Brody.

"Nine!" cried Thumim excitedly.

"Nine and a half," said Brody.

There was a crack of thunder. One of the electric lights over the reading-table dimmed, and went dark.

"Nunny," said the President to his little son, "go call the *shfartse* to bring a new bulb."

Nunny ran down the aisle, bouncing a rubber ball on the red carpet.

Throughout the synagogue conversation became general. Comments about the weather. In the rear there was a burst of laughter where some one had just told a new joke.

My friend Leo, the seminarian, at last gave an opinion on the status of the widow Podolnik's offer that had been outbid. "She fulfilled a commandment in starting the bidding," he said in my ear. "It is a *mitzvah* to start something. *Sof ma'aseh machshava tehila*: the end of the deed is the thought of the Beginning!—"

Afire, the Jewish joke progressed from bench to bench, greeted at each telling with a burst of hilarity.

"*B'reshith*—in the Beginning God created the heavens and the earth," said Leo.

"Shh! shh! this is a synagogue!" admonished the President pounding the palm of his hand loudly against his open prayer-book. The buzz fell an octave lower, as happens on a meadow in the month of August when the sun passes momentarily behind a cloud.

"Twelve dollars!" rang out the voice of Thumim in a last desperate raise.

"Twelve-fifty," said Brody.

"*For heaven's sake,* Marcus—" said Brody's brother-in-law, tugging at his sleeve.

"So?" Brody turned to him with a bland smile. "Did I say I want the bid? I'm just—*raising* a little."

"Twelve-fifty is bid by Mr. Meyer Brody for the honor of opening the Ark for *Tal.*"

"*Fifteen dollars!*" thundered a new voice on the left.

"Ah," said the Rabbi, "now we're getting somewhere."

"Sixteen," said Brody.

"*Seventeen!*" boomed the voice.

"Seventeen-*seventy-five,*" said Brody.

Preceded by Nunny, now bouncing a different ball, a small red ball at the end of an elastic string, Aaron, the grizzled-haired Negro, came down the aisle carrying a ladder and a frosted bulb. He climbed on the ladder, stretching up his arm to unscrew the burnt-out light. The ladder began to wobble. The Reader lent his hand to hold it firm.

"The question is" I said to Leo, "whether he should lend his hand to *hold* the ladder—"

"The answer is Yes," said Leo sharply. "This comes under the rubric of helping to preserve a man from injury."

"Twenty dollars!" said the booming voice on the left.

"Twenty dollars is bid!" cried Rabbi Horn joyously. "What is the name please?"

"Samuelson—Ely Samuelson."

"Ah, Mr. *Samuelson!*" exclaimed Rabbi Horn with the joyous and flattering quaver that he mostly reserved for weddings. "Mr. Samuelson is not a member of our Congregation," he explained. "He is a visitor from Providence, the capital of Rhode Island. His uncle, however, is our dear President, Mr. Sonnenschein; and I am sure that you will all join with me in telling Mr. Samuelson that he is just as much at home in this Congregation as in Providence, Rhode Island."

"I'll give just one more hike," said Brody quietly to us. "After such a build-up by the Rabbi, how can he get out of taking the bid? But why should I make him pay more than he can afford?

"Twenty-three dollars," he called, after judicious consideration.

"*Twenty-five!*" said Mr. Samuelson, on the left.

"Good—take it," said Brody, and turned round to us triumphantly.

"I bid them up from four dollars to twenty-five!— Why shouldn't the money go to the synagogue? Have I been playing auction-pinochle for forty years for nothing? *Always* you can tell when you can bid them up and when there's nothing doing! Seventeen-seventy-five: there was a bid! Who could refuse to go to eighteen? But in a game of pinochle, *never* three-forty; always force them into it. Then just drop your cards and say Good! take it!

"Sometimes in a game," said Brody, "they think *they're* boosting *me*. *I'm* boosting *them*."

The pinochle-player of the Lord.

The Cantor and his choir of black-robed boys had begun to gather at the reading-table under the light that had been repaired and that shone dimly in the brightening space. The young soprani were downstairs in the cellar playing punchball, and their piercing cries could be heard in the distance.

At last, after its triumphant progress from the rear of the room across the entire congregation to us in the front, the joke arrived at our bench; but it proved to be the antique story, that I have already set down elsewhere, about the little Jew in the crowded trolley-car who sings "Deedle-deedle-dee, it ain't my setchel."

"Look, Brody," I said, "supposing the Rabbi decided to knock it down to *both* of you, and have both of you grasp the cord to open the curtain. Ha, then what?"

"It shouldn't happen on *Pesach*," said Brody.

The Cantor, who had a white hat with a pom-pom, stood up on a stool to tower, with his pom-pom, above the boys. For unfortunately, though he was very broad-shouldered and had a powerful black beard and a bass voice, he was only five feet high. Like Ulysses, "when he was seated he looked imposing, but when he rose to his feet you saw that he was of small stature." From the top of a stool he dominated the scene, and often, holding a long note, he would dart a sidewise and upwards glance at the women.

He smote the table with his little tuning-fork and held the sound to his ear, while the vibration wheeled out amongst us with the unpleasant ring of pure tone. (At one time he had been accustomed to use a pitch-pipe, but this was considered by some of the orthodox as playing a musical instrument.) The choir, catching the note, sang an A-minor chord. And as if created out of nothing, the tranquillity of nature, the natural harmony, crowded into the corners of the space.

"Will the Congregation please rise," said Rabbi Horn, "for the repetition of the Amidah and the singing of *Tefilas Tal*. Mr. Samuelson, will you please come up and stand alongside me on the platform."

"Barukh . . . Blessed art Thou, O Lord, our God and God of our fathers—" began the Cantor in a deep voice, accompanied by a humming continuo of the boys.

"God of Abraham, God of Isaac and God of Jacob; great, strong and awful God, God most high, who grantest goodly favors and art the owner of all that is. Thou rememberest the piety of our fathers, and Thou wilt bring a redeemer to their children's children, for Thy name's sake, in love. King, Helper, Savior and Shield: Blessed art Thou, O Lord, the Shield of Abraham.

"Strong to eternity, O Lord, who quickenest the dead and art mighty to save."

The progressing chords of the choir, and the flowing

line of the Cantor's voice, now baritone, penetrated every corner and we were (for the most part) still.

While Brody looked on with an ecstatic smile, Mr. Samuelson smartly pulled the cord of the curtain over the ark and disclosed the ranks of a dozen scrolls of the Law, dressed in white silk, wearing silver crowns.

The Congregation of Jews rose.

"Our God and God of our fathers, grant Dew!" said all.

"Grant dew, to quench the thirst of Thy land—" sang the Cantor alone, for all.

"In holy joy, sprinkle on us Thy blessing—
with quantity of wine and corn
establish the City of Thy desire!"

"B'tal! . . . with Dew!" shouted all, while the choir sang a loud paean.

Now the thunderstorm had moderated to a light steady rain, tapping on the skylight, flowing down all the drains. The space had become brighter, and the artificial lights shone dim and pale.

There were many stanzas to the poem, each comparing, in some trope or other, the state of the Jewish people in exile to that of a land thirsting and without water.

"With dew and contentment fill our barns—" sang the Singer of this agricultural people, accompanied by the continuo of the choir.

"Renew our days as of old—"

"B'tal!" shouted all.

". . . with Dew!"

New York City
1935

A CROSS-COUNTRY RUNNER
AT SIXTY-FIVE

The list for the cross-country run was tacked up in front of the Post Office; the small boys crowded round, looking for only one name, and there it was:

NO. 6—PERRY WESTOVER

"He's going to run again!"

"Let *me* see."

"He ran a thousand times."

They crowded up close to the bulletin board.

"How could he run a thousand times, stupid, when the race is only a hundred years old?"

"I saw him run last year and before that. I saw him run twenty times!"

"What! you little liar; you're only eight years old."

"He *used* to run, my mother told me."

"Why does he run? he's too old to win."

"How do you know he can't win? He's just kidding around. He could win any time he wants."

"I saw him once in the woods when nobody was watching, and he went like a streak."

"If he once put on the steam!"

"He has so many silver cups the whole cellar is full and there's no place to put the coal. Right, Danny?"

Danny was the runner's grandson. "My grandpa has lots of cups and medals," he said.

"He must be more'n a hundred years old."

"My grandpa is sixty-five," said Danny.

The Winchester Borough Cross-Country was the oldest race in the state. It was forty-five years old. Runners from all the neighboring boroughs and even from neighboring counties came to run in the event. Perry Westover, however, had run all forty-five times, he had not missed a year. In his prime, he had once won three times in a row, and twice beside that. Even now he came home among the first third, which was attributed to his "experience," as if he knew short cuts. There was more talk about where Perry Westover placed than about the winner—it proved the superiority of brain over brawn.

Mrs. Perry Westover disapproved of her husband's racing.

"I hear you have again handed in your entry," she said.

"Yes," answered the old athlete.

"Why do you do it, running with a lot of boys! You old fool. Don't you see that you are an old man?"

"I used to run to win; now I run just for the race."

"Running under the broiling sun—you don't know how it aggravates me or you wouldn't do it, to see you come home panting. How long do you think your heart can last? One day they'll bring you home on a stretcher. Well, it will give them something to talk about again."

"Of course they talk. Living close to us, they think I ought to do what they do. So I seem eccentric. But to people farther off, perhaps, there's nothing ridiculous in my devoting myself to a race; perhaps it's even natural."

"Do you suppose I care what people say, Perry?" said the white-haired woman. "I am thinking only of you. What a pity it is a person of your intelligence should waste his life away running across the fields. Almost every morning you are out before breakfast. The closet is crammed with old hobnailed shoes and dirty running-pants hung up. And half a dozen tarnished silver cups."

"Could you name me a career that is obviously preferable, that everybody would rather choose?" said Perry excitedly, for it was a point much thought of by him. "Don't you believe it! In the long run, the cross-country runner is as wise as the banker or doctor—rain and shine. One life is as good as another; mine is no worse. Anyway, haven't we done well enough and brought up three children?"

Perry had evolved this doctrine of the indifference among careers partly by a long reading of the book of Ecclesiastes. He kept this book by him so often that it began to infect his speech, and he sometimes bewildered a person talking to him by saying, out of nowhere, like the memory of a dream: "Time and Chance happeneth to them all," or "Ere ever the silver cord is snapped asunder, and the golden bowl is shattered, and the pitcher is broken at the fountain . . ."

The Westovers were well fixed, for the village of Winchester, almost rich; this despite the fact that, all his life, Perry had never chosen a career, unless to be a cross-country runner for silver cups is a career. He was "lucky," always falling into money-making ideas, "hunches," "windfalls." One time he saved the State a quarter of a million dollars by demonstrating that a new bridge ought not to be built where they intended building it, at the road, but farther upstream, since the road would have to be made over anyway within a year or two. For this he was paid $10,000 as a "consultant-engineer." Again, he set up his eldest son in a prosperous hardware business by inventing a patent can opener, sold by mail order. The secret was that he alone was not tied down to anything but could look about him disinterestedly. In a freely competitive society (such as this rural country used to be in his youth) a person like that could always make money.

"Do you want to know something?" said Perry. "I run cross-country in order to see the country."

At this moment, Cummings, the eldest son, entered the house—an alert, well-groomed, rather portly gentleman of forty. Like his mother, he disapproved of Perry's running in the race. So did his brothers, and so, aping their parents, did all the grandchildren excepting Danny. No one could see any *sense* in it, in being a cross-country runner at sixty-five! They would have felt less ill at ease if he were guilty of kleptomania or a lust for little girls.

"To see the country!" said Cummings. "If you want to see the country, papa, I can drive you around in a yellow Stutz, from here to Denver!"

"One need not go so far; a little territory thoroughly explored."

"By God, you've had time enough to do that."

"Think it through, son. To know something you have to return to it when you change your mind. You wouldn't trust your childhood memory of a man, would you? Most often, when asked for a judgment about anything, we have no clear present idea of it, but judge it with the same words we once used, although they have lost their meaning. This is why we so often contradict ourselves. But luckily we suffer that vague uneasiness of conscience which tells us (though nobody else knows) when our words are opinion and when they are knowledge. By running across the country again and again, I hope to keep my judgments up to date," said the old man, smiling.

"You intrigue me, papa," said Cummings. "What is there to see in the environs of Winchester? Perhaps I have been missing something."

"Not very much."

"For instance?"

"There seem to be at least five temporal layers. When you first pass by, different patches of land seem to have completely different dates—a spot beside Beaver Brook has not changed since the time of the Cayuga Indians, whereas the macadam highway, Route 4W, seems exclusively 1930. But the more you look at each, the more you see all the others emerging from it."

"What are the five?"

"In tabular form:

"1. The rough brook poppling among the green rocks and, under the high pines, the quiet carpet of brown needles: this is a hunting ground for the ghosts of Indians.

"2. A stony field baking in the sun, a few cattle penned in with a wall of stones and a wooden fence; the land cleared but full of stumps, with wild grass for grazing and four trees where the cows lie down.

"3. A cultivated field with tomato vines, a sow lying in the mud nuzzled at by seven sucklings; a barn with a nag, a well with a windlass. You see how crowded the scene becomes. A wire chickenhouse strewn with corn grains, and loud with clucking, cackling, crying, and crowing. A post box of the RFD.

"4. Next is the tarred road, the tar spattered on the brittle leaves of the huckleberry bushes, and the reek of gasoline; a road turning and bumpy—the wreck of an old Packard with the door in the back; telegraph poles leaning in different directions; a red gasoline filling pump, painted over for the third time, outside a hut of corrugated iron. This Age of Iron is the most crowded of all. The billboard CASTORIA, 'children cry for it.'

"5. And most recent is the concrete speedway, Route 4W, bright buff broad way across the State, crossing valleys and hills with hardly a rise or fall; the road signs are made of little mirrors that catch the headlights or the sun and burst into brilliance; the bridges are of gray steel. Lying on the road, like a metal jewel, is a smashed radio tube, the plate, grid, and filament entangled."

"What do you know about that!" said Mrs. Westover. "Look, Cummings," said the old runner, "when you skim by in your yellow motorcar, you see all these in flickering succession, as in a moving picture: woodland, steel bridge, farm, woodland, pasture, rapidly coming into being and vanishing. But when I break my way through the woods and emerge on the concrete speedway, the viaduct arching over my head, I am bodily into a different time. Sometimes, at the end of a long, hot run, fagged, a little sun-struck, it's as hard for me to drag my way from a hunting to a pastoral economy as it was for our ancestors. I break out of the forest like a tired replica of the Race of Man!"

"Is it true, what they say, grandpa," said little Daniel, "that you sometimes run so fast in the trees that a person can't see you?"

"Who said that?"

"Alec van Emden."

"What else do they say, Danny?"

"They say you must be one hundred years old."

"What else?"

"They say the cellar is so full of silver loving cups we have no place to keep the coal."

An automobile drove up to the porch. Cummings looked out the window.

"It's Roy Wiener of the *County Recorder*."

The reporter came in without knocking, explaining that he was after an interview with the famous cross-country runner.

"Is it true, Mr. Westover, that this is to be your forty-sixth annual race?"

"Just so."

"Do you mind if I take a picture?" he said, setting up his apparatus.

Perry likewise gave him a photograph of himself snapped over forty years before, when he was twenty-two or twenty-three. A blond, curly-headed youth stiffly posed, with a serious face, in the manner of that time, and holding up an absurd little silver loving cup in his right hand. The reporter thanked him, this was just what he was after. Little Danny kept looking away from the white-haired old man to the youth in the photo.

"In the course of years, I suppose there have been many changes in the itinerary of the race, isn't that so?" said Wiener. "What was the course of the Winchester cross-country forty-five years ago?"

"Substantially what it is now. Then also we started at the Post Office, went as far as Hemans Hill, and came back by way of Gaskell. There has been only one considerable change, and I was the one who suggested it."

"What was that?"

"When the road was built through Chapone, I suggested that we run along the road for a mile or two, rather than go out of the way across the fields. It was a cross-country race, I argued, and it would be a strange view of the countryside indeed that failed to take in the roads as well as the fields."

The old man searched in a trunk and brought forth a complete set of charts of the course, dating from before 1890 and indicating all the minor variations. The first drawings were rough, blurred pencil sketches on brown paper; the later ones increased in elegance even to the point of having the printing in red ink. It was clear that with the passage of the years the old man had not lost interest in the race, but now he paid more attention to the formalities and perhaps less to the actual running. Wiener noted the marginalia: "If a warm day, cross at M; if not, at N." " 'Ware of the bull in this field; sprint to get here first."

"You see, there is a certain science to it," said Perry.

"Tell me, Mr. Westover, are you always consulted by the sponsor when there is to be some change in the course or the regulations?"

"Yes."

"Do you mind if I ask something a trifle more intimate, Mr. Westover?"

"No, no. Go right ahead."

"The readers of the *Recorder* would like to know just what you see in cross-country running, just what is its peculiar attraction, that you have devoted so many years to it."

Perry laughed briefly. "How do you mean?" he said.

"Why, I mean, some men go into a thing for the money in it, others because they want publicity—"

Suddenly, for no cause at all, Perry became cross and excited. What infernal crust, he thought, to ask a man for *reasons* for what he has devoted fifty years to!—as if we lived for some ulterior end outside the act of living.

" 'He that observeth the wind shall not sow!' " he quoted, " 'he that regardeth the clouds shall not reap . . . In the morning, sow thy seed; in the evening, withhold not thy hand—for thou knowest not which shall prosper, this or that—' "

"Where is that from? It sounds like the Bible," said Wiener.

" 'Enjoy life with the wife whom thou lovest all the days of thy vanity . . . *Whatsoever thy hand attaineth to do by thy strength, that do.*' That *do*. That DO!"

"My husband is a little tired; couldn't you come back some other time?" said Mrs. Westover.

"Oh, no, thanks, thanks. Thanks very much, you've

been too kind," said Wiener, hastily packing up his camera.

" 'VETERAN ATHLETE QUOTES SCRIPTURES,' " he thought viciously, as he climbed into his roadster.

"Will I last till fifty years?" thought Perry anxiously.

Next morning, practicing, he slowly jogged the entire course, glad of the opportunity to move his limbs; he was very disturbed, very nervous. He had lost his temper at Wiener's brass and had not recovered his mental balance. At the same time, the realization that he had become an old man made him sad. Formerly, he had kept withdrawing from the surrounding countryside to the thoughts and memories inside himself and then moving back to the environment as if awaking, shuttling back and forth until the two regions became inextricably mixed. Running year after year over the same course and carefully noting, as he did, the slow transformation of every part of the countryside during two generations, the houses demolished, built, moved from place to place, again demolished, brick replacing wood—it had still not really occurred to him that he also was being slowly transformed. Now, as by a flash of light, he looked at himself with the eyes of all the children of Winchester; he realized that he was not just a runner, but an old institution, ancient, almost fabulous. Likewise, an old man. "Perhaps after all," he thought, "I ought to be thinking about getting ready to die, rather than running across the country. Why fifty years? just because it's a round number." These ideas obsessed him successively, and kept recurring in various combinations—as the idea that he was a kind of institution led to the the thought of Wiener's brass and this to the thought that it was inappropriate for such an old man to run across the country; but again, the idea of Wiener's interview led to the thought that he was a kind of institution, something like a house, more permanent than those that had been moved away, soon to be demolished in turn—so that he soon realized that they were all expressions of one basic idea, and it made no difference which one of them he proposed to his mind, anger at Wiener's brass, or bewilderment at having grown old in a second, or the strange humor of being a ghost while still alive. Thus, without a thought of the road, he ground away mile after mile.

But suddenly, in the heart of Winchester Wood, in a little clearing, he found himself in front of a small house of logs that seemed strangely familiar to him; for instance, he knew, without counting, that it was so many logs high, and, without looking, that the fourth log in the rear was pointed on one end as if cut for a different purpose. Then he remembered that he himself had built this cabin: he had sharpened the log to drive it into the ground as one of the corner posts, but had finally decided for a different mode of construction. How many years ago, he had no recollection. During the past twenty years at least, he had apparently passed the house by without even seeing it, as he ran by (unless indeed he had now missed the trail and was lost in the wood!), without regarding it even as a milestone to identify the course.

He pushed open the door—which was provided with new brass hinges—and went in. The room was in the best of repair and very clean. There was an unpainted deal table with a book and a couple of cans of tomatoes on it. The fireplace had been several times rebuilt; now it was cemented and mostly of brick; but the two big conical stones, almost twin, which he himself had built into the front, stood there still, after many years, the wardens of the fire. Perry picked up the book from the table, half expecting to find it a Bible; but it was a tattered copy of an old edition of the *Boy Scout Handbook,* with a boy scout on the cover in khaki shorts and a flat-brimmed hat, signaling semaphore with a pair of red-and-white flags.

The back wall was thick with carved initials:

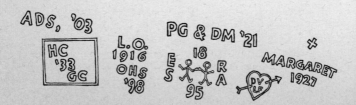

Some were fresh and yellow on the varnished logs, or stained red, or some were dark, worn, and painted over. Among these, the 85's and the 92's, Perry looked vainly for some carving of his own. Quite by accident he lighted on:

Cummings, Gerald, Lawrence Westover, his three boys. But there was no PW, no Perry Westover; he had never thought of carving his own name in the wall. To be sure, it was he who had built the wall . . . To Cummings and Gerald, evidently, this cabin must have seemed part of the immemorial wood; how could it have occurred to them that their own father had built it. P.W. *struxit*— Perry Westover built it! For a few moments he became absorbed in the contemplation of each separate carving in the wood—so that he could hardly drag his eyes from one to the next.

On the way to Chapone, he again lost all sense of his surroundings; he clambered over stone fences, his thoughts two hundred and forty thousand miles away.

"Were Wiener to ask me again," he thought, "I should rather quote the passage from Ecclesiastes: *There is a time for every purpose and for every work.*" "But, Perry," Mrs. Westover said (he thought), "all the same, perhaps some works are more proper than others." "All come to one end!" he cried. He quoted, " 'He hath made everything beautiful in its time; also *He hath set the world in their heart, yet so that man cannot find out the work that God hath done,* from the beginning even to the end.' Even a wise man can't find it out! What does this mean? It means that one thing is as good as another!—

'Strange things I have in head, that will to hand; which must be acted ere they may be scanned.' "

"Is that how you interpret Ecclesiastes?" asked Roy Wiener, arranging his apparatus to take a picture. "The book is a long sermon against idolatry," said Perry; "some men experiment, as it is said, 'how to pamper the flesh with wine'; others make great works, houses, vineyards, gardens, and parks; they gather gold and silver and servants. Others, again, try to become wise. All this is vanity. 'Let me point out,' says the Preacher as I read it, 'that to put your trust in such works is idolatry and vanity. Yet it is proper to turn to something or other,' he goes on to say, 'whatever your strength is capable of, for "to everything there is a season, a time to every purpose under the heaven"—only do not put your trust in *it*.' "
"In what shall we put our trust?" asked the reporter. "In God," said Mrs. Westover. "Is this the meaning of the book?" asked Wiener, trying hard to understand rather than to cover a story. " 'Then,' " quoted Perry, " 'then I beheld all the work of God, that man cannot find out the work that is done under the sun; though a wise man *labor* to seek it out, yet he shall not find it; though a wise man seek to know it, yet shall he be unable to find it out. Chapter IX. For all this I laid to my heart: that the righteous and the wise and their works are in the hand of God; whether to be love or hatred—man knoweth it not; all is before them. All things come alike to all. . . . *This is an evil that is done under the sun!*' " " 'Whether to be love or hatred—man knoweth it not,' " said Mrs. Westover. "Yes, yes," said Wiener approvingly, " 'the race is not to the swift, nor the battle to the strong'—I am a reporter, I have seen it often!—'neither yet bread to the wise, nor yet riches to men of understanding; but time and chance happeneth to them all.' " "Ah, I see I have convinced you!" "Bravo, Perry! Who would have thought that there was so much philosophy behind being a cross-country runner at sixty-five!" said Mrs. Westover.

Triumphant in this boyish daydream, he emerged from a copse of birches at the white fence of the State Road, 4W. A green roadster, with flashing glassware, shot by at eighty miles. Perry sat down on the fence for a breather. On the road was lying a broken spark plug, the porcelain insulation broken. There was always some such broken relic on the speedway. He kept staring at this spark plug.

He knew from experience that by staring long enough at one spot, and thinking hard, he could revive the whole history of the place—the steam rollers would return and the tar-men light their fires; the salvos of dynamite level the hill; and before that, a nag drag a peddler's cart up the grade. And he ran a few yards along the road. On the right hand was a battery of signposts: GASKELL 2½ miles. MIDDLETON 10 miles. MALORY 15 miles. CICERO 125 miles. From the lowest of these signs could be seen dangling an old shoe that Perry had hung there, in case the owner ever drove back that way; but by now it was spoiled by the rain and shine. It struck Perry that, just as these signs marked the distances of different towns, it would be a natural thing, and not useless, to set up signposts of the passage of time: 5 years ago. 50 years ago. 150,000 years. (As if abruptly, on a local signpost, there should appear: THE MOON ↑ 240,000 miles!) . . . At the signpost, the course left the road, and once again Perry plunged into the wood.

It was the fall of the year, the beginning of October. In the wood, four urchins, playing hookey from school, had built a fire among the colored trees. They were telling dirty stories and were playing cat's cradle, passing the intricate cord from one set of fingers to another.

Perry sped out of a scarlet thicket near by; his white form appeared and vanished among the tree trunks.

"Look! there is Perry Westover, practicing for the race!" cried one of the kids in an awestruck voice.

"Where? where? I don't see him," cried the others. He was unable to point because of the game of cords in his hands. "Where is he?" they said.

Perry kept appearing and vanishing in the wood.

"*There* he is!"

"There he is!" they cried.

New York City
1936

HANDBALL PLAYERS

I.

Often, playing handball, I am paired with the weakest player, as if I were the strongest player; and often we two win.

In fact I am a mediocre player, but I have a strong service. Once play is engaged, my weakness appears. I follow the ball tenaciously and place my own shots cannily, but they are progressively feeble (against a strong player); by the fifth or sixth return I'm a dead duck. I inhibit my shots, yet tenaciously keep the ball in play: as a child agrees not to do whatever it is and nevertheless will not let the issue close (waiting for her softer nature to reassert itself?) Desiring not to win, but to fight a *drawn-out* losing fight.

But when I crouch in the corner to serve the first ball, no one is yet in motion, and then, watching where they lie, I can spin the ball to within an inch of any line on the court or at the toes of my opponent. No one is in apparent motion, yet because of the previous serves they are already about to move this way or that, one may easily judge, or they are uncertain: then is the time that they bungle the set-up and their confusion is perfected. They are prematurely engaged; I am isolated, motionless, adequate— the world lies open for me to put it at a disadvantage. Against even a strong player, my tricky service, darting every way from my little corner, is worth half a dozen points.

When I am thus isolated, not socially engaged, I do not inhibit my strength and I am a formidable opponent. Woe to those who do not recover their aplomb but become more and more prematurely engaged—really engaged in the memory of the play that is over, but I start afresh, I speed up the tempo—I could sweep them off the court: except that my softer nature reasserts itself and I cannot do it. Once I see my own advantage too clearly I am ashamed, and soon I relax both the tempo and my deadly serve. But strong players, of course, stall and recover their aplomb and then they pound me, though I hang on tenaciously.

Playing alone, I dislike to win, to have to win. I like to prove to my own satisfaction, not my superiority, but my adequacy. But I do not like, playing alone, to be guilty of victory. Perhaps I even prefer to lose, if it is a good contest and I am closely engaged, especially if I have shown flashes of power to make me respected. But the victor is terribly isolated, and cannot get back in. Because the game is over.

II.

Thus I often choose to be paired with the weakest player, especially if he is also the youngest.

Now some strong players crowd their weak partners out of the game. Such persons want too much to win and assert themselves; they are disgusted to see the weak partner bungle the shot that they could have returned with effect. But this is bad policy, for (if the sides are evenly matched) no player can stand against two. Meantime the boy, feeling inferior to begin with, becomes more and more worthless: crowded out of the play in prospect, he is not there when he is called on; and sure that he is inadequate, he bungles even when he is adequate. His partner's disgust doesn't help.

Merely as policy, though I do not do it as policy, it is best to allow the weak partner his full court, but to support him close on his weak side. When he feels himself relied on, approved and supported, then most often, since his weakness has been in part his conviction of weakness, he plays a little better. Momentarily he enjoys the naturalness of "beginner's luck." If he can confirm this good new habit, he's not such a weak player after all (supported on his weak side).

I support him and approve of him like a father. I do it because he is myself: I am the weak player.

Next, in two minutes, because he gratefully listens to me, he has learned the simple secret of never making a random shot without an angle, just to pound the wall with blundering power like our opponents. See, now it is they who are behind on every play. The boy imagines that he is an adequate player after all. At least—we are a team. He fancies that he is a *strong* player—at doubles.

More and more I withdraw from the volley, leaving most of it to a weak partner! But in this way I have re-captured, even in the midst of the close volley, the isolation and the power that belong to me when I crouch in the corner to serve. My boy is engaged *for* me: shall I not suddenly step in, crowd him from the court, and hit again the angular bounder that passes them by? (I have no killer.)

They try to keep the ball away from me, as if I had more than this one shot. They hit it outside the court.

Under these circumstances, when my boy is playing most of the game, my softer nature does not reassert it-self; my boy is asserting it for me. We do not relax the tempo; I do not relax my deadly serve; we are not ashamed to sweep them off the court with brutal victory and cry, "O.K., next victims!"

III.

What I like best is not to be closely engaged in the social game at all, not to risk the weak nature and the weak player to the chances of the game that scene by scene re-create the earnest episodes in which I learned to inhibit my strength—but for my favorite, by no means a weak player, to play in there for me, while I coach him, and we win.

He has not yet learned not to follow through and to become weak in the volley, but he pounds it with first nature. And as for the canny cross-purposes by which a child recovers and tenaciously keeps the ball in play—I see to them. Then I feel the freshness blowing in my soul when he crouches, in isolation, and spins out my puzzlers, the low-darting serves, an inch within any line!

Have I done morally to teach the boy, who never earned it by fatal losses, to crouch so cunningly disengaged when all the rest are in premature motion playing the memory that is dead and gone? And *then* he follows through by his own first nature, for it is only a boy!

Yes. Why should not at least one exhibit his fearless power? as if he never had a mother and it's no fatal loss.

Nevertheless there is something too young and terrible in this fearless victory, scouring the court by nature and teaching, freely, not like the poor devils who drive themselves to brutal victory because they have been hurt.

I think that it is only partly in resentment of my favorite that I feel sadness at his triumph.

Freely victorious, both in isolation and when closely engaged, in despite of my mother and all the poor grown-up folk.

But the ball is no longer in play.

Sitting here on the sidelines disengaged, the more closely engaged for *every* dancing player, I can see how the killer has put an end to the social game; it has destroyed them one and all.

Better, clenching one's will and power, to kill on the serve, immobile and solitary, before one has ever joined at all. To specialize on the serve in order to prevent the play from starting, that will end in our hurt.

"Let me in the next game, fellows," I say. "It looks like Duffy's the best, so pair *him* with the weakest." Ha! and will he be able to support and enhearten his partner?

IV.

It seems to be I who must support and enhearten us all, both the weak player in his insecurity and the strong in his disgust, and my own partner—and myself; crying, "Too bad!" or "Partner!" or "Beauty!"

I do not omit the human cries among the dry noises of the act.

We are not playing against each other. Whom are we playing against? against what are we playing?

We are playing against the wall! No pun; the act of the game is the essence of the game. The competition is our ruse to make us go to the extreme.

Pounding the immovable wall in order to keep the ball in play.

One will not break down a stone wall by pounding it with a rubber ball. (Hard to reach orgasm.) But at least return it again and again. Why break the spell of the offering with murderous skill?

Yet unless it is heightened by the excitement of speed, power and skill, and skill against skill, and will against will, going to the extreme, always within the rules— the rules are just so we may go the extreme—how should we come to devote ourselves to the sacred offering, beyond ourselves and getting out of ourselves, in the social agony?

No fault in the young hero, victorious, the fool! that he hits the shot impossible to get; but that the rest of us do not rise to the height to achieve that impossible, and so miraculously offer ourselves. Doing miracles, forced to do miracles by the difficult demand. God forbid that out of resentment I should be saddened by a pure feat of first nature and second nature. What has a father to do with hurt pride?

Hurling our planet again and again—I am speaking of every ball game. At the immovable wall. The world is returned to us alive, so long as we keep it in play. We try, as far as possible beyond ourselves during the brief time that the ball is breathing with life, to devote ourselves to the sacred dance. The line divides the court into the Houses of Night and Day. The planet is in play. The wall does not move, but it is consenting. The power is in our own two hands (though one will not break down a stone wall by pounding it with a rubber ball). By my cries I continue to support and enhearten us all. And the young hero, by creating the situation impossible to achieve, has raised us—one and all, not privately—to do miracles.

V.

Handball players do not play to win, but they think they play to play. Sometimes they play for a dollar in order to convince themselves that they are playing to win and are not childishly at play.

Yet they do not even play to play, but to keep the ball in play. Vainly they pretend that, relaxing from earnest, they are merely playing and not giving an offering to the implacable wall that stands up against them.

Acting—and renouncing the fruit of action, just as Krishna urged Arjuna. This is to act sacredly, there is no guilt in it.

The ball game is not an arbitrary convenience merely to enable us to act; but we act precisely, according to the rules, renouncing the fruit of it (nor is there any fruit of it), in order to keep the ball in play, the wall consenting.

A rubber ball is a similitude of a *live* thing. This is obvious when suddenly it bounds away in freedom, beyond the reach of the players or under their legs, across the courts, unwilling to give itself to the power of their hands. Then it dies. Indeed, when you see an eager, awkward child playing with a rubber ball and "hitting it with all his hard might," you would think that they were both equally live things, bounding to and from each other.

They play in order to bring to life the little animal; in order to preserve alive the breathing life in it.

The four players, competitively and with their best and sacrificial effort, are generating an immense power to impart to the homunculus and make it leap with life.

To spin our microcosm across day and night and make it wring life from the wall, for it seems to rebound from the wall of its own will.

The sheer wall is the will of the players that does not fail, relax or soften—but it returns each blow as hard as it is struck.

Now here is the sheer, immobile, immovable and impending wall. But there happens to be no other player to make a social game, so the man desultorily pounds the wall himself. It is hard thus to enliven the ball, playing with oneself like a masturbator. There is no external excitant, nothing unforeseen and distracting the conscious attention, to carry him beyond himself. Even so, desire and image well from the unknown. Does he think, desultorily pounding the ball, that he can so carefully control his strength and the enlivening animal? "Return me *that* flicker of Mercury! between the black night and the rising sun."—But he cannot, and it bounds away from him and dies.

At least the wall itself is immobile; it will not move forward against the players, but stands there consenting. (There is nothing unusual behind the blank wall: it is the wall of a warehouse.)

But I used, when I was ten years old, to have a recurring nightmare: that the walls along the street crumbled as I passed and showered down their bricks upon me. The achievement of this orgasm roused in me a terrible anxiety.

But now the walls stand firm, and the live animal is only a rubber ball, as we develop, figure by figure, faster and faster, the devoted dance of our social game, within the rules, renouncing the fruits of action.

> "Casting action upon Brahman,
>   abandoning attachment—
> Evil does not cling to him
>   as water not to the lotus-leaf.

> "Rid of attachment, freed,
>   his mind fixed in knowledge,
> acting for worship only
>   —all action melts away."

New York City
May 1945

THE BREAK-UP OF OUR CAMP

✳   when the ice is soft enough to break through
and fall in,
the water ain't as cold as it might have been.

CHAPTER I

The Canoeist

I.

In mid-lake, Armand in his canoe woke to singing. He
had drowsed, the paddle loose in his hand; his eyes
opened wide. Darkness was on the water, and on the
shore, whence came the gusts of music, was a row of starry
fires. The young Canadian felt wide awake, but increasingly
so continually, so that he was surely in no normal mood.
Pointing his prow toward the camp fires, he paddled rapidly ashore.

Here I, patrolling the waterfront, stood waiting for
him. "What are these fires and singing?" he asked in a
French-Canadian accent. "This is Camp Katonah, a summer camp for Jewish boys," I answered in French; "who
are you?"—flashing a light on him—for we did not approve
of strangers coming into our camp after dark. At the
same time, he was a traveler, to whom we owed hospital-
ity. In the circular light he crouched thin and red, somewhat intimidated. He explained that he was from St.
Pierre, Province of Quebec, and was paddling to Burlington. "I dozed off," said he, "and I awoke and saw your
fires on the shore."

"Any other night," I said, "lights would have been out. Wednesday's camp-fire."

He opened his eyes wider still when twenty-five juniors rose to do a swift hora among the fires.

"It must be dangerous on the lake at night," I thought.

"This is like coming in to a family," he thought.

There was a can of tea, and I offered him a dipperful.

"Roast us something to eat, Danny," I said to the tall boy who ran my switchboard backstage. I was the teacher of dramatics at this Jewish boys' camp on the shore of Lake Champlain.

Singing began again.

"In what language are they singing?" he asked with a frown.

"In Hebrew." It was the Zionist marching song, *V'im lo Achshav, Eimatai!*—"It means," I said,

> And if not now,
> When?

"That was what the old Rabbi said—" Then I saw how absurd it was, to try to explain to this Canadian into what kind of world he had come. The song itself, a song of the East European Jews, was in three languages, in Hebrew, Yiddish and Russian; how to explain it? What a curious thing for a hundred small boys to be singing, in northern Vermont, in Yiddish,

> Pioneers, quickly!
> pack up your packs,
> for the train is starting off—

"At the same time," I thought, ruffled (for no one likes to think that what he has grown used to is curious), "any combination of circumstances would be equally improbable. What if they were singing English beside the ancient lake?" *Proschaiti psedruja!* the small boys now sang in Russian.

> Good-bye, comrades!—

Where were they all going, sitting down?

The singing was rapid and smooth, had none of the wildness of the boys; they sang like a learned choir.

"What a peculiar place and what a peculiar crowd of people!" thought Armand. He bit into the steak sandwich; the meat was black and tender, with a sprinkle of salt on it. "I like it here," he thought. "Everybody is singing and eating." The more he looked about, the more mystified he became, and at the same time the more he seemed to become wide awake—becoming mystified and seeming to become wide awake were to him the same. "Your camp is a wonder box," he said.

"I'll show you around," I said a little annoyed, for I absolutely did not approve of strangers appearing out of the night to call our camp a wonder box. His phrase, nevertheless, was not so very different from my own, that "any combination would be equally improbable." "Danny," I directed, "watch the shore so nobody falls in and drowns.—This waterfront is very dangerous."

"My boat?" said the Canuck discreetly. "I shouldn't like to be stranded here," he smiled broadly. ("Is that so?" I thought.)

"Put Armand's boat with the other canoes."

We went along Company Street, preceded by the circle of my flashlight. On either side stood the ghostly tentalows with white canvas walls, and as we withdrew from the singing and the fires, the quiet of the night and the noise of the frogs spread round us. "Is this where you all sleep?" asked Armand but this question made me very cross. "Where do you think we sleep, in the trees?" I was cross at his asking obvious questions, as if he were a tourist and we were exotic, but the deeper reason of my antipathy to that stranger—it was only in the course of time that I came to be aware of *this,* my own disgust, and boredom, with our camp. *"Go away, canoeist, before you spend one night here!"* I ought to have warned him. "How many sleep in each bunk?" he asked. "Five. Isn't that a good number?"

"What is your job here, you seem to give orders?"

"I put on the plays. Here is my theater."

I led the way inside and, leaving him in the darkness among the seats, I leaped on to the stage and threw on the green borders.

Immersed in this pea-soup gloom and beholding me, a ghastly spook, on the stage, Armand faltered. At

which, in momentary triumph, I flashed my most powerful spot full in his eyes and he recoiled and spoke a
cry.

"Where am I?" he cried.

Slowly I filtered the atmosphere away from the green
until stage and theater were bathed in deep rose—wasting time while an idea that had struck me could become
formed; then I left the stage white and bright. I was content. For weeks I had been thinking what play to give as
the last of the summer; and now, beholding the stranger
in the white spot in the gloom, I decided on *Macbeth,* in
a version for my boys age 8 to 15.

He climbed onto the stage and began to manipulate
the switchboard, which I perfunctorily demonstrated. He
was extremely childlike; he could not conceal his pleasure
at the number of toys. His lips revealed his gums in a
wide grin as the wonder box proved more and more productive. Happening on the siren, he tirelessly sent lugu-
brious howls into the night. He sent a howl of wind up
my spine, while the bluewhite tops of the cyclorama flickered on and off. In time to the lightning, I punched a
metal sheet—*Double! double! toil and trouble!*

"I seem to have been here all summer!" thought Armand, because he was busy.

From down the lane came the strains of taps.

"Let's go up to the Lodge. They've put them to bed
over in the girls' camp."

"Oh! are there girls, too?" said the Canadian.

I looked sharply at him—he was wearing white duck
trousers over a bathing suit of Canadian red. "Don't you
think you could put on a shirt or a sweater—" I started
to say—"skip it," I said.

Now, just as we were mounting the hill to the Lodge,
the full moon, whose light from behind the low hills had
been more and more irradiating the eastern sky, rose
large and yellow; and, as if creating them from nothing,
its light brought into view both the boys' camp and the
girls' camp across the covered bridge: the equal-sign
of the boys' tentalows below, and across the face of the
hill the arc of the girls' houses where now everybody was
asleep, and the dying fires along the shore each circled
by seated people; and a quarter of a mile away, shining

in the milky light (for each moment that we watched its effects the moonlight became whiter and brighter), were the markings of tennis courts and a baseball diamond.

"You have large grounds," said Armand in a flat voice. He decided not to paddle off on the following morning before breakfast.

The moon rose high and bright. Out of the covered bridge came three young women, my girl Maitabel, Louise the dancing counsellor, and Naomi. These three came noisily laughing through the bridge. When they saw Armand they stopped short.

"This is Armand," I said; "he's paddling down to Burlington."

"Hello, Almonds," said Louise.

"Look," I said in Yiddish, "will you take away this mad dog before I shoot it?"

"O.K., let's go to town, *Almonds!*" cried Louise, sizing up the situation in her way. She clung to his arm. "Can you wrestle?" she said.

"Why shouldn't I stay here for a few days?" thought Armand, bewildered and happy. "They all seem to like me, except that dramatics teacher, who doesn't know what he likes (I've met that type before). I have never fallen into such a curious place. They have no manners and talk over my head in an incomprehensible language; at the same time I feel at home, as if I had been here all summer. I seem to recognize people. I wonder if I am really so wide awake as I imagine."

Inside the Lodge, a radio was playing

> You're the tops, you're molasses candy,
> You're the tops, you're Mahatma Gandhi—

"Good-bye, Armand," I said, holding out my hand, "I probably won't see you again. You'll be gone in the morning before we get up."

2.

When I came into the mess hall next morning for breakfast, there, at the main table, *in my place,* at the right hand of the head counsellor and next to Dr. Kleinberg, sat Armand, grinning broadly with his brown face and eating spoonfuls of cornflakes. Seeing me enter, he did not stop eating but waved a greeting with his left hand.

"Look," said Danny, who came in with me, "there is Armand your canoeist."

"For Christ's sake, Werner," I said in Yiddish, "what is this *shaegitz* doing here in my seat? Don't you see now we'll never be rid of him?"

At this main table we were at the heart of our camp. Behind, one could hear the conversation of the girls' dining room. Ahead, through the windows, spread the whispering lake. Out of the corner of my left eye I could see sullen Winkie, who did not yet know that he was going to be Macbeth.

"He claims the water is too rough for sailing," said Dave, "he'll leave this afternoon."

"Too *rough!*"

"I was telling Matt," he said to Armand in English, "that you were going to be with us till this afternoon." The Canadian smiled.

"*Attention, everybody!*" proclaimed Dave, getting to his feet and emitting a shriek of his whistle, so that the clamor of the mess hall fell an octave. "I want to introduce Almonds, a Kanuck. Almonds is on a canoe trip from St. Pierre to Burlington, down the St. Lawrence River and down Lake Champlain, a distance of two hundred and fifty miles. Almonds will stay with us all morning and he will be glad to give any and all a lesson in sailing. *Give him a big hand, everybody!*"

Armand rose to his feet and there was loud applause.

"Rabosai," said an authoritative voice: "Let us say Grace."

The noise hushed and Armand looked about while a voice began a prayer in a different foreign language.

The surface of the lake was blue and glassy, crossed once in a while by a fan of quarter-inch ripples glittering in the sunlight. Armand did not find enough breeze to put up his lateen-rig to give the instruction in sailing; instead he performed canoe tricks, of which he had a large repertory. He could make a canoe stand on end, or make it roll over without shipping water. The excited Senior boys splashed round him and climbed on and off. He introduced to our camp the sport of canoe-jousting with brooms, which has since become a popular tournament amongst us with a bronze medal for the champion (in this particular, Armand played the role of the Culture Hero who came from afar and founded the institution). Finally, seeing our large pink war canoe, twenty feet long and meant for eight paddlers, he decided to perform also on this instrument and launched the boat into the open; but it was too heavy for him—a gust of wind, the single gust of the morning, swung the nose around into the pier and broke the canoe's back.

"Very good!" I said to Dave.

"You were the one who brought him here," said Dave, reddening.

"Mark my word, he'll be here tomorrow morning, too."

"What do you advise me to do?"

"Let it run its course! Let it run its course!"

The eleven-year-old Intermediates were the next group to meet Armand and make him feel at home. He was thus welcomed by one after another of us, by myself, by Louise, by the head counsellor, by the whole camp, by the senior boys, by the inters. "Almonds, tell us how you shot the rapids!" the kids cried in their high voices, crowding round him—it was perhaps something he had promised earlier in the morning. In their gray sweaters they came crowding round him in his flaming red and white, forming a pretty flower. "Tonight after supper—" said Armand, laughing, trying to break loose. "O.K.!"—and they ran off to a new sport, forgetting all about him and his promise; but to Armand it now seemed that he was welcome in the evening, too, and would see the camp fires actually being lighted, not merely burning from afar. He did not know that there were camp-fires *only* on Wednesday nights.

Bernard, who was five, the smallest child in our camp, came running and said: "Uncle Almonds! piggy-back me to the wash-house!"

In the afternoon, Louise said to me grimly: "Please, you'll have to tell that nut you brought around not to follow me or I'm going to crack him. He wants to wrastle all the time."

I grinned at her uncertainly. By this time I was no longer cross at the coming of Armand, but ill at ease.

"He comes when I'm trying to teach a class and the girls aren't dressed."

"You gave him a good time last night, didn't you?"

"I! You were the one who began it. He says that you took him into your theater and flashed a spotlight in his eyes."

"Yes, I did—and he cried out."

"What did he cry out?" she said (I thought).

"I couldn't understand the word. It was in bad French."

"You told me he was going away in the morning," said Louise, "or there were things I wouldn't have let him get away with. There's a way of acting with a person who *is* staying for only one night and you're never going to see him again."

"If our camp were not only for the summer, and we ever expected to see each other again," I faltered—and the tears began to flood my eyes—*"we, too, should have behaved more circumspectly.* But there is no time."

And it seemed as if this canoeist, who had paddled in out of the night, seeing our fires from the lake and hearing singing, had also been around all summer. When he walked down Company Street between the rows, and could look through the wire-screen walls at the activity, the naked boys with towels around their shoulders and the counsellor stealing chocolates from a trunk, he was a familiar figure, greeted by each one he passed, by the little boys and the big boys and the young men, with an off-hand nod or a strained smile, or by some such phrase as "Nice going, Admiral!"—to all of which he replied with a flashing smile and a characteristic wave of his right arm bent at the elbow.

3.

Yet by the next morning he was frozen out; and when he walked down the windy street, for it proved to be a wretched day, every head turned slightly away, not more than a few degrees, but just so no one would be obliged to notice him. Twenty times, amid the gusts of wind, he half raised his arm and the smile decayed on his lips. The animosity against the stranger, which I, like a delicate barometer, had felt almost at once, had reached its full storm; and there were many ways in which it broke forth that I shall not set down because it is unpleasant. The small boys, who were as sensitive to what their counsellors did not express as they were disobedient to what they did, peered with fright at Armand out of the corners of their eyes, so that the whites of their eyes showed like the under-sides of leaves before a rainstorm. Unable to find anyone to talk to, Armand walked across the empty athletic fields, and the more woebegone he looked the less willing was anyone to notice him. But I, who could rejoice in the general acceptance of my own dislike—and was this not what I desired?—instead found myself in pain. I could not watch him loitering on the baseball diamond, amid the first drops of rain—yet I could watch nothing else. "Hasn't he had enough!" I thought—and I shadowed him at a distance from place to place, hiding behind a tree, so he would not see me.

Were it not for the troubled weather, he would have left already. The wind, slowly accelerating through the night and morning, had attained a formidable speed, tearing to shreds the canvas doors of the tentalows and whipping up foam of the lake into rapid bullets against our faces. The tossing sea of Champlain was white and black, yet despite the high wind the cloudy ceiling lowered so heavily that nothing seemed to move.

Late in the afternoon, far out on the pier's end among the whitecaps, Armand ate his lunch, while I, from the porch of the theater, unable not to watch him, looked on.

Turning around, he caught my eye, and I was obliged to come down to him on the pier.

"I am afraid I have overstayed my welcome," he said.

"Are you going to go away?" I asked in anxiety.

"It's lonely, paddling down the St. Lawrence River and in this ocean!" he said, indicating with a brusque gesture the tossing lake. "I thought by luck I had come amongst friends and pretty girls. For a moment yesterday I was about to ask to remain here as the boating counsellor."

"We have a boating counsellor, my friend Mike," I said. "He's been sick."

"Up to a certain point—" said Armand, "up to a certain point from the time I awoke and heard the singing and saw the fires on the shore—up to a certain point from that time it kept seeming to me that I had come to a good place. Then!—without any real reason for the change, mind you, for your camp is well enough in its way—all this was impossible, inconceivable. . . . The fact is," he said, and broke into a quiet smile, "beyond a certain point your camp leaves me cold!"

"You yourself said you didn't want to be stranded here," I said.

"After all, those friends and those girls—" he said with a grin.

"They're well enough in their way," I said.

"Well, good-bye, Mathew, and thanks for everything," said Armand, holding out his hand. "Tell Dave thanks for me, and give my love to Louise."

A few large drops of rain now began to fall and I left him on the pier. Furthermore, it was time for Sabbath evening services, to be held in the theater because of the weather, not outdoors as usual.

I was in a black rage. It was very well for *him* to talk cheerily about the camp leaving him cold, but *I* had to stay! I scowled at the ninety boys and the eighty girls, and at the counsellors of whom I had seen too much, collecting in the theater where I had staged too many plays, for a prayer service that I had said too often. Up to a certain point! Beyond a certain point!

"Look!" pointed Danny, standing at the window with his legs apart, "there goes your Canadian."

I peered through the square dusty window, into the rain that was now coming down forcibly, the drops splashing on the unquiet surface of Champlain. Struggling in the teeth of the south wind, his double-paddle rising and falling courageously on either side, rode my canoeist, forced back three-quarters of a length for every length of advance. A bolt of orange lightning split the sky, silhouetting his figure with a brilliant glow around his outline. Three of the electric lamps in the theater went dim and dark. "I pity him," I told myself, "if he intends to be out all night on that sea." But the truth was that I did not pity him at all but envied him, because he was going away.

Behind me, as I stood looking out of the window, the collected camp broke into that marching song, *V'im lo Achshav, Eimatai?* and this question,

> And if not now,
> *when?*
> And if not now,
> WHEN?—

this question broke in so hard in my depression that I had to lean with my hand against the window frame, not to fall.

> Pioneers quickly! pioneers surely!
> . . . the train is starting off.

I felt ashamed, standing with my back to the others and my eyes flooding with tears that at a shock would begin coursing down my cheeks. Yet this extraordinary uneasiness meant, I knew from experience, that I was in the presence of what I should do well to disregard not lightly.

CHAPTER II

The Break-Up of Camp

> ※   The deeper sinks the sun, the longer grow the shadows.
> —NIETZSCHE

> ※   The owl Minerva flies at dusk.
> —HEGEL

I.

Groggy with the lights, I stumbled out the back door of my theater, gulping in the air. The sun setting, red and flat, called attention to itself. The shouting of the kids was retreating up the hill. The lake was turbulent.

Mike was gesticulating to two kids to bring a canoe in.

When they got close enough to clamber up, he beat them
on the head. With a heave he lifted the boat onto the dock
and drove his heel through the belly of it. This scene,
this action of my mild friend, was so unbelievable that I
observed it with simple curiosity. The feat of strength was
such as persons perform when they become heroic in an
emergency. The pink war-canoe was already lying with its
back broken on the rocks, in the waning light, like another stage-property of the same fiction.

At supper the racket was extraordinary. The fourteen
tables raged. Maybe it was always like this, and I myself—
no longer occupied with the old show and not yet preoccupied with the next—was suddenly hearing while they
cheered and sang—punctuated once a meal by the terror of a falling tray of dishes. But there was an extra
energy in the banging on the table, and that tray was not
dropped but flung down. Above all, there were barbarous
quarter-intervals in the tunes, as if these booming boys,
well-behaved Jews from Brooklyn and Montreal, had forgotten thousands of years of civil culture.

A counsellor was bellowing whatever popped into his
empty head. It was of course Ostoric, the repulsive counsellor of arts-and-crafts.

Munching a roll, he approached my table. "Marvelous
show, Matt!" he bellowed. "You done a wonderful job!
The fire under the cauldron was—ah!" he kissed his fingertips.

I stared at him in stupefaction. This was the character
who had been hired to *help* me backstage, with the prop-
erties; and never once had he driven a nail or laid a brush-
stroke,—but my lads and I, we did it all. I was resentful
by disposition—

"*Keep* your hands off!" I warned.

"Three big cheers for Uncle Matt!" said Huey Ostoric. "Rah! Rah! *Rah!*" And they cheered.

The color left my face. We were accustomed, in our
close society, to cheer each other, to cheer each other on,
to cheer each other up. These loud cheers would almost
have repaid me for the whole season, if I did not hold
back my answering gratitude.

The "whole" season? Aha.

Beginning quietly in a corner, then taking fire and

spreading in chorus, a well known song swept away all other cheers and consolations:

> Three more days of vacation!
> Off to the railway station!
> Back to civilization!

So.

As for me, it was my last little show and I no longer had any function at this place. For me too this stripped away a mask and put on everything a different face. "Mike! Harry!" I shouted across the dining-room.

"Rah! Rah! *Rah!* Zuppy!"

"Let us say Grace," said an authoritative voice, and there was a pause of silence (not *yet* to be disturbed by the mere break-up of our camp).

> Rabosai n'vorech,
> y'hi shem adonai m'vorach me-ato v'ad olam

—"May the name of the Lord be blest from this time and forever."

But even while they were saying the prayer, there was a curious pantomime framed in the window. Mr. T., the owner, was nervously roping a trunk onto the back of his car. "Good-bye, boys!" he shouted suddenly, and climbed in and drove off, and his lights were eclipsed in the dark.

"Where in hell does that mad dog think *he's* going?" said Dave.

Ostoric laughed loudly.

Still we looked thru the window, at the untouchable reality in its frame. Two sheriffs in starred vests drove up, to attach the person of Ben Tumpowski for debt.

The prayer ended: "Blessed art Thou, Lord, who nourishest the world."

The sheriffs hung around, as if they expected him to come back. Ostoric said, "There's no use waiting, he's not going to come back."

I therefore went down to my theater, because it was the last summer. I turned the stage-lights on full, as if for rehearsal, but I sat, where I never sat, on a wooden chair in the middle of the vacant stage. Amid the tag ends of the final scene of our childish version of the great melodrama—the branches and saplings, already drooping, of Birnam Wood, and the red tissue-paper uniforms of Malcolm's soldiers torn to bits. The broken end of string of the Dagger Scene dangled near my nose—loose, motionless, as if no one had walked on this stage since the days of Edmund Kean. I fell to thinking, without thinking, of many performances, of many wonderful and famous performances. One of the footlights brightened and went dark.

All that summer I had wanted to get away from this boring place and these child-plays that no longer fitted me, and now I had what I most desired.

There was a sound. I wheeled round, half out of the chair, and caught two kids fiddling with the door-latch, to get out. They froze fast, crouching, and I half out of the chair, looking across my shoulder—like a scene from a play rehearsed until it passed over into reality; like the reality too precisely adapted to the circumstances, till it became merely a play. The two kids froze, an arm half-lifted,

a hand outstretched, about to grasp,

and I watched them out the corner of my eye, the broken string dangling, as if this moment were the end result of the long process of time, which was indeed the case.

"Mad dogs! where do you think *you're* going?"—They were Ottawa Red and Ba Ba of Manhasset, not bad actors.

"We needed rope to tie up our trunks," said Ba Ba.

"Who said you could take it?"

"Uncle Matt said we could go backstage and take it," he lied mechanically to my face.

"Take it tomorrow morning," I said in a voice that surprised me by its tiredness.

The two made no offer to drop the rope they were carrying, but they crossed and stood in front of me.

"Well, are you sorry the camp is over?" I asked.

"What I remember *best*," cried Ba Ba passionately, "is Almonds the canoe-man paddling off in the lightning!"

"But they never fished up his drowned body!" said Red.

"Sonny saw his speerit over in the girls' camp."

"Ke-ram! he smashed the war-canoe."

"An' he's the one that breaks the other boats!"

They turned to go.

"What was that?"—my attention came alive, betraying me into an interest that was out of season. I clutched at the greatest thing, that I wanted most, the social legend, when the time for plays was past. "*I* am in charge of the stories," I said, and they left.

Instead, I took out the electric bulbs, just so they wouldn't be broken for kicks.

The wind, meantime, that had begun to rise earlier, was howling at thirty miles. I came outside and my flashlight blew out of my hand and shone in the grass. The canvas doors of the tentalows were torn to rags that flapped in the wind. It was near freezing.

Since no one else seemed to be on duty (it was in fact my night of duty), I made the rounds among the younger ones, flashing a light on every bed, restoring the blankets that had been kicked off. The kid lay there naked, shivering in his sleep, in the round beam.

2.

In the fresh sunlight there was a masquerade. On Company Street, some of the boys were parading city-clothes, others went quite naked. Some of the naked boys had on ornamental hats and were carrying tin swords from the rifled theater.

The boy most disguised of all was our pitcher, Arky, for Arky appeared for the first time all summer in his college baseball-suit, as if he were a college ball-player, and not just our pitcher.

It blew *Fall-in-for-Inspection,* but no one paid any attention to this ludicrous command.

Now was evident the form of the confusion: Decadence, the accelerating dissolution of the parts of an organism when once the unifying soul has perished. Sports and varieties appeared. There were spontaneous powerful social combinations, enduring for two hours, of members loosed from their conventional associations, finding often more natural associations (but not yet the fatal natural associations of Brooklyn and Montreal). Last day friendships were sealed that have survived the years, for they sprang from instinct. And old forgotten practical jokes and nicknames from the ancient history, like *Huffski Puffski Ben Tumpowski,* were turned up in the universal overturn, and shone brilliantly for a moment like first-water jewels.

But Mike and Harry and I were friends from before we ever came to this place, so were not *in* it.

"No," said Harry, "this is precisely *being* in it. We make comments."

"My conscience is clear," said Mike. "I kicked in the last of the boats."

But I said, "Listen, do you remember Almonds?—" For I was not reconciled to it. By disposition I am never reconciled to anything. I turn to each blow *after* it has struck. Yet at the same time (therefore) I kept repeating to myself my little motto: *If not now, when?*

Ostoric had on a red bandana and was carrying a bowie-knife unsheathed. He was contriving to look like a pirate. The idea of his being in it, at this level, aroused in us a deep disgust. Yet the truth was that he was not *in* anything; he looked just as he had always looked; he had always worn a red bandana and carried a bowie-knife unsheathed, and tried to look like a pirate.

They began to march in step, up the hill to breakfast, a step satirically heavy, as soldiers use on furlough. *One* two *three* four; and to the rhythm of old slogans of the Color War: *White* will *Fight! Blues* can't *Lose! White! Fight! Blues! Lose!* . . . The last, since it made opposite sense, caught fire, and could be heard, all day, in every distance, *Mad! Dogs! Blues! Loose!* The first part barked, the second howled.

I suspiciously did not touch the food. There were announcements about the trunks: how they were to be labeled, when they were to be ready for inspection. These announcements were official recognition, on the part of the head-counsellor himself, that the camp was *over*. But the announcements should have been made by Mr. T., the colossus who bestrode the gap between the cities and our camp. Who was Dave Werner to make such announcements, as did not concern the shore, or the Teams, or the calls to my rehearsals? His voice lacked authority.

They howled while he talked—*Blues! Loooooose!* He
dissolved the camp, but he did not represent the Fathers:
no one accepted this idea. The only existing world was the
dissolving one, and *Blues! Loose!* and *Huffski Puffski* were
its outcries. "We want Huffski Puffski!" "Fuffski Huffski
Puffski!"

"Why aren't you eating?" said Harry angrily.

"I'm not eating," I said.

"You don't have any *evidence* anything is spoilt, do
you? Then shut up."

"Not eating," I said.

I took some eggs. They were not poison.

"Oh Christ, why should *I* be the goat!" cried Harry
bitterly—for he was responsible for the smallest ones.

—Tomorrow! tomorrow when they would be waiting
around, and watching the trunks piled into the truck,
and the Montreallers already gone; regarding the grounds
as no longer their own, hesitating to suggest a set of tennis—then the campers would become resigned to the fact
that the summer was over, we'd never return to this
place; then they'd feel bad and burst into tears. Oh yes
they would! But not today.

"Mad! Dogs!" I said absently.

It was melancholy to see, on the far side of the
field, vanishing into the woods, Harry and his tiny train,
off on a hike, out of harm's way.

3·

Dave Werner, the head-counsellor and brother of my
pal Husky, caught up to me.

"You're staying over with us, aren't you, Matt?" he
asked.

"Over?"

"Over the week-end."

"Staying?"—I stared at him.

"Yes, ten or eleven of us are staying. We're counting
on you," he said.

"No, I'm not staying," I said. "What the devil does he
want?" I thought. "Why ten or eleven?"

"Some of the girls are staying," he said, aggrieved. "I
think Maitabel is staying."

"No, I'm not staying," I said.
"They'll all be gone," he said.

4.

The masquerade was wearing off. It was becoming nature. Far across the baseball field Harry and his tiny train were vanishing among the trees.

I joined Mike, going down to the shore. Maybe I would spend the morning skipping stones.

A dark kid of fourteen passed us, coming up. "Hi, Mike, Matt," he mumbled, hurrying past.

"Hey! mad dog! where in hell do you think *you're* going? The shore is out of bounds."

"Mr. T. sent for me," he lied.

We let him go. On all sides the campers were streaming past, howling their howl. I had the impression that, going downhill, I was lapsing into confusion. But if I went uphill—in the direction that the dark boy had taken—the matter would become clear. . . . I stopped in my tracks. My homosexuality revived hot.

"Who is *he?"*

"Who?"

"The dark one, who lied to us?"

"Oh. Bayer. Julie Bayer. Free-style medal, junior division."

"Has he been here all summer?"

"For years. He's one of the Canucks. They leave early in the morning."

We went out on the dock. The boatman was satisfied. The boats were beautifully decommissioned. So far as he was responsible, there was not a lethal weapon in existence.

"Mike," I said, "you called him a 'mad dog' . . ."

"Who?"

"The boy—the one who went up. I heard somebody else use that expression. Has that expression been common this summer? I'm interested in such things."

"Are you *well?*" said Mike.

"Do you think he knew Mr. T. was gone, and that maybe we didn't know it? I mean, do you think he was lying?"

"*Are* you well?"

I faltered—"Don't—don't you think he's an interesting-looking boy?"

We went into my theater.

—Too late! It was too late to stage the legend of Almonds the canoeist, to show the kids indeed—and this was my sense of my function as their counsellor—that there is poetry, all the poetry that there is, in our common incidents; that the poetry springs from their own fantasies, considering what our life in this camp is worth. Too late to stage the delicious little comedy of Mr. T., roping on the trunk and skipping out half a minute ahead of the sheriffs—his farewell gesture with the left hand, fingers outspread, as if to ward off the answering look. *Leaving the camp to us,* to ten or eleven—all the rest would be gone. Wasn't this the typical condition for a romantic comedy, genre of *Twelfth Night* or *As I Like It?*

But it was, is, too late to fall in love with the boy, myself, just because my world has fallen into chaos. Longing for immortality.

I am painting my name in red on the back wall of the stage:

**MATHEW WAS IN CHARGE
OF THE STORIES**

1932—1933—1934—1935

"Somebody is on the water!" hissed Mike, and rushed out of the theater.

Two hundred yards out, on the glassy lake, Red and Ba Ba were in a canoe settling up to the gunwale.

"Bring that boat in."

"We can't. It's full up."

The voices came thin and clear across the water, followed by the echo from the Cove, Full up! full up!

Splashing in the sunlight, they swam slowly toward the shore.

5.

"We only went out to play Almonds. But he got mad and we sunk."

"Why does he want to sink the boats?"

"Because we give him the cold shoulder and he was drownded."

"No, the opposite. He don't want *us* to stay here, he busts everything 'cause he's an anti-semite!"

The Lonely Stranger came by water out of the north, looking to establish himself at some campfire or other, instead of wandering any more. Fighting for this happiness, as he regarded it, he became a demon of Persistence, wherever the slightest occasion offered.

We, however, took our blessings for granted.

He happened to come to our camp on a special night, Campfire. We were off our guard and temporarily made him welcome. By his charms and stories he cast a brief spell over all. But how soon the true canoeist was revealed to us, trying to oust Mike, the waterman, and to become *too friendly* with the girls. The spell was broken and now, in great fear, we drew back from any contact with him. And while we of the camp went to our religious services, he had to paddle forth into the storm. He was drowned.

But his spirit, freed from the body but fixed by the longing that had governed him when alive, returned to haunt our camp. It appeared among the girls when they were stripping for gymnastic dances; it appeared to little Sonny Benjamin on the outer baseball diamond; it appeared to Matt backstage. But at the words *Ma Tovu*— "how goodly are thy tents, O Jacob!"—he had to paddle away again.

From camp-site to camp-site he went, this stranger, creating unease, discomfiture, dissatisfaction with our lot; causing doubt in the evidence of our senses, by preternatural pranks; spoiling present fun by alluring tales of *other* places. Woe to him who would be seduced! To be swallowed in the lake. Even while he paddled away he was heard to laugh out loud. Though he was gone, he was not forgotten; no one in our camp would ever be satisfied. The Senior boys wanted to go on a long canoe-trip; the women counsellors did not respond to the men's caresses. Like a kind of *Poltergeist* he tipped trays of dishes in the dining-room, and he stove in the canoes.

Also he was Kwee-Kwee, the Algonquin that first founded our camp, long ago.

He came from the water as a man is born; he departed on a journey as a man dies. And in-between—stopped at our camp for three days; just as we were all stopping, just as we were all stopping for three days; just as we were all stopping at our camp for three days.

But with an effort of the will I dismissed this afterthought for another time, and I went up the hill to look for Julie Bayer.

6.

The sheriffs were still hanging around. Farmers with starred vests, they were the outposts of the reinvading countryside, with which, despite many efforts, we had never established an easy relation.

There was a new functionary in the office, a Burlington accountant going through the books (he would skin them all, natives and foreigners both). He and Miss K., the secretary, were in the office; and Ostoric! apparently in a position of confidential importance.

"Well, soon the Jew-camp won't be here any more," said one of the policemen affably.

—The slogans were corrupted, the morals became perverse. Rhythms were syncopated and quarter-intervals permitted. The owner ran away, the scholars delved into the legends. Moralists prayed for the destruction of the instruments of production before irreparable damage was done to mankind.—I told myself I was confused, when all the while we were passing into the Very Last Times.

Miss K. came out of the office, shaking her head.

"I'm sorry for you boys," she said to Mike. "There's no train-ticket for you and Matt. You'll have to get home the best way you can."

"Please. How do we get home the best way we can?"

"Don't shout at me. It's not my fault."

"What's Ostoric doing in the office?" I hissed.

"Why, he's Mr. T's nephew; they need him for information."

"*He's* got a ticket!" I groaned.

"No, he hasn't got a ticket either."

"It's O.K., Mike. We'll stay here, you and I, with Dave and Husky Werner and the rest, and we can drive to New York in Dave's car."

"*Stay?!*"—Mike looked at me with genuine awe.

"So Ostoric is T's nephew. At last I have something impersonal against him."

7.

We spent the time with Julie Bayer and his pals. I had no function in this place, and now, as it turned out, I had of course the one function that I ever committed myself to, to have a hard-on in impractical circumstances. Starting from this premise all my further acts were predetermined, and sure to end by making me frustrated, irritable, mournful.

A light rain began to fall, the elements themselves turning to my advantage, for it assured our proximity. On piled-up trunks we played chess and contract-bridge. Julie had a brilliant card-sense and made a psychic bid, but Tony excelled at chess. It was now too late, but I dressed Teddy to be Malcolm in the play. We went swimming in the drizzle. We drove an overturned canoe out into the lake, and Mike and I, treading water, watched the four bronzed figures clamber on and off and dive.

And during this happiness there was death in my heart —such death as we erotics have—because it was the end. Nor am I ignorant of the truth that that happiness was only a cunning forepleasure for the releasing of a grief much sought for—yet still not deep enough for tears. That I praise the object in order to bewail myself. That I love and praise the future peace of the world in order to lament the present state of the world. Because we *still*, as Franz said, do not eat of the fruit of the Tree of Life; *therefore* we are not in Paradise.

The rain stopped, and gave way again to an unusual

sunset. On the indigo clouds stood a granite rainbow, whose colors were

> turbilous, pearl, and dizimal,
> the colors of September brilliance

—urging us to hope forever.

In the west, the light fell down in striped rays, then when the fiery ball itself appeared, half-set, the bronze clouds in the pallid sky lay in horizontal tiers of cirrus to the pole.

Husky Werner confronted me.

"You *are* staying with us over the week-end."

"Why?" I looked at him frankly. "Why ten or eleven?"

"We need ten men for a *minyan* for Kaddish. Otherwise Dave and I can't stay."

The brothers had lost their mother, and now morning and evening they said the mourner's prayer,—but in the orthodox rite ten men are needed to make a congregation of Jews.

As for me, I was going to stay because I had fallen in love with our dead camp. What luck!

"If Maitabel stays, I'll stay," I said.

8. MANIFESTATIONS OF THE VERY LAST TIMES

Even before breakfast one father, who had driven since midnight from Toronto, took away his son. This boy, C. Haskell, is remarkable as the first one to have left.

The meal was eaten in silence and in great haste, by even the New Yorkers, who were not to leave till the evening. We who were *not* leaving found ourselves still eating, disregarded, when the others had walked out. It was remarkable that we, who were staying on and still possessed and used the property of our camp, no longer belonged to the actual world. In this apparent world, the dining room where the head-counsellor was making his announcements, we fitfully passed in and out of the actuality. Dave had many announcements to make, but when he was talking of anything connected with our camp, of where to pile the mattresses or where to return the equipment, it was as though he were not saying a word, his remarks vanished on the wind. But if he mentioned the word "train" or said "those leaving this morning," his speech glowed with communication; and when he read off the list of the Montreallers, the room had a suppressed excitement.

During the night, Ostoric had committed the expected act of vandalism, the excessive act that would survive as a memorial of, no doubt, our vices. On the side of the theater, in red letters a foot high, were painted the words

FUFFSKI YUFFSKI

Dave, who was responsible to Mr. T., flew into a towering rage about it. *"No one will be allowed to go home until the damage is paid for!"* he shouted; but this foolish boast vanished on the wind.

In a flash were made manifest the relations of brothers and cousins, of neighbors in the city who shared a common trunk but who all the summer had seemed barely acquainted. The older brother who had sedulously avoided the younger now sought him out to check the tag on a valise, and at once you could see that they were brothers, the family features, speech, manners. These were the relations among us not made in this camp, not made for the camp, but recollected in the crisis, for the crisis. The stress of the last day brought us to the recognition of the real families, and real natures, overlooked in the distractions of the life of our camp. The counsellor who had promised mama that he would carefully watch her boy, to see that he took a certain medicine, now frantically sought him out; but the boy had grown three inches and was unrecognizable—and the counsellor sweated with anxiety.

We others, I say, were rejected, or had elected ourselves to be out of it (it comes to the same thing). Yet we were assigned certain auxiliary roles *in* it, and we hung around. That is, we were in the position of devils. A devil is one who takes part without sharing the common aim and drift; he has his own aim.

My job was to certify the baggage-tags. And so I noticed that Tony was the cousin of Rosalie; but *she* was Maitabel's tent-mate. So! If Maitabel was staying because I was staying, I schemed, and then why not Rosalie, then there would be grounds for Tony also to stay; but Tony was one of Julie's pals! To be sure it was not Tony that I was interested in.

But scheming was hopeless, for we who were not in it, were not in touch with the real tendency; by contriving one could successfully be neither in it nor against it. We should have drifted off by ourselves, retired; this would have spared us plenty of resentment and impotent rage. We hung around.

I followed Julie Bayer with my eyes, but without determination. There was no common ground to move across to him.

Unstudied textbooks were discovered in the cobwebs, and newspapers dated June 28 blew up and down Company Street.

They began to give away their belongings. Everything was considered too troublesome to pack at the last moment: sweaters, comic-books, candy-bars, the things that had been invaluable. Tony offered me a silver-plated pencil, which I accepted. "These gifts are souvenirs," I told myself. But they were not souvenirs, because, although the thought of home was so powerfully influencing them in camp, it was not the case that they thought of the thought of camp influencing them at home. But we counsellors, who had no past, present or future, were eager to have souvenirs.

Or again seeing their friends continually going away, they were *binding* them by generous gifts.

Mike's opinion was: "No kid any longer has a bunk of his own; no one has a responsibility for his belongings, because it is only when he has a bunk of his own that he has property. But the sweaters, the cameras, the blankets, the tennis-racquets, the silver pencils, have all reverted back to their parents. Some of them are going to be held responsible for the things they are now giving away.—

"And there are also those!" he cried, "who all summer have been *careless* with their belongings, and now they are frantically searching for everything that has been lost, because it is their fathers'."

9.

Well! in their desperate haste to be ready in time, so that many of them omitted breakfast and were now hungry, the Canucks now had time heavy on their hands. It was an hour and a half to train time, and the New Yorkers had the whole day before them. The truck did not come, the horn did not blow. There spread an intolerable ennui.

Hereupon (it was the moment I had been waiting for) we manfully took up again our duties as counsellors, and I set to entertaining the Canadians with a police-investigation: *"Who painted the name on the theater?"*

"Maybe it was the Greek (the chef)?" I suggested. "He had it in for Mr. T."

"No," said Tony. "How would he have known the name Fuffski Yuffski?"

We stood in front of the red painting.

"It's good printing," said Irving. "Maybe Huey Ostoric did it, he can print."

"Look, here is the paintcan underneath the steps."

(He had broken into my paint-box! It was *still* my paint-box.)

"It's paint from the theater," cried Irving, the actor, excitedly. "He took it from behind the stage. I'll show you where."

We went backstage.

"What won't Dave Werner do to the character when we find him out!"

The chest had been jimmied open.

"Maybe *I* did it," I said. "I knew where the paints were."

"No, you would've had the keys."

"What time is it?" said Julie Bayer, asking with keenest cruelty the crucial question.

"*It's a quarter of ten,*" I said. I could not take my eyes from the face and body of Julie Bayer.

"No proof," Mike went on—even though some one had already asked the crucial question. "Maybe Matty didn't use the keys in order to divert suspicion. Isn't that possible?"

"No. Matt would have used the paint and put it back. I know him."

"That wouldn't help. Anybody'd know the paint came from here. Where else is there paint except backstage."

"There's paint in the arts-and-crafts shack," said Julie Bayer.

"Well, anyway, Huey Ostoric did do it," said Irving, " 'cause I saw him."

"Look, Tony," I said, "would you like to stay on a few days with your cousin Rosalie, if she says you may?"

"Yes!" he cried. "Gee! Maybe. I don't know. I'll ask her when she comes to say good-bye."

A horn sounded. A whistle blew. With a grinding of brakes the truck from the station came slowly down the hill.

10.

The Montreal boys climbed up into the truck. They were near to tears. Blinding tears came into the eyes of some of the smaller boys and they had to be helped up. At this moment, being hurried off, they saw in a flash that the summer was over; their vacation had come to an end while they were thinking of something else. *Once in, it was forbidden to get down from the truck.* So lively and promising now seemed the visible camp, spreading all ways in its almost limitless grounds.

Still Rosalie did not come. Tony was near to tears, because she had promised—and he wanted to ask her the question. "Can't you find her?" he kept asking me. I ran through the covered bridge and searched the girls' camp. But I could not find her.

"Good bye, Red," said Ba Ba of Manhasset. And the next moment this truck rolled away, this truckload of Julie Bayer and his pals. This company of angels—but we were only flesh and blood.

I grew slowly into a cold fury: that all summer I had never known Julie Bayer and his pals (to be sure I had known them all summer; Julie had acted in the first show of the season). That never had we acted out the legend of Armand and his canoe. That they were taking away from me forever my beautiful stage and my actors with their ringing throats. That my time of life was slipping away. What was the use of this desert camp-site?

Rosalie came. "You might have been on time," I choked. "The kid was crying.

"All summer you have been late to everything! And now you have to be late to this!"

I spoke so bitterly that she too began to cry.

"Why don't you 'phone the station and have him sent back here to spend the weekend with you at least? Or are you too selfish for that?"

She 'phoned, but the truck had not yet arrived.

Finally Tony called: No, he didn't want to return; since he'd come this far he might as well go all the way home. No, he was not unhappy, he said, and hung up.

When I heard this, that my connection was gone, I called Rosalie a damned bitch.

CHAPTER III

A Congregation of Jews

I.

The red light of the caboose rapidly diminished down the starlit tracks, carrying away the children of our camp. The Great Bear hung already a little northward, at the end of summer.

"Matty! Mike!" Husky, the brother of the head-counsellor, called us to the circle near the truck. Gathered in a close ring were we men who had stayed over: Aaron, Leo, Dave, Husky, Artie, Harry, eight of us, counting Mike and myself. (A ninth was Mr. Tobias, the silent partner, who had stayed to supervise the closing up, for Mr. T., the owner, had fled ahead of the sheriff.) And there also, standing uneasily behind Husky, as if looking to squeeze into the circle—but there was no place—was a tenth man, Ostoric, the despised ex-counsellor of arts-and-crafts. We were all ex-counsellors now.

When Mike and I came, a place opened for us in the ring. "For Chrissake," said Husky in a tense voice, "how do we get rid of Ostoric? Nobody asked *him* to stay over."

The stout untidy fellow heard this, blanched, and stepped back away. And I saw it and broke up the group.

On the way back to camp, Husky rode in his car with his brother and Mr. Tobias and Sweeney the caretaker and Ella, who was Husky's girl. That car had five seats. Ostoric rode with us in the back of the truck, with Mike and me and Rosalie and Maitabel, and Harry and Leo and three other girls. I am telling all these numbers because it takes ten men to make a congregation of Jews, and Ostoric happened to be the tenth man.

It was cold and we clung together for warmth, but Ostoric was offended and sat by himself sucking noisily on a dirty pipe. As we bounded along on the stony road, Rosalie began to moan the song-hits of that time, and we all, also Ostoric, joined in the joyous choruses. "Violate me in violet time in the vilest way that you can!" Mike sang in a surprisingly loud and happy voice; it did not occur to me that he was feverish.

Sweeney, who had got back ahead of us, came running down the road with a lantern, shouting that the farmers were everywhere like cockroaches.

No one had remained behind to watch over the deserted camp.

"Half go over to the girls' camp and half to the boys'. Pile up the cots and mattresses. I'll have the truck along. When we got here there was farmers with flashlights carrying things off."

We got down numb with cold.

Ostoric did not join either group, but went into the lounge to go to bed. He had made up his mind to leave in the morning and he did not intend to be more helpful than was necessary.

In the girls' camp the flashlights went out. Some one could be heard moving in the underbrush. We were afraid. It was dark. The hundred thousand stars and the Milky Way shed no light below. Our flashlights cast a gray illumination on the street and on the bungalows. A mattress, a book, a hat-box, a paddle, vestiges of those who had left. On the backroad a car rattled off; there was a loud backfire.

We had left for our city; why should not the natives come back and take possession? But we few had unaccountably stayed on.

Some of us had allowed ourselves to be persuaded (and we persuaded the others) to make up the ten men needed by Dave and Husky for a *minyan*. But why were they staying? It is not in a particular place that one has to mourn a mother. We were staying by inertia—absence of another force. We were staying to celebrate the gone world that God had once created, such as it was.

The girls' trunks, the duffle-bags, the valises had not yet gone to the station. All this was to be called for next day. The Jews assumed that there would be a next day. The porches and rooms were piled with baggage tagged and labeled to New York and Montreal.

We dragged out the fifty trunks from the black rooms, and the flashlights held in our armpits cast swift shadows on the walls. Bent under servile loads of bags and boxes, unwillingly, we sweated and then stepped into the chilling night.

No. It is reasonable for one to do this if he is here, on behalf of those who are not here.

At last came Sweeney with the truck, the headlights shooting long beams on the towering piles of bedding and baggage. He blew his bass horn till we collected.

"Listen, Husky," I said spitefully, "Mike and I expect a lift to New York Monday in your car."

Husky stopped loading. "It's tough," he said, "you're the fifth person asked me. There's only three empty seats, so I sold them five dollars apiece to Aaron, Artie and Ella. Why didn't you ask first?"

"*Sold?*" I cried; "why do you think Mike and I stayed, just so you and Dave could have a *minyan* to say Kaddish?"

"Do you need any money?" said Husky.

"No, I don't need any money; no, I don't have any money. Skip it," I said. The cry "Sold!" held a moment in my ear; and then, suddenly, I began, intermittently, to take pleasure in these things.

"Skip it," I said.—As for me, when the day came I was going to hitch-hike home, alone, taking my chances on the road; and the prospect of it already gave me pleasure.

By midnight, everything was in safe-keeping. The baggage was piled to the ceiling in the lobby; in the music-room, which was furnished with wicker sofas and a broken piano, were the heaps of old mattresses.

We began to laugh. We laughed at the trunk we had stoven in. The thought of Ostoric, provoked by a gesture up the stairs, made us choke.

Halfway down the stairs, warily creeping, were a pair of fat little twins, Melvin and Phyllis Kalman. Their father had arranged to drive them to Montreal, but he had failed to appear; and we also forgot them when we went off to the station. They had run upstairs to hide and cried themselves to sleep. Now here their round red faces, roused by our laughter, shone like twin suns—and it was, of course, the peak of everything funny, that from this Adam and Eve our camp itself should spring alive again (such as it was).

The telephone rang.

It was Sam Tobias, the brother of our Mr. Tobias. He had been expected to arrive from Montreal early in the morning, but he was phoning to say that he could not make it. This news was indifferent to us,—nevertheless we had counted on Sam Tobias of Montreal to be the tenth man.

Our friend Mike, meanwhile, was pale, and trembling in every limb. Maitabel and I went into the kitchen to brew him some tea.—

We turned away. The unpaid kitchen-help had left without cleaning up. The garbage of several days lay on the floor; the unwashed dishes in the sinks were clouded with flies that swarmed in our faces as we turned on the light. There was a fearful stink. On the stove stood a great cauldron of cocoa, made for the last meal, still tepid, but with a thick scum on the surface and many flies drowned. In the adjoining dining-room the tables were not cleared. Pieces of lettuce lay on the floor, a tomato squashed under my heel. On each table a milk-jug was overturned and the streams of spilled milk, in slow drippings from the oilcloths, united on the floor in a gray network. The flies awoke with a cry.

2.

In the morning, Friday, Mike was very ill. Despite the appalling color of our room, with its crimson and gold wallpaper and the bedstead of tarnished brass, he had about made up his mind to stay in bed. But the sunlight outside was warm and moist, and the wasps buzzed angrily against the windowpane trying to escape.

A call from below decided it. "Matty and Mike, downstairs please!" Downstairs our *presence* was needed to make up ten men for morning-prayers. Mike put on his shoes. It's comforting to be useful by one's mere presence.

We came into the music-room where the prayers were to be said amid five heaps of mattresses and we made ourselves hats out of newspaper.

Dave called to Mr. Tobias on the porch. The old man, six and a half feet tall, his gaunt jaw covered with white stubble, came into the room cramming an old felt on his head.

Now as soon as he entered, being the tenth man, there was a congregation of Jews; and at once Aaron, who was our Reader, faced to the Orient and took up the hum and mumble in which the orthodox hasten thru their lengthy prayers: from time to time it is punctuated by a sentence, either by way of a period at the end of the psalm, or when the person praying is suddenly moved by the meaning of what he is saying and so says it, or when he takes a breath.

The sounds of prayer rose from all corners of the mattress-filled room lit by the moist sunlight. Yet only a few were praying. I allowed my eyes and my attention to wander from the blue-covered Siddur in my hand: to take in all ten of us, those praying and those not praying. Whatever unity there was present amongst us was not the unity of morning-prayers.

"Ribon kal ha'olamim," said Aaron.

"Sovereign of all worlds! Not because of our righteous acts do we dare lay our supplication before Thee, but

*because of Thy great mercy . . . What is our life? what
our piety? what our strength? what shall we say before
Thee, O Lord our God and God of our fathers?"*

Sprawled in a wicker chair, Mr. Tobias lit a cigar and
was reading a week old copy of the Montreal *Star*.

Leo, Husky, Dave and Georgie had put on the phylac-
teries, little boxes on brow and biceps and a leather thong
wound seven times around the forearm and thrice around
the middle finger.

Artie at the piano sounded three crashing chords.

Aval Anachnu Amcha—

"Nevertheless, we are Thy people," continued Aaron,
*"the sons of Thy covenant, of Abraham Thy beloved to
whom Thou didst swear on Mount Moriah."*

My eyes fell on Ostoric.

He was so clean! Washed and combed and without the
whiskers of a summertime. He was wearing a polka-dot
bowtie, gray flannel trousers with a knife-edge crease
(where did he get them pressed?) and black and white
shoes. His blue jacket was carefully folded on the piano.
All summer he had kept this finery in hiding. Now helter-
skelter, each thing jammed where it would fit, ties wrapped
around shoes, he was cramming a small valise—preparing
to leave.

But he was our tenth man. It was not the time to leave.
In the dining room, with brooms and a pail, the girls were
restoring a little decency.

Artie climbed on the mattresses to stretch out.

"Get down! you'll knock them down!" said Mr. T.
crossly.

"Hear O Israel, the Lord our God, the Lord is One!"
said Aaron in a loud voice.

The moist sunlight poured into the room, impartially,
among those standing and those not standing and the
heaps of mattresses, and on the black letters of my book.

Mr. T. began to count the mattresses.

I anxiously watched Ostoric. He stepped outside to
knock his pipe against the porchrail. At such a moment
was there or was there not a *minyan*? Did the congregation come to be and cease to be, moment by moment, as
one would switch an electric-light?

With fearful eyes, the white showing, Dave Werner kept looking at Ostoric and the progress of his preparations to depart.

"Thirty-eight, thirty-nine, forty," muttered Mr. Tobias. So we came to the great prayer of the Eighteen Blessings, of which Nachmanides once wrote to his son:

> During the prayer of the Eighteen Blessings, remove all the affairs of this world from thy breast; think of no other matter but that of fixing thy mind on this prayer with perfect devotion; prepare and purify thy heart and mind unto God, blessed be He—*thereby* will thy prayer be pure and untainted, devout, and acceptable before the Holy One, blessed be His name.

. . . "Lord, *open* Thou my lips, and my mouth shall utter Thy praise." So we began.

"Will you sit on this valise," said Ostoric, "so I can lock it."

"Wait till after the *Shmoneh Esre*."

"Eighty-four, eighty-five, eighty-six," said Mr. Tobias. Happy and dancing, washed and comforted, the twins descended from above.

V'l'yerushalaim ircha—

"And to Jerusalem Thy City, return in mercy," read Aaron in a flat voice, for it is a hard passage for the Jews. *"Dwell there as Thou hast promised it; rebuild it soon, even in our days—an eternal building. Set up there again the Throne of David!"*

Dave and Husky repeated the mourner's prayer and the service was over.

3.

"You aren't going away, Eli?" said Husky. For the first time all summer he called Ostoric by his first name, which was Elihu; but he refined the affectation too far, as a nickname Ostoric prefered to be called not "Eli" but "Huey."

The ex-arts-and-crafts man said that he was leaving.

"Why are you leaving?" said Dave aggrieved. "There's nothing in the city. The best part of camp is after the kids go. Now is the time to take a rest."

Ostoric carefully explained that he had to get to Stroudsburg in Pennsylvania where his fiancée (he said) had also finished a camp season, and then they were going to the World's Fair in Chicago. It was clear that he was really going to leave.

"Why didn't you go yesterday then, with the others, if you're in such a hurry?" said Husky bitterly.

"I don't want to get to Stroudsburg before tomorrow, because then I'll have to help Margot pack. She always leaves it for me."

"How you going?"

"Hitch," said Ostoric. "That's why I'm all dressed up. Looks sharp, no?"

"You're the tenth man," said Dave, the head-counsellor. "If you go there is no *minyan*. We expected Mr. Tobias' brother from Montreal, but he can't make it till Sunday."

"Ostoric!" pleaded Husky, "stay over the weekend. Tuesday morning I'll take you as far as New York by car."

"What about us?" I said. Mike and I were also the tenth man.

But then I remembered—and the thought of it brought me peace—that when the day came I was going to leave this place, alone. So I did not protest. I said nothing. I smiled with inward joy and esthetical contemplation. Lo, Ostoric!

Last night Husky was itching to be rid of him; now he offered him the coveted prize of the place in the automobile. The stone that the builders rejected was become the capital of the pillar.

"Will you drive me as far as Wilkes-Barre?" said Ostoric, pretending to bargain.

"Yes! Yes!"

"I think—I'll think it over. Now supposing you drive me into Burlington now," he suggested blandly, "and I'll think it over on the way. Maybe I'll change my mind and come back with you."

As for me, I *loved* this Ostoric and could spend with him the eons apportioned to us in Paradise. Even Mike, who was ill and pale, spread his lips in a thin smile.

"O.K.," said Husky, almost with a sob, "you think it

over." But he took the keys out of his pocket and brought the car around in front of the Lodge. Dave climbed in with Ostoric's valise.

"Good bye, fellows," said Ostoric warmly, and insisted on shaking hands with each one. "Maybe I'll be back; and if not maybe I'll see you next summer at some other camp. Who knows?"

He got into the car and they drove off.

"Let me wash my hands," said Leo, "to get the feel of that lizard off my hands. Let's shave," he suggested.

It was Friday, and we were accustomed, all except Ostoric, to clean up for the Sabbath Eve.

But when we went to fetch our shaving-kits, we made a curious discovery. The holders of our safety-razors had been robbed of their blades, and the spare blades were likewise gone, though the little boxes seemed untouched. We looked at each other, the whites showing in our eyes.

It was a practical joke of Ostoric's.

4.

To get away from the others, I took the twins for a walk. We went down to the boys' camp.

John Wells, a farmer from up the lake, was stripping the torn canvas from the tentalows. "Morning," he said, continuing.

On the beach the wrecked canoes and rowboats, parched and warped, seemed a hundred thousand years older than yesterday. The pink war-canoe with its broken back lay like the skeleton of an ichthyosaur. Our camp had been bankrupt and badly equipped this last summer; but now today, the day after, the effect was not of decay, nor even of abandonment, but of reversion to the natural environment. Ossification, petrifaction. Not as if the Jew-camp had ceased to exist, but as if it had never existed in these late days.

"There are some good bulbs in the footlights on my stage," I said to Wells. "You can get in the back way by forcing the latch."

"Got 'em," he said.

The twins cried out in horror and seized me by the hand. It was Rollo, the little alligator, escaped from his tank and crawling away down the middle of the dusty street. "It's only Rollo, from the museum," I reassured them; "don't you remember him any more?"

"What kind of thing is that?" said the farmer, paling a little. "No lizards grow round here as big as that."

"No they don't. He's an alligator, from the South."

The little beast (alas, no dragon!) proceeded slowly between the shacks down toward the lake.

"Good-bye, Rollo!"

"What will happen to him if we let him go?" asked Melvin.

"He'll jump in and drown," I said, turning up the hill.

"Bye," said Wells, holding out his hand. "Shan't see you again."

"Oh, we'll be around a day or two yet," I said acidly.

5.

Late in the afternoon the brothers returned from Burlington. They were not speaking to each other. At the last moment both had not punched Ostoric in the nose and their pent-up aggression turned against each other. There was no longer a congregation of Jews at our camp.

"We called on a rabbi in Burlington," said Dave. "He said that in a pinch you could count in a boy not yet *Bar-mitzvah,* so long as he's circumcised."

"If you're thinking of Melvin Kalman, the father called for them an hour ago."

A bitter wrangle arose between Aaron, who was a rigorist, and Leo, who began to remember things convenient to our case. "So long as there are 9 Jews it is sufficient, for Elijah can be counted in," said Leo. "Number two: there is a difference between a servant in the household and an ordinary *goy;* so Sweeney can be counted in. Three: why not count in one of the girls? In our times the status of women is not like what it was in the days of the Tannaim; isn't their religious status different too?"

"Good!" said Aaron. "Why not have a Jew present by telephone and make use of all modern technology? If you're trying to be funny you're old enough to go on the vaudeville stage."

"Don't be so sure of yourself," said Leo. "If Hillel

were alive, who knows what he would say about it all?"

But there was one memory of Leo's that Aaron conceded to have the earmarks of an opinion. In case a man is missing, it is permissible to regard an open *Siddur* as symbolic of an absent reader.

Dave too remembered it. "Yes—" he said, trying hard to remember it. He remembered, twenty years ago, when he was just *Bar-mitzvah,* he had been part of a *minyan*—they called him from the street—and there for some reason that he did not understand at the time, but now it was clear—they called him away from a hockey game—an extra prayer-book was propped on a table, and somebody turned the pages.

"Maybe for mama's sake we ought to leave," said Husky.

Maitabel uttered a wild laugh, and stuffed a handkerchief in her mouth and rushed outside.

I followed her in anger. "What are *you* laughing at?" I shouted.

—Where now were Julie Bayer and our boys? my actors? the roaring lions in *Daniel* and the midget girls who could dance? The summer camp was over. I am an artist, and the fact is that in long art I have never had a happy moment except contriving plays of adolescents and children; I steal the art from their plastic gestures and their ringing voices, and then I am not dying. When, on the night, I touch the head of the kid who is on-stage, and signal for the curtain to rise—

"What are you *laughing* at?" I said with tears in my eyes.

"What are they haggling about? What difference does it make whether there is a minyam or not?"

"The word is *minyan.*"

"Minyam!"

"Don't be so sure of yourself!" I was repeating Leo's anguish. "What you would save is a little trouble and making a fool of yourself. What *they* would save"—I did not say *we,* because it did not make any difference to me—"what they would save is to make it possible to have mama die.—

"To hell with it," I said. We kissed and made up. I do not mean that this contact was an answer, but at

least it was the bedrock of community. If we stayed on
another weekend at this camp, it was to be with our girls,
in the pleasant season, beside the lake, without the kids.

6.

We prayed in a third floor bedroom where Maitabel, who
was a registered nurse, had forbade Mike to get out of
bed. The tired overhead light on the crimson and brass
was not like one's home, one's home. My friend's head,
at once pale and burnt, lay nobly on the pillow, but except that his fever was down you would have thought
that he was going to die.

Open to the Friday evening service, a book was propped
against a wash-pitcher. As we progressed, Leo turned the
leaves for the absent tenth man. It was not to be seen
that the Prophet Elijah turned them, nor that the Son of
David sat anywhere, anywhere, on any throne of glory.
It was not to be seen that the Son of David sat on any
throne of glory.

The brothers came once more to their Kaddish, saying
Yisgadal V'yiskadash—

*"Great and Holy be His immense name in the world
that He created according to His will!"*

What!

What is this thing that we say at the opened grave,
when they have let down mama's body there? The place
is strange to me and I have been unhappy anyway. Let
me be more glad in the mutual aid of love and labor,
maybe I'll weep. But to say, *"Blissful! Famous! Glorious!
Uplifted!"*—encouraging ourselves with an identification!
not otherwise than unhappy children fantasy that they
are the heirs of a prince, but they were kidnapped by
gypsies.

The prayer itself forbids it. *"Although,"* it says, *"although indeed! He is beyond all the blessings and hymns,
the celebrations and the consolations that are uttered
in the world."* What does it mean? Consider it, draw it
to its conclusions, perhaps it is not false. It means first, of
course, that we are not to worship idols; this goes without
saying. It means then that we are *not* to make the proud
identification, but to be humble; it is likely that the au-

thor (the Aramaic indicates a desperate period) meant
to urge this humility. But there is a further conclusion,
implied in the prayer, to be explicated by us—if not by
us, by whom? and if not now, when?—it means that we
are to look to the prosier things that *can* be uttered in
the world. I do not mean that we are to rely on our
strength, for it is quite unknown to me for any good thing
to come of my own will and plan without better help;
but that we should look to it.

(Now it is again in Hebrew) : Oseh Shalom—

*"He who makes peace in His heights will make peace
also among us, and all Israel. Let us say, Amen."*

So we were all collected in Michael's sickroom, entertaining ourselves and him, making him laugh, and raising
his fever, into the Sabbath morning.

CHAPTER IV

Ostoric

I have since come to ask myself about Huey Ostoric. The
meaning of the rest of it I understand well enough—in a
history that I have drawn from experience, but I myself
willed the experience for that history; but wouldn't Ostoric have the right to say of me, like that canoeist long
ago, "This dramatics-man doesn't know what he wants;
I've met that type before"?

Let us suppose that Ostoric stole the razor-blades, carefully abstracting them from their boxes and touching
nothing else besides. It was immediately before the Sabbath Eve, and we must say that his intention was that
on this Sabbath at least, after the camp had departed, we
would be unkempt, as unkempt as he used to be on *every*
decent Sabbath at our camp. What then? Did not also I
speak of the "service that I had said once too often," in
the "camp that I was tired of," among the "friends of
whom I had seen enough"? What if he perhaps felt a
certain—disgust, that on this especial Sabbath, after the
camp had departed, we were *still,* just as if nothing had
happened, prepared and in readiness,

prepared and in readiness

as the hymn says? This disgust he expressed in a practical joke.

All summer he carried on such a practical joke, slovenly, unshaven, unkempt, unpunctual, letting me down and not trying to be any more helpful than was necessary. In this way he cut a figure in the camp, in our camp, not in his camp. It was also his camp, but he was not enthusiastic about his and our camp; likely he was not so enthusiastic about us; certainly we were not so enthusiastic about him. Then why not show that? why not act that? The *fact* was that if one looked at the broken boats and the ripped canvas, and then looked *quickly,* before the illusion grew, at Huey Ostoric in his dirty sweatshirt and canvas pants, matching pebbles on the shore, one saw a natural and proper scene, not so highly colored by mere ideas. And was *I* so enthusiastic about their camp that had broken up long before the first of September? and about my childish theater? But I used to be betrayed by a certain curiosity as to what these people wanted, and I expressed this by punctilious attention to my job.

What if all summer Huey Ostoric went in dirty clothes because he had no change of clothes? I do not mean that he had no clean clothes at all, but that they were packed in his valise. Throughout the summer he did not unpack his valise. Then when the rest of us put on blue polo-shirts and white ducks for the Sabbath, Ostoric, who also possessed those things, could not wear them because he did not want to unpack them. Nevertheless, *he had not come to camp with the intention of behaving in that way.* (I wonder if I could say as much.)

Mr. T. was not open-handed with the salaries of any of the staff; so far as I was concerned, he left me stranded, without a railway-ticket home. But Huey Ostoric was his relative, so it was unnecessary to pay him a salary at all. The rest of us had had an advance, and for better or worse we were established; but to Huey, on the contrary, Huffski Puffski made it clear that he was "on trial," he was really just enjoying a vacation and might have to go home at any moment when the "regular" arts-and-crafts man arrived. (There was no such person.) At the same time, being a relative, Ostoric was more or less in his uncle's confidence and he knew, when the rest of us did not, that the camp was bankrupt. For the same salary he helped Miss K. with the books.

In these circumstances there was not a single day during the entire summer that the stout young man thought that he was justified in unpacking his little satchel. But when the camp was over! we saw that Huey Ostoric too had a blue polka-dot tie and flannel trousers with a knife-edge crease.

It was easy!—I see it now—it was easy for me to identify myself with that Canadian canoeist, and to follow him with my heart when he paddled away, silhouetted by an orange flash of lightning. That canoeist with his three day disgust was a mere *idea,* and such an idea has always been easy for me. But Ostoric was *always* there and I was supposed to work with him. He was the arts-and-crafts man, and I was promised that he would help me backstage with the carpentry and the electricity. What did I expect? that the *real* expression of my alienated heart would not *annoy* me, and that he would be there conveniently day by day as a reminder and not *offend* me? but thank God, when he dealt our Congregation its death blow, merely by going away—in the glory of a straw hat and a polka-dot tie—I was able to watch it with a certain—joy! for I too had made up my mind to travel on my own.

In my remembrance, Huey never said a resentful word to any of us. (But I enjoyed plenty of resentment, and that canoeist was burning with resentment.) Huey was friendly by disposition and he tried to be easy-going with us at the very same time as he was not cooperating on the stage and was not enthusiastic about the War,—as if to say, "We are all fellows of the camp—such as it is." He was disturbed to learn that we relied on him to be the tenth man, for it had never occurred to him that just by his existence he was necessary, he was one of the *minyan.* He went away anyway, of course. Was it *his* fault that just by absenting himself he became the powerful judge of the Congregation and condemned it to dissolution?

CHAPTER V

A Hitch-Hike

※   *A rolling stone gathers no moss.*
"It means," said the refugee professor,
"that he does not become stodgy or as you
say mossy."
"No. We use it to mean that he doesn't
make any money."

I.

The farmer called for us at sunrise and drove us to the
station.

No more days of vacation!
Off to the railway station!

On the contrary, it was just the beginning of my sweet
and hard vacation. For to those of us who have lapsed
into, or achieved (it comes to the same thing), a careless
and unscheduled way of work and love, it is the times of
general vacation, the weekends, the summers, that are
painful. From our habitual distraction, that occasionally
yields a good fruit, we are distracted by the demands of
the others who are bent on distraction. There is nothing so
tiresome as a person concentrating on having a good time.
Till all men are clockless, I prefer to serve as a waiter during their leisure meals or as a crewman on the excursion
boats.

With passionate eagerness I put my sick friend on the
train, so eager to be rid of them *all,* and my old friend
the last of them, that his bad luck was my good luck.
"Goodbye and good luck," he called from the moving
window. The noise and the vapor of the engine engulfed
us, and his goodbye rapidly rang and diminished into the
thousands of goodbyes that constitute, I guess, the ringing
in my ears that I hear when I lie relaxed, before the sadness rises in my gorge. The tail-end of the train diminished, it was swallowed by the hungry present, bloated

and empty all about me, as again the tail-end of a dream vanishes on awaking: into the free, beautiful and senseless present moment that thrives on the lie that I have no past.

As the young man once I saw, at the top of the steps of a gray-painted house, carefully closed the door and threw wide his arms and cried "Freedom!" (I had my doubts), so almost—having disembarrassed myself of an old friend—I threw wide my arms; but I was holding a valise.

I crossed the street to the store and mailed the bag ahead of me. It would be odd when my clothes arrived home without me. As I thought it, the stout matron behind the counter looked at me candidly. I dismissed the suicidal afterthought for another time and scooped up the change from the counter. Then again, I reopened the valise and took out a pencil and my little pad. Like others, I have *paid* for my immortality.

It was the beginning of the fall. The sun shone clear and bright, but not hot or brilliant. It served rather to give adequate illumination, to "put things in their proper light," than to attract attention to itself,—yet I was attending just to it! as we watch a smiling prestidigitator whose gestures have a wonderful appearance of naturalness. Even so! everywhere, on all the apple trees and pear trees was edible fruit; by stepping momentarily off the highroad I could enjoy a piece of fruit. It was ideal weather for seeing New England from side to side, and why shouldn't I poke into Massachusetts and New Hampshire for a day or two? New York one could always reach, for everybody went there. Only, provided it didn't rain. . . . Struggling to keep hold of the present, I could see only, through the dusty window-pane, Armand in his canoe struggling in the teeth of the wind and the rain, forced back three-quarters of a length for each length of advance, his double-paddle almost vainly rising and falling on either side; the orange lightning drew the outline of his figure, and they burst into the marching song:

> If not now,
> *when?*

—Well! I'd wanted to get away, and now I was away!

The recollection of the canoeist and of the camp vanished from the morning.

I took my stand on the south side of the highway, Route Thirteen of my country, and began to signal to the high-powered automobiles. They were coming at the rate that one vanished in one extreme as another appeared in the other, so they seemed to draw each other elastically from the infinite poles. The notion, my notion, was for one of them to stop at my gesture and give me a lift on *my* way as far as *it* was bound. Then by the accretion of these short and long rides, by the interplay of our contrary purposes, I should eventually reach my destination! There was a post of signs by the roadside:

100,000 years	THE GREAT STONE AGE	
1,000 years	THE DAY THAT I WAS BORN	
400 years	THE FOUNDING OF OUR CAMP BY KWEE-KWEE	
0 years	THE CREATION OF THE HEAVENS AND THE EARTH	0
	THE REVOLUTION	?
	THE DAY I RECOVER CONFIDENCE	??
	A FREE SOCIETY	???
	THE TIME OF THE MESSIAH	????

The bright day, the flashing motorcars by-roaring, the unending highway roused in me a calm excitement. Who would stop? And how far would I go?

I was at the whim, but willingly, of whatever vehicle might choose me. Each car of these hurrying along, with anonymous exteriors of flashing glass, had some private career that I, with my lifted right, was willing temporarily to share, entering into the contract beforehand. It was very different from being at our camp.

"Dreams are the royal road to the unconscious," said the father of the psychoanalytic movement. The *King's* Highway to the Dare-Not-Know!—With mounting despair I watched flash by these uncommunicative images,

manifest reflections of the stupid daytime, not yielding up
their inner secret.

2.

With a startling hiss of air-brakes, a great red oil-tanker
ground to a stop on the gravel twenty yards beyond. The
driver thrust out his red head—Apollyon up from Hell,
as Hawthorne would say it, his hair still full of smoke and
fire. But I hastened to clamber aboard.

"We ain't supposed to pick up anybody," said the
driver, as we gathered speed. His thick forefinger touched
a legend on the windshield,

ИO RIDERƧ

"Who knows? You pick up a character who pulls a blackjack and throws you in the ditch. *You* look harmless."

There was an equal risk for those within the flying engines?

"But it gets lonesome on the road and a fellow likes
to have somebody to talk to. Other day a character fell
asleep at the wheel."

"How far down are you going? I'm going all the way
to—" I whispered the name of a very far place.

"You come a long way from there!" he said admiringly.
"But I turn east this side of Burlington."

"Maybe I'll ride along," I said in a high voice. "Why
shouldn't I see it all, from side to side?"

"Nothing to see," said the driver bitterly. "What's to
see?" he said (I thought). "I've traveled the other routes
as well, and it's all the same, boring!"

"Not if you're a hitch-hiker," I stoutly maintained (I
thought). "Trouble with you is you always have a sure
ride, eight feet above the road, you giant!"

"Is that so? Let me tell you, young snot, it's only human society that has an interest continually renewed."

"I can see that you've never been a counsellor at a
summer-camp!" I cried triumphantly and refuted him.

He bit his lips.

Meantime we were steadily eating up the road, and for
several minutes we exchanged no word. Suddenly, without turning his face from the road, he said to me be-

tween his teeth: "The chain! the chain! Do you hear the chain rattling on the road in back? They wouldn't let me remove it. Why not? Why in hell do I got to have this chain? *That's* why I picked you up; you looked like you would know."

"Sure!" said I cheerfully. "Sure I know. That's because the oil is swishing around in your big can and generating static. And if you don't keep continually grounding it, the whole works might blow up sky high."

"This they never told me," he hissed. . . . He jammed the brakes. "You get out. I don't like you. I never liked you from the beginning."

"O.K., O.K.," I sang. "I'm sick and bored with this highway anyway. And thanks for nothing."

A moment later I was flying into the sun, up a less traveled road, with a trio of blonde girls in a two-seater roadster that made eighty without a purr. The white posts of the road formed a continuous blur. The hair of the girls was whipped by the wind. One head was copper blonde, one golden blonde and one ashen. Now this last, black blonde, is the color of hair that I love most; and I was seated beside her in the rumble-seat. At my remarks the girls burst into fits of giggling; and soon they began to tell jokes which, I must confess, were excellent.

"What is it, Matt," said the copper girl at the wheel, "that men have but don't carry and women carry but don't have?"

"It's not dirty!" cried the other two.

"Repeat it," I said.

"What is it that men have but don't carry—men have it but don't carry it—and women carry it but don't have it?"

"Well, I can think of some things—"

"Yes, but they're all dirty. And it's not dirty!"

"I give up."

"Hemophilia," cried the girl at the wheel.

An added spurt, up to eighty-five, and we zipped through Little Giddy.

"Do you want to guess another riddle?" asked Eleanor, the black blonde.

"Yes," I said eagerly, knowing that my friends would appreciate these fine riddles.

"What is it—listen carefully—what is it whose shape belies the function—what is it whose shape belies the function of one of its nicknames?"

"Well, what is it whose shape belies the function of one of its nicknames?"

"A doughnut!"

"Why a doughnut?"

"Because it looks like a life-saver, but it's called a sinker."

It was so pleasant and joyous touring the countryside on so bright a day with such vivacious girls! There hovered on their faces, as those in front or the beauty beside me turned momentarily toward me and away, their moist teeth in the wind and wisps of hair in their eyes, many other lovely faces, recalled, in this one's smile and that one's laughter, while the greenery flickered by and the white blur of the posts stood still and the copper girl stepped on the gas. I had a joyful anticipation. The dampness of that summer camp was dissipated on the wind. Was I not becoming my real self again, untired, beginning over, back to a time before I could remember anything at all?

With a roar, that seemed much like a warning shout, our car came to a stop at a little road turning up into the hills.

"Duxbury: here's where we turn in," said the driver. "I hope you have lots of luck exploring New England from side to side," said the ashen girl.

I would have said, "I'll go up this little road with you as well," but my tongue clove to the roof of my mouth.

Because my tongue clove to the roof of my mouth, I could not tell even myself (and cannot now) what it was that simple happiness was, and what forbade, nor what it was that had occurred long ago.

But I know, in *general,* that much of the misery made amongst us is avoidable.

I was standing thunderstruck, by the roadside, whether for a short or a long time I cannot tell, when a black frock-coated bespectacled grandfather in a yellow calash, driving a smart dappled nag at a brisk pace, said "Whoa!" and stopped beside me.

He said, "Hop in, sonny."

Mechanically I climbed up beside him, and for a good while in dead silence we rolled on at the new pace.

On the left, as if belonging to a different order of things, for we rolled on the gravel shoulder of the road, flew the high-powered automobiles, passing us by.

The old gentleman was a schoolmaster.

—Now once, when I was a child, as punishment for a hair-raising misdeed (that I would gladly repeat) I was put back to a far lower class in school; I was made to sit, humiliated, in a seat too small for me. In my dreams this wished-for punishment recurs—except that, worse, I am lost and cannot even find the room, no less my home-room. Avoiding the room of the punishment; looking for the punishment; willing to endure the punishment again in order to have repeated the childish crime.—

We came, on the other side of Middlesex, to a traffic jam on the road, with scores of autos and farmers gathered to look on. It was a railroad crossing. During the night, just at the crossing, a big locomotive had jumped the rails, and it lay, half-over, with its nose in the ditch. Two of the great wheels were bent on a rock and the searchlight was shattered.

It had monstrously turned to confront us, in the night, with its violent force and the light blazing to the back corners of the soul.

It was a rare spectacle! The great iron animal was hurrying through the night, darting along the endless track the long beam of its eye, and drawing on a copious store of energy in its forward rush, while the lengthening plume of smoke stood suspended for miles in the calm air. But it turned. Without *even* a warning shout, the engine was lying in the ditch.

"How many were hurt? how many were hurt?"—The automobiles kept continually augmenting, mingling their raucous voices. The farmers were in high spirits, lighting their pipes.

On all sides streaming past with their howls. *Bluuuues! Lose! Mad! Dogs!*—"Who is *he?*" I said to Mike. "Who? who?" said Mike (I thought)—"*Who? WHO?*"

Surely it was *somebody, somewhen*. But I cannot recall it. And what if it was nobody, but only the wish of my need? Then, how? For nothing comes from nothing.

A haywagon was waddling into the side road. I leaped onto it and buried my head. I had hit on a methodical scheme—choosing always the less traveled road of the fork, and the less traveled of the next fork,—to come to a pause.

3.

The middle of the afternoon of the next day I was sitting, stranded among the daisies, beside a back road not marked on any maps. I was munching violet sickle-pears that I had gathered from the field. A little brook trickled through a clay pipe under the road. And to while the time, I was making parables and poems.

It was not probable that I should progress further, so long as I remained on this back road.

In the meadow, a dark-haired man was mowing with a busy, horse-drawn machine, but so far off that the noise of it was softer than the brook's.

Supposing I dropped a twig into this brook. Now this water ran into a stream and the stream into another and this into another that would eventually become the River Thames flowing into the ocean past New London. It did not follow that the twig would float all that way, because it might be snagged anywhere along the way. Indeed, with the keenest agitation one would see it being snagged and hope for it to break free, perhaps unsnag it (though that was cheating) to float further. Yet supposing the twig finally did break free and floated to the end! —then all that anxiety, and release from anxiety, would have been for a senseless twig in the sea.

The September sun was again a little golden, a little warming, not a featureless illumination. The solitude was not so lonesome, not so menacing with lonesomeness, but that I could relax my midriff and, ceasing to deceive myself, grieve for my condition and the condition of injured people, they being not there. Also recognizing the salient fact that it had not taken many rides to bring me to a relieving pause here, now; in general, the moment— each moment—was the end result of the long process of time.

My midriff, I say, was loosed; but my face—I could not
see my face—was watchfully waiting.

The declining sun cast a hue of bronze on the grass.
A fish slipped through the long moss of a rock and fled
downstream. From the distance rang the cry of the
reaper, to whom had occurred a sudden thought: "Leonard!" The time of day was between four and five. And
a white cloud, flying freely on the left, moved just beyond where I could glimpse it out the corner of my eye. I
blinked. And when I opened my eyes, the world as a
whole had passed on to a new configuration. I summed it
up:

> The King's Highway to the Dare-Not-Know!
> —but I beg my rides, and well I know
>
> the boring roads where hundreds and hundreds
> of cars fade by in hundred-hundreds
>
> of flashing mirrors much too fast
> to see my face. I am steadfast
>
> long hours of the morning sad.
> An old-time trap, an ancient sad
>
> horse and his master stop by the way,
> they'll take me one mile on my way
> —out of my way—is this the Way?
>
> I used to think I might be happy,
> but is it possible to be happy?
>
> What is it like?—like Plato oh
> we'll copy it at large and oh
>
> plan a city where all the distances
> (where? where?) are walking distances.

Towards evening, a large dark touring-car appeared on
the hill against me and rapidly approached. A startling
sight. The shadows of trees had gotten hundreds of yards
long, the red sun was touching the horizon, and the reaper
had left the field. There was an edge of chill in the air
and my jaw began to chatter, loosening my fixed stare. As
the car approached I got to my feet.

"Take me far as the main road," I shouted.

For I would not get far, even out of my way, if I did not get back to some kind of highway. Further I became aware of the expression that had been fixed on my face, the while I thought that I was breathing easy—anxious waiting.

With a quiet click of the brakes, as though it were a matter of course, by appointment, the dark-colored car stopped and the door flew open. I heaved a strong sigh as I stepped in.

4.

It was Ostoric.

"For God's sake!"

—"Get in. Got to keep going."

"Where'd you steal the car?"

—"Sure I stole it. Those fat greasy slugs, going by by by."

"How long've you been on the back roads?"

—"Third day."

"I thought you had to get to—where was it?—Scranton?"

—"Stroudsburg."

I finally took courage to look at him. He was not so natty as last we saw him.

—"Too late!" he cried. "If you're not there at the moment, nobody waits. There is a tide in the affairs of men which taken at the flood leads on to fortune! Keep going. Mustn't let people down! They don't forget it."

"It's O.K. by me," I said. "I'm glad to see you," I said frankly.

—"I know what you're thinking! 'That lazy son of a bitch never did a stroke for me all summer, and now he says, Keep going! It's a joke!' What the hell do you know? I came five minutes late the first time."

I did not pursue this puzzling line. Maybe he was right; I didn't remember. I was afraid to say what came to my mind, "Poor kid—" But I said, "Did you pick the car up by the road, or did you—"

—"Right! I shoved him out on his ass, into the ditch."

"But *he* was the one who gave you a ride, not like the others."

—"Saaay! Do you want to ride 'long with me or don't you? 'How sharper than a serpent's tooth!' Ha! *that's* what you're thinking!"

"Stop telling me what I'm thinking. You don't know anything about it. How long do you expect to cruise these fields before they catch up to you?"

—"Never never never never never."

"What do you mean, never?"

—"I still got bucks for gas."

He fell silent, while we tore the rubber off our wheels on the rocks. I felt that his silence was a bad sign.

—"All summer Nuncle lied to me. There never *was* going to be a regular arts-and-crafts man. All for a hundred lousy bucks, when I trusted him. He said he didn't send the wire because I nudged him. What do *you* know about it! . . . Oh God, I'm so sick and tired of begging, rubbing up against your leg just to gain admittance. . . . Then he skips off anyway in his fat greasy car. *I* was supposed to drive him to the city."

"Well, he didn't really have much time," I said to mollify him.

"Poverty," he recited,

> "Poverty who lately made
> more wholesome the common diet,
> now has cast me in the dark,
> for I cannot pay the Company,
> the giant that turns switches on
> and floods our rooms with light.—"

I was eerily moved. It was a poem of mine that he was quoting, a poem of long ago that I could never have remembered—it must have been written during the Great Depression—so I heard it not with my present ears, but surprised into the emotions of *those* times, before I had perfected my defenses against hope. Tears started into my eyes.

It was nearly dark. I reached to switch on the lights. He jammed the brakes so suddenly that I cracked my head on the shield.

—"Hand over the $200," said Ostoric.

The bowie-knife was pricking my ribs, as I had feared it all summer.

"What $200?"

—"You know what. The August pay."

"*What* August pay?"

I emptied my pocket of a dollar and a quarter. "Here's what I have and you can't have it, because I need it for supper and breakfast.

"Snap out of it, Huey Ostoric. Put that pig-sticker away. You saw the books, you know who got paid and who didn't get paid."

His reaction to this was terrifying.

—"Poor Nuncle Ben!" he blubbered. "He *wrote* down in the books that he paid you. He was ashamed for me to think it otherwise. He was ashamed. And now, you weren't superior ones after all, shouting there with your authoritative voices: pointing with your thumb to the switchboard script, and the other one, the admiral o' the ocean. Silent! silent upon a peak in Darien.—I never knew it. You're right. I never knew it at all. I only wanted to be able to share in." He burst into deep sobs, saying, "Poor Uncle Ben—poor Huffski Puffski."

I switched on the lights, calling into being the beautiful sylvan world. The knife dropped to the floor. He threw in the clutch and we rapidly accelerated.

"You're *lying!*" he cried, reaching his hands high.

The wheel gave a smart spin, and we crashed.

5.

It was gray among the trees. A runnel of water was flowing into my collar and out through the sleeves, emerging from my last dream. The rain was loudly pelting the woods. I was stretched on a blanket in the shelter of a tree. I had a headache. I reached for my pipe and tobacco, to suck a little security: everywhere there were dolorous twinges—in the spreading continents and the rivers of water and the mountain ranges, but especially in the skyey dome—yet nothing excruciating, nor unresponsive to searching. But the matches were wet.

There was a flame. Ostoric was offering the flame of his lighter and I got a light. I noticed that the stem of my pipe bore many tooth-marks of suppressed rage, and it was (I think) this observation more than the draught of smoke that brought the electric spirits tingling back into the torpid places.

—"Are you all right?"

"I think so." I squirmed some more.

—"Why did you do it? why did you do it?" he said, weakly wringing his hands.

An answer slipped out of me, like a thunderbolt: "I'm bewildered too." It was the hardest admission I ever made in my adult life, more than to confess the jealousy or cowardice that take from me the savor of the world. I got to my feet. My headache made me sick and I leaned against the tree. But it passed, it passed. It was simply suppressed bewilderment, and I whimpered—not for the pain, there was no pain—but because my eyes did not focus—I was frightened.

—"Are you all right?" he kept saying, hopping about.

The place, the road, was much more rough and sylvan than when I had gotten into that cursed car. It had needed a Cadillac to get further into the woods. The road gleamed with yellow puddles in which the raindrops were bouncing, through the overhanging trees. I stepped gingerly through the mud, from island to island, though I was soaked through and through anyway. "Come along," I said to Ostoric, though at the same time dissociating myself from him.

—"Yes! got to get going!"

To my astonishment I emerged (that is, we emerged) almost immediately onto a through way, a broad route of the Commonwealth whose marking I easily found on my rain-soaked map. This macadam road was not, to be sure, one of the great national ways, nor one of the international ways, yet even this road was traveled, even in this weather, by many cars, darting their yellow flares feebly in the dawn, through the rain; and it boasted many promising signs on the post, as well as the warning words

SLOW
DANGEROUS
S CURVE

Out of the fog and rain swished the high-powered cars, breaking the law moment by moment. We cowered on the side, almost invisible.

Every minute or so the noise of a car grew louder, and we stepped out from the shelter of an oak-tree to signal it. But no car was willing to stop. The yellow lights briefly illumined us as each sped by.

"Trouble with begging," I said bitterly, feeling terrible and losing my sense of humor, "is that we turn to each blow *after* it has struck."

In the teeming rain must not every car stop and pick us up? How could they not, seeing us with the water flowing in runnels into our ears and eyes?

"They don't like the idea of our wet clothes and muddy shoes soiling the upholstery," said Ostoric apologetically.

I looked at him in disgust.

"If I had a car," I said, "I shouldn't pass by *anybody* in such weather—even you."

CHAPTER VI

A Memorial Synagogue

※ It is not incumbent on you to complete the work; but neither are you free to withdraw from it.

—RABBI TARFON

We willingly commit some folly, just to live on a little.

—GOETHE

I.

We three came to the city where, despite much busyness, there was little useful work; despite much art and entertainment, little joy; despite many physical comforts, almost no sexual happiness; where among thousands of thousands there was almost not one person exercising most of his human powers, but every one pursued with earnest concentration some object not really to his advantage and which, perhaps fortunately for himself and us, he could not achieve. Yet such as it was! so I remembered my city from early childhood and I shared its ways; and Lord! I was glad to come back to it, as each time I come back.

Yet for conversation, we three exchanged only sighs. There were many fine things here and many distractions, but as it turned out, it was not possible for us to turn our minds to anything but recent disasters, unfinished disasters, wreck of our happiness both by our own stupidity and by compulsion, inextricably involved, both by commission and omission, with the many disasters of other people. The suggestion of any distraction decayed on our lips, but heaving each his own sighs we communicated with each other—the Canadian and Ostoric and I.

2.

Also we—and I think many many others at this time—were simply *floundering*. One cannot help saying that the young persons of the end of the first half of the century, those who have intellectual energy, are floundering. Floundering: that is, willing to give ourselves, and *giving* ourselves, to what we *know* to be unlikely. It is not even a matter of faith, or of misplaced faith. But what would you do—just to live on a little?

3.

We came to a crowded part of the city and at once began distributing our handbills.

The proposal of these bills was neither daring nor modest, but in the middle; it was what seemed appropriate to us in the circumstance that we could not succeed in turning our minds from the recent disasters. The fact is that one *cannot* do nothing but sigh, without a more athletic and social exercise. But if the reader's response to our proposal is just to heave a tired sigh, that is not inappropriate.——

> **A PROJECTION,**
> **IN HEAVY MATERIALS,**
> **OF OUR GRIEF**
>
> The Jews ought to make, of heavy materials, of medium size, embellished by great artists, a synagogue dedicated to Grief for their own recent disasters and the disasters of all peoples.

On corners of a busy intersection, we stood giving out these bills.

4.

There are some persons who, when offered a free handbill, harden their jaws and stare stonily ahead, and will not take it. Sometimes they jam their hands defensively in their pockets, for the hand is naturally apt to give and take. The reasons for this behavior are obvious: those that spring from fear are contemptible, but those that spring from wounded dignity are not (in our city) contemptible. But what is disheartening is to see a young person behave in this way.

Other persons accept the bill by an absent-minded reflex or out of courtesy, but they at once repent and angrily throw the offending paper into the mud.

Now still others courteously put the paper in their pocket, unread, perhaps carefully folding it. This delaying behavior creates a relation of complicity, almost of conspiracy. The moment will come—one may imagine in what dramatic circumstances! a man after the fourth ineffectual drink gives in to the distraction of emptying his pocket, to escape from the personal problem he is faced with across the table—and out of his pocket emerges this forgotten message, that he holds up to the light.

The man who has stonily declined a bill on the other corner stoops in the gutter to pick up a bill thrown away, now he is no longer face to face.

There are those who read and laugh nervously or snarl —for most handbills contain unpleasant matter; or who stand stock still, screw up their faces and seem to be spelling out the letters; or who, the experts in the kind of matters treated in free political handbills, give a cursory glance and at once engage you in argument.

5.

Before long fellows of mine (I am an anarchist) came by. They gave the bill a cursory glance.

"What's this!" they cried. "Have you taken leave of your senses? War-memorials! Do you think that war-memorials stop wars?"

"No, I don't," I said.

"Why the Jews? And *why* a synagogue? Have you suddenly become religious?"

"No, I haven't. But the city is full of Jews."

"The city is full of *people,*" they corrected me.

"Look, Matt," one of them said, troubled. "What's the use of making Yom Kippur? The thing to do is to prevent a recurrence."

"You're right, you're right," I said wearily. "There's no use crying over spilled milk; the thing to do is to make a change. But when I try to do it, the fact is that when I try to do it, it comes to nothing but sighing."

My friends respected me enough not to greet this remark with a hoot. But, a small knot of people having gathered around us, they at once began to harangue them about more hair-raising immediate and long-range action than we were proposing.

"I think," said a little old woman to me, "that the idea of a war-memorial is beautiful; there should be a great war-memorial. But it ought to be something useful, not statues. People are proposing that we build a community-center, with social activities and sports for boys and girls."

"No no," I said stubbornly, "it has to be something heavy, of hard materials like stone and bronze, because there is a heavy place in my breast that I want to get rid of, out there."

6.

A man who had been listening to the harangue cried out, "The speaker is right! But he's too god-damned reasonable. We don't need so much sweetness and light; we need more anger."

I touched him on the sleeve. "Not anger. Not just now. Let me tell you something I remember. I remember when the war was just breaking out in Europe, that Toscanini gave a concert, they were playing the *Eroica* symphony; and in the performance, in the performance by Toscanini, there was an edge of anger—even in the variations at the end. Anger. What do you think?"

Another man read the leaflet carefully. "You boys are floundering," he said.

A policeman dispersed the crowd.

7.

"You Jews ought to grieve for yourselves," said a woman. "You had enough trouble without grieving for other people's troubles too."

"That's just what the Canadian said!" I said, "—my friend on the other corner. He was wrong. Because we have a saying: *Im ein ani li, mi li? Aval im ani l'otzmi, ma ani?* It means: *If I'm not for myself, who is for me? But if I'm only for myself, what am I?*—"

I stopped short.

The saying had a third part. But when the third part came to my tongue, I stopped short. *V'im lo achshav,* is the third part, *eimatai?*—

And if not now, WHEN?

When this third question, this crucial question, came to my tongue, my tongue stuck to the roof of my mouth and I stopped short.

Next moment I burst into heavy sobs and stood on the corner with the tears streaming down my face, not even handing out the bills.

Hereupon (such is our city), whereas previously a

knot of people had gathered, now they gave me a wide berth and a space opened around me.

8.

> ※ The oxen that drew the Ark brought it, without a guide, to Beth-Shemesh, singing.

The sculptor who had chosen himself to embellish the building (as we had all chosen ourselves, for so comes into being the project that people only potentially want: it is forced on them)—the sculptor said:

"The chief object of embellishment must be the Ark, the box where the scrolls of the Law are kept, because this is the center of attention.

"Now for the right and left sides of the Ark I have designed two Cherubim, and they are these: Violence and Nature. But—but—"

He began to stammer, and then he began to keen.

"What's the matter, sculptor?"

"When I look at my designs," he said, "I can no longer remember, I can no longer distinguish, which is Nature and which is Violence.

"Once it was clear to me—if indeed it ever was.

"See, this one. His wings are spread across the top of the box, his hair is streaming: he is going aloft, from it, or with it—

"Ach! if I meant him to be an ideal motion, then he's Violence: raising, raping, tearing by the roots, it's all one. But maybe I meant him to be soaring and spreading wide, like growing Nature.

"Well, the other Angel has his feet firmly planted, that's clear. He's standing in the live rock, and that's how we'll carve it, too! But isn't he dragging the structure down, like a terrible wrestler? Good!—between us, I don't believe in the Law.

"I see that the two are fighting for the box—I didn't consciously mean this—the raised wings are trying to cover it, the wrestler is wresting it away. Maybe they aren't Nature and Violence at all. Yang and Yin!" he cried.

"Don't worry, sculptor; these are only designs. When you come to the execution and can think with your hands again, it will come back to you which is Nature and which is Violence."

"They aren't fighting at all. They're trying to embrace each other. But the box is in the way. Ha! I can fix that."

His face had a crafty look.

"I have planned the box as a movable furniture, according to the ancient way. It's a box of books in a dead language. If I—remove out this box—a bit—or *push* it back out of the way! won't they fall into each other's arms?"

"What! will they move?"

"Certainly they'll move!" said the sculptor arrogantly. "When my dolls move, you'll cry out, and the musician will blow the horn!"

He laughed raucously. "A pair of brawny movingmen," he said contemptuously, "tugging at that little box as tho it were as heavy as a safe."

9·

The painter had a different personality. A tiny Polish Jew, he was famous as a creator of wonderful whimsical animals. He said:

"For my part I wanted to use stained glass. But the architect says we must have white light for reading. Why must they read so much when they can look at my pictures? O.K. I tell the story on the walls."

"What story?"

"A fable I heard in the old country, unless it came to me in a dream. It goes like this:

"God said to Noah, 'Build the ark, three stories high; then the animals, two of each kind, will go up in it and be saved from the flood.' This was the arrangement and Noah set to work and did his part. But when the animals heard about it they called a world Congress. (Maybe some of the finest animals didn't even come to the Congress.) They chattered and jabbered; finally it came down to two factions. The first faction was superstitious and they thought they'd better do as they were told. But the other faction was indignant and didn't trust the arrangement at all.

" 'Since when,' said they, 'have these men been so good to us that now we should put our trust in them and, to be quite frank, walk like boobies into a trap. I for my part have a lively memory of Nimrod, that mighty hunter. Ha! you turn pale. So.

" 'And what do you think of the accommodations? We go by twos; but Noah! he doesn't go alone with his wife, but he also takes with him those three fat boys, of whom I need say no further. *And* their wives. Include us out.'

"The others only said, 'We'd better go.'

"So the day came and Noah blew on his shofar a loud blast—"

"Excuse me," said Armand, "what's a shofar?"

"A shofar—is a shofar."

"Yes, but what is it? Noah blew a blast on his shofar; what's a shofar?"

"A shofar is a shofar, dummy," said the painter angrily.

"What is it, a kind of bugle?"

"Yes, it's a bugle. Noah blew a blast on his bugle!"

"What's to get angry about? Why didn't you explain it was a bugle in the first place?"

"Please—" the painter screwed up his face in pain, "*is* a shofar a bugle?

"—He blew a blast and some of the animals came, and then came the rain and the flood. But the others *didn't* come, and they *drowned. Ach!*—So perished from the earth the wonderful snodorgus and the kafooziopus, and klippy, and Petya, and the marmape, and Sadie—"

It was impossible to believe one's eyes and ears, for suddenly the little man began to bawl in strange little sobs at the top of his chest, for his fantastic animals whose names he was making up as he went along.

"So died," he screamed, "the loveliest and the shrewdest. Petya! Petya! And my sister's little girls, and my brothers, and long ago my friend Apollinaire.

"But I shall paint these beauties into existence again, on every wall in the world!"

10.

The architect started out with firm logic:

"In a building of this kind the chief thing to communicate is the sense of the Congregation. The sense of itself *by* the Congregation. Therefore we must be careful about the sight-lines."

He hesitated. "The sight-lines. I arrange the seats in two banks, facing each other across a plain. The Ark is at the eastern end of the plain. See, the sight-lines: everybody is in full view."

He hesitated and began to draw lines on the tracing-paper.

"They flash across the space! Sometimes they get tangled in mid-air. It means that a man gets the impression he is being stared at.

"Don't misunderstand me," he apologized. "I'm not saying that it's embarrassing to be looked at; if that were so it would be the end of architecture; but—not just now.

"Strictly speaking there is nothing else to see in the Jewish service except the Congregation itself. There is no sacrament.

"A few men are called up to bless the passage; that's all the service consists of. That's what we have to keep in view. Here they open the scroll to read it, and quidam is called on to bless the passage. *Everybody* is suddenly looking at him, a fine representative figure of a man!

"Suppose he turns and stares at *you!* You don't like that, huh?

"Maybe the visible Congregation is not such a good idea after all and something is to be said for the stained glass.

"The old men cover their heads with their prayer-shawls, but you could never get the young ones to do it. They are ashamed to be ashamed."

He began to slash the paper with heavy lines, as if the sight-lines were clashing in the space like knives.

He hesitated. The hesitation endured, but there was no moment at which you could say he fell silent.

Finally some one prompted him. "What about the sight-lines? What do they see?"

"The people are crying," he said.

He heaved a sigh of relief. "That solves the problem!" he said more cheerfully. "People crying can't see much."

New York City
1935-1947

LIKELY AND THE DRAGON

I.

"Stand still, Texas!" they shouted at the horse.

"Stay, Texas!"

"Good Texas!"

The three of them—Matty, Laura, and Likely—kept shouting at the old horse. The field was full of flowers, in white and orange patches. The horse stopped walking and stood for the children to climb on.

They brought the ladder. "Stand still, Texas, so we can climb on," they said.

The patient horse stood and let them lean the ladder against him. One by one—Likely first—they climbed up and jumped off on the other side.

Likely sat on Texas' neck. Matty followed her up the ladder and he was the first one to dare to jump down on the other side into the grass. Laura, who was smaller, climbed halfway and clung to the horse's mane.

With a groan Likely saw her little brother Larry coming across the field. He was a pest, always following.

Old Texas was a pinto horse, white with great patches of brown, like maps. There were patches of white and orange on the field and patches of white and brown on Texas.

Larry was a pest because he couldn't do anything, he could hardly talk, yet he wanted to play in the games of his sister and her friends. He began to scream, "Yeow! Up! Me! Up! Me!"

"Scram, Lary, you're a pest," said Likely crossly.

The little boy began to cry.

But the others climbed up the ladder onto Texas' back and jumped off on the other side. Larry kept on crying. The three friends kept on screaming with excitement. The colors kept on shouting.

Suddenly the horse moved forward and the ladder fell. Texas took three steps forward, but he was too old and tired. With a sad whinny he fell over on his side in the field, and died.

The children were suddenly quiet. Except for Larry who kept saying, "Yeow! Up! Me! Me!" But the other children stood around Texas and said fearfully, "Good Texas! Stand up, Texas!" But he couldn't stand up any more.

They were going to run away but they didn't.

Suddenly they knew that he was dead and they began to murmur.

It turned into a sad song, which they sang over and over,

> "Texas is dead!
> Poor Texas!
> He can't get up any more!"

They picked some of the field-flowers, the white-eye-lashed daisies and the devil's-paintbrushes dipped in fire, and threw them on the dead horse, singing,

> "Texas is dead!
> Poor Texas!
> He can't get up any more."

The farmer came across the field to see what was the matter with the horse.

II.

In September, Likely and Larry came back to the city.

Sometimes Likely thought about Texas. She remembered—she could not forget—how he walked forward three steps and gave a whinny and fell down on his side in the field, and died.

Her eyes became hot and she said angrily, "Everything I love is going to die! Texas has died already. The summer flowers are gone and the autumn leaves are beginning to fall."

The sycamore leaves were falling slowly into the street.

"Mommy is going to die. Larry too. But I'm going to die before Larry, because I'm older than he is."

When she said this, Likely burst into tears.

Aunt Liz, who was her father's sister, tried to cheer her up and said, "Don't cry, Likely, God isn't going to die."

"No!" said Likely. "Everybody is going to die."

"No!" said Aunt Liz. "God is and God always was and God always will be."

"Oh, how awful!" said Likely, who did not want to be cheered up, "God doesn't have a birthday! He never had a birthday-party."

She didn't want to be less sad, and she began to cry out, "Ow! Oh-ow!" until she was screaming.

Aunt Liz was at a loss what to do.

III.

But by the afternoon Likely was happy again and forgot about Texas and that God had no birthdays.

Everybody went for a walk in the sunshine, Mother and Aunt Liz and Larry and Likely. Likely wore her skates and Larry sat in a red wagon, but the grown-ups were only walking.

Likely skated ahead—she was always the leader—first on *this* foot, then on *that* foot. *This* foot, *that* foot, this foot that foot, faster and faster. She liked to go like the wind.

"Look!" she cried, "there's the redbird again."

"Where?" said Mother.

"There! it's a tanager."

"How do you know it's a tanager?" asked Aunt Liz.

"By the black wings. Can't you see it's a tanager?"

"I can't even see the bird, no less the markings," said Aunt Liz.

"Yeow! yeow!" crowed Larry, standing up in the wagon.

"Little brother can see it," said Likely. "Only he thinks it's a tomato. Zip! there it goes to *that* tree."

The streak of red burned in the sky and sat in the golden sycamore.

"I'll draw a picture of it," thought Likely, "with Larry standing up in the wagon."

"I still can't see it," said Mother.

"Now you can't see him because he flew away."

"Oh."

"Don't be disappointed. He lives in that nest—see? He'll surely come back."

"I see the nest. I can't see the bird."

Likely saw her friends skating around the corner. "Hi!" she shouted, and flew like the wind to catch up.

"Bye, Likee!" called Larry, standing up again in the wagon.

"Sit down, Larry," said Mother.

After a moment Likely came back around the block. She had gone all around the block. "There are five ways of going places," said Likely. "Walking, running, skipping, and jumping, that's four. Rolling on wheels—*this* foot! *that* foot!"

IV.

Mother said, "Watch Larry a moment, while we go into the tailor's. It's steamy there."

"But I'm *skating*," said Likely. Her friends vanished around the corner like leaves blown by the wind. It was fall, and the leaves that had fallen in the street were blown by the wind.

"We'll be only ten minutes," said Mother. "If you don't want to, I'll take him in. I thought you might *want* to take care of him."

"All right," said Likely, and Mother and Aunt Liz went into Mr. Abrams'. "Sit down, you," she said to her little brother.

"Larry stand! Up! Me up!" said Larry.

"I hate you, lousy Larry," said Likely. "Why do I have to take care of *you?* But if I don't, Mother will be angry."

She hated him because he was messy when he ate.

Larry could hardly even talk. He was contemptible. He kept shouting, "Yeow! yeow!" and bouncing in the wagon.

Sometimes she didn't mind taking care of him. Other girls had only dolls.

The wild race of her friends again came around the corner. They were skating round and round the block.

"Hi!" cried Matty, as he flew by.

"Hi!" cried Likely happily, because she loved Matty. She could skate as fast as he. Sometimes she wished she were a boy, like Father. Other times she was glad she was a girl.

"Hi!" said Laura, her best girl friend, and neatly stopped by dragging her left skate and swinging in a circle, ending in front.

"Let's drag Larry in the wagon," said Likely.

"Horses! I'm Texas!" said Laura.

"I'm Texas," said Likely.

"*I'm* Texas!" said Matty in a terrible voice.

"We'd better go slow or he'll fall out," said Likely.

"Roger! Texas will go very slow!" said Matty.

They grabbed the rope of the wagon and began to drag it. *This* foot. *That* foot.

"Yeow!" cried Larry happily.

"Giddyap, horsey!" said Likely.

Soon the three horses were dragging the wagon as fast as they could go.

"Yeow!" cried Larry, for everybody likes to be dragged in a wagon.

"He'll fall out and hurt himself," thought Likely frightened.

"Larry's not afraid! he loves it!" said Laura.

Their iron skates made sparks on the pavement and a terrible noise.

"Heigh-ho, Silver!" cried Matty.

This side, *that* side—the wagon careened.

BANG! The wagon crashed into a hydrant and Larry fell out.

He was so surprised he didn't even cry. His nose was bleeding and made spots on his clean suit. Then he screamed and Mother rushed out to see what was the matter.

Likely said to Mother, "It was my fault. I knew he'd fall out and get hurt."

Mother and Aunt Liz looked at her.

"I'm not angry with him any more," said Likely surprisingly. She was frightened at what she had done, but his nose stopped bleeding. "He's brave," said Likely. "He didn't cry once. He gave only two screams."

Mother was displeased at how Likely took care of Larry. "Now you can go skating if you want," said Mother, in her tone when she was displeased.

"I don't care if I do," said Likely, dragging her feet.

V.

Mother was not displeased for long, and at night, when Likely went to bed, she sang her some of the old songs which Mommy loved and Likely was learning them too.

She sang the old Scotch song, *Annie Laurie,* explaining the words of it, especially the strange Scotch words. If a song is beautiful, it is twice as beautiful if you understand the words and sing them with the tune.

The song *Annie Laurie* has three parts, and first Mommy explained the first part.

> Maxwelton's braes are bonny
> where early fa's the dew.

"Maxwelton is a place in Scotland across the ocean," she explained. "It's named after some old family Maxwelton that lived there. *Braes* means fields in Scotch, and *bonny* is the way they say pretty. And in these fields, the dew—you know what dew is—falls early in the evening, because it's cool and shady. Anyway, it means that those fields are very nice."

"*Fa's* is Scotch for falls," said Likely, who was smart.

> And 'twas there that Annie Laurie
> gie'd me her promise true
> that ne'er forgot shall be.

"This man who is singing the song," explained Mother, is in love with Annie, and she promised to marry him or something, and he won't ever forget it. *Ne'er* means never, in poetry."

> And for bonny Annie Laurie
> I'd lay me doon and dee.

"Bonny is Scotch for pretty," said Likely.

"*I'd lay me doon and dee* means I'd lie down and die. He says this because he loves her so much."

"What a curious thing to say!" said Likely.

Mother then explained the second part of *Annie Laurie*.

> Her brow was like the snowdrift,
> her neck was like the swan,
> her face it was the fairest
> that e'er the sun shone on.

"He says her forehead, that's brow, is white and smooth as a snowdrift. And her neck is pretty as a swan's—he doesn't mean it's as long as a swan's."

"Of course not," said Likely. "I catch the rest. *E'er* means ever. In poetry."

> And dark blue was her ee.

"Her ears!" cried Likely in astonishment. "Her ears were dark blue? That *is* curious!"

Mother laughed. "No no! *Ee* is Scotch for eyes. Her eyes were dark blue."

"So what?" said Likely. "Mine are blue too."

> And for bonny Annie Laurie
> I'd lay me doon and dee.

"I'd lay me doon and dee—same foolish remark as before," said Likely.

Then Mother explained the last part of *Annie Laurie*.

> Like dew on the gowan lyin'
> is the fa' o' her fairy feet

"*Gowan* is a grassy meadow."

"That's light!" said Likely. "She walks along like dew on the grass, shiny and hardly touching."

"Exactly."

> And like winds in summer sighin'
> her voice is soft and sweet.

"Yes, I get it," said Likely drowsily.

And she's all the world to me.

Mother did not explain this, but kissed Likely goodnight.

Likely was fast asleep. Mother turned out the light and left.

VI.

While Likely was lying there in the dark, she heard an awful voice. The sound of the voice was so frightening that her eyes stared and her tongue stuck in her throat. But what the voice said was even more frightening than the sound of it.

"Likely," said the voice, *"you killed your brother Larry. Anyway, he's not here any more."*

She moaned in her sleep. "I didn't kill him. He's inside in the next room." She called out, "Larry! Larry!"

But there was no sound, because she was asleep.

She lay there, covered with a cold sweat, and she moaned, "Help! help!"

To her help, in walked an old friend.

It was Texas!

He was changed. He was not pinto now but all white, except for his warm friendly eyes. And he had blue ears, which would have made Likely laugh if she weren't frightened.

"Don't be afraid, little Likely," said Texas, in a rich baritone voice. "Larry isn't dead, but he *has* gone away. We'll go and bring him back.

"Also," said Texas, "you didn't do anything especially terrible when you let Larry fall out of the wagon. All girls and boys hate their little brothers and sisters. It can't be helped. They're messy, and Mother has to take care of them because they're so little and can't do anything for themselves. Then, of course, she can't pay as much attention to you as she used to. Don't worry about it. Mommy understands how you feel, and she loves you the same as ever."

"Where *is* Larry?" asked Likely. "I called and there was no answer."

"He has disappeared over the horizon, and we must go and fetch him back. You know what the horizon is, but let me tell you about the Dragon."

"Dragon? I don't like Dragons. Yes, I know what the horizon is. It's the circle all around, where the sky comes down to the earth."

"Correct," said Texas. "Around this circle lies a Dragon who bites his tail with his mouth, so he makes a big circle. He is and always was. Now that Dragon—don't be frightened—has swallowed up Larry, but we'll go and fight him, and cut him open! And out will step Larry, better than ever!"

"Let's go!" said Likely, springing from bed. "How do we get there?"

"You may ride on my back," said Texas patiently.

Likely looked at him—embarrassed. "Won't you fall down and die?" she asked at last.

"No. I'm not going to die any more," said Texas.

And he stood against the bed and Likely climbed up on his back.

VII.

Although he had no wings, Texas could fly like the wind. He had roller-skates on, which Likely hadn't noticed before. In a moment they were flying through the clouds and across the black and starry sky, for it was night.

Round them was falling the gentle dew.

When you look at the stars you can see that, if you draw lines from one star to another, they form the shapes of animals or giants or whatever you imagine. In one part of the sky is a quiet Lion. In another part is a giant Hunter who never catches what he is hunting. Among these shining shapes rode Likely on the back of Texas.

Texas pointed out the sights in the sky. "Here's the Big Bear, and here's the Small Bear. And there is the starry Crown, overhead for us all."

Then Texas said something so curious that Likely hardly knew whether or not to believe him.

"Do you play the game of Hopscotch?" said Texas.
"Of course," said Likely.

"Well," said Texas, "listen to this. You see how the sky is divided into the houses of different starry animals and giants. There's the Lion's house, there's the Crab's house, and there's the Ram's house, and the rest. Now these houses are the same as the squares in the game of Hopscotch! each one of which has a different number. But you must be careful and throw the little stone into each numbered square in turn, and visit all the houses!"

"Yes, that's how we play. Why must I?" asked Likely.

"Then you will have crossed the sky and you can come home and be happy. This is why children really play the game, but they don't remember any more."

A shooting star fell close, across Likely's left shoulder.

"Don't be alarmed," said Texas. "People say that's good luck."

Likely was riding on Texas' back. But somehow, at the same time, she could also see them both riding across the sky, and the stars shone through the horse's sides.

VIII.

Thus, they came to the Horizon. There, sure enough, was the ugly Dragon with his tail in his mouth, enclosing the world in a circle.

"Let me out! let me out!" cried voices, but nothing was to be seen but the endless Ocean. That was the dragon's name.

Likely climbed down from Texas' back.

"I'm ready," she said. "How am I supposed to fight him?"

"I'll dress you up as a knight in armor," said Texas, "and I'll give you a sword and a shield."

She knelt.

"Likely," said Texas, touching her with the sword, "every girl and boy must fight with this dragon. Do not be afraid."

And he gave her armor to put on. But this was a mistake. Her open face disappeared in the iron helmet that had a black plume. On her shield was a picture of the

Winter Sun trying to shine through a snowfall. The armor was too heavy to wear, and Likely began to shake inside of it and be afraid.

And when, in the heavy armor, she went up to the ugly Dragon's head, he spat smoke and fire at her, as dragons do, and gave forth a bellow. He struck her with his claw and knocked her down.

"Oh-ow!" moaned Texas. "All is lost."

"Nothing is lost!" said Likely. "It's the armor that is too heavy!"

She stepped out of the heavy armor, and she took off the iron helmet so that you could see her face again. She threw away the shield, but grasped the sword.

Then she easily stepped up to the Dragon and cut his head off.

"I'm sorry to hurt you, monster," she said, "but you must give me back my brother Larry."

"Don't be sorry," said the Dragon's head. "Thanks! I'm glad at last to be able to let go biting my tail. Now I can go swimming, which I enjoy."

And the head dove into the sea and disappeared.

Likely cut open the body and out stepped Larry, happy and new, and able to talk very well.

"Hi!" said Larry. "It's God's birthday. You know, God has a birthday every couple of weeks. Sometimes, when all's well, He has a birthday-party every morning at sunrise."

Likely was glad to hear it. She had never learned anything from Larry before.

She helped her brother up onto Texas' back, and she climbed up herself, and off they flew across the sky.

"Texas," said Likely, as they moved across the sky toward dawn on their homeward trip, "you are old and wise and we love you, but you don't know how to fight dragons. You must never wear heavy armor, but just swing your arms with all your might."

IX.

The sunrise came into Likely's bedroom and she woke up.

It was the world's birthday. The world has a birthday-party when all is well. That happens sometimes, and it happens more often if you let it happen. Likely did not hold herself back with foolish fears. She could, if she wanted, fly into the very next moment; or she could sometimes sit still and let the next moment come to her. So she sang,

> Happy birthday to you!
> happy birthday to you!
> happy birthday, dear world,
> happy birthday to you!

The question is, how many candles are there on the world's birthday-cake? The answer is, One. It is the *extra* candle that they put on birthday-cakes, the one to grow on. That's really the only candle you *need* to have a birthday-cake.

Aunt Liz and Mother and Father and Likely and Larry sat down to breakfast and ate the birthday-cake. Since it was breakfast, the cake was toast. For it's not the chocolate icing that makes a birthday-cake, but the shining candle in the middle. You can make a fried egg into a birthday-cake by lighting a candle on it.

"Put a birthday candle on the heap of toast," said Likely.

"Why on earth?" said Mother.

"Because it's a bright sunrise," said Likely.

"It is. But we can't have a candle every time it's a bright morning, you silly girl," said Mother.

"No, but once in a while, for a change," said Likely.

"You're right," said Mother, and got a candle from the drawer and stuck it in the heap of toast and lit it.

"I want toast and cereal," said Larry in perfect English. Aunt Liz marveled that Larry had learned to speak so well. "It's as if he learned to speak overnight," said Aunt Liz. Likely knew why.

X.

Likely decided that it was better to have a real brother than a doll.

Matty and Laura came with their skates. You could

first hear their skates clattering in the street. *This* side, *that* side. Then, after some scuffling, they came in carrying the skates.

Likely and Matty kissed each other because they loved each other.

"Is everybody here?" asked Likely. And she called the roll of the people in this story.

"Aunt Liz?"

"Here."

"Mother?"

"Here."

"Daddy?"

"Here."

"Larry?"

"I'm here," said Larry in perfect English.

"Matty?"

"Here."

"Laura?"

"Here."

"Where is Texas?" asked Likely.

"Texas is here in his absence," said Father.

"Yeow!" said Larry, to show that he could also remember his old words.

"I'm going skating," said Likely. "Larry can come along if he stays where we put him. As soon as he makes a fuss, he comes upstairs again."

"No fuss," said Larry. "Skate on sidewalk. *This* side, *this* side. With one skate. Yeow!"

Larry could skate with one skate.

"Do be careful, children," said Aunt Liz. "Don't go where the cars are."

"For heaven's sake, Liz," said Father, "Likely has sense and she can go wherever it's safe."

"Right," said Likely. There was nothing to argue about.

Soon you could hear their skates speaking in the street. *This* side, *that* side. This side, that side—faster and faster —then softly purring.

But Larry's skate said, *This* side, *this* side.

MARTIN

Larissa happened to mention that she had a brother
named Martin. For the rest of the evening Johnson
moved the talk around him. He felt that this topic must
be interesting to her, intimate and yet not so personal
as to be embarrassing, since he had just picked her up. It
was a quiet tavern without television, and their voices became warm, earnest, and soft. With gray eyes glowing,
she described how tall and dark was Martin, unlike her
own ashen blond to which she thereby called attention.
He was so slim as to be almost skinny, unlike herself. He
was three years younger. He was interested in baseball
and astrophysics and baseball. He had a certain way of
saying "Wow!"—"very boyish!" giggled Larissa, "just like
you." Indeed, before the night was over, because of the
very animation of her recital, Johnson came to feel another, erotic, interest in Martin.

He thought it would be remarkable, an experiment
fraught with doubt and difficulty, to have an affair with
both the brother and the sister at the same time. Without
jealousy in the very lair of jealousy. This idea struck him
just as he looked up at the clock and saw that it was 2:32
in the morning, a time when resistance is low. Larissa was
at this moment describing Martin's best friend, an Italian
boy with violet eyes named Andrea, and how inseparable
the two were, at which Johnson became perturbed and
tipped over his glass of wine on the tablecloth.

In love Johnson was disinterested and creative and this
diminished his own anxiety so that he could have sexual
pleasure. By withdrawing and, like a sculptor, arranging
the male and female figures in a group, he could then take
his place in a niche left for himself. Sometimes, to be sure,
the group worked harmoniously without him being in it;
but he was reconciled beforehand to the disappointment

and self-sacrifice that come from trying to make something worthwhile with recalcitrant material.

"When am I going to see this paragon?" he said briefly.

"Oh—I mean—if you and I are going to see each
other again—"

"Of course I am going to see you again. Tomorrow. I
must see him too. Now don't you miss. It's more important
than you think."

She looked up at him with timid gray eyes as he arose.
She was already in love with him.

"What's this name Larissa?" he said. "Where did you
ever dig up a name like that?"

"Oh—I mean—" she said. She explained that her
mother had wanted to call her Laura, but her deceased
grandfather's name was Isidore, so they called her Larissa. "We're Jewish," she explained. It was evident to her
that Gift of Isis was a Jewish name.

Sexually, Johnson *was* a Judeophile. "I'm going to call
you Sarah," he said approvingly.

"Oh no!" she cried.

But when Larissa came to the appointed place the next
day, she came without her brother Martin. She was late,
too.

Johnson was in the habit of being on time, especially
when he kept the appointment. Now, after waiting, walking up and down in front of the Lions for twenty minutes and wondering how he could have so miscalculated
the girl, he had the added disappointment of finally seeing her running up Fifth Avenue alone, without Martin.
She was always late and she always arrived running, taking off the edge of insult to injury.

"I couldn't find my hat," she said in a fluster. She
pressed his hand warmly in both of hers and clung to it.
He had to shake her loose.

"Where's Martin?"

"Oh. He couldn't come. He had to finish eating supper."

Nevertheless, Johnson soon recovered his accustomed
cheerfulness and devoted himself entirely to Larissa. He
did not so much as mention Martin, for now he felt he
knew her well enough to talk about herself and it might

seem unflattering to the girl to be talking always about her brother. So he just kept starting her off—"wound her up," as we say—and let her prattle on. Mainly she talked about her former lovers, how she had loved one person 75% and another person almost 90%.

"She really is stupid," thought Johnson wonderingly. "After all."

"You remind me of some one I used to know," he said suddenly. "Some one that *I* was in love with. 100%. He was a man, named Leonard. When you stick your tongue out, that way."

It was true that she reminded him of Leonard. At this time almost everything still did, any lisping speech, any off-color hair, or mention of vacation spots that had either lakes or meadows or mountains or beaches. For just the opposite of his esthetical withdrawing mode of approach, once he had gotten hooked he could never cut loose. She also pouted and lowered her eyelids at the same time. He could not help but love her.

It was good to mention Leonard to lay a groundwork for making a pass at Martin.

When he left her that evening, he kissed her warmly. They were very sympathetic with each other.

"You won't forget I want to see your brother Martin," he said.

"Oh no," she assured him. But she said this smiling complicitly; she understood.

For suddenly, precisely because of his slightly forced manner, she began to entertain a singular notion about Johnson and Martin, that, far from wanting to see Martin, Johnson wanted the very opposite. He spoke of "seeing Martin" in order to have a pretext to see *her*. The expression "I want to see Martin" meant "when shall I see *you* again, but I am embarrassed to ask straight out"— just as for Swann the expression *faire cattleya* meant "let's screw."

Larissa was happy at the success she was having with Johnson. He had soft hair. When he kissed her, she caught her fingers in his hair. His hair was streaked with different colors. He was a man of the world. He was the most sympathetic person she had yet met, the only one to whom she could say certain things without his getting edgy; for instance, when she explained hesitantly that she had been in love with somebody not altogether but about 90%. He understood, he really understood. He showed the same finesse in his ruse about "seeing Martin," avoiding embarrassment for them both. But since it was evident that he wanted to be alone with her, there was certainly no advantage in putting a fifth-wheel on the carriage, especially a younger brother.

Despite his best efforts at communication, it did not occur to Larissa that Johnson might be interested in boys.

"I must make up a really clever excuse to explain him away this time," she thought as she ran down Broadway. But she couldn't think of anything.

When he saw her coming across the opera lobby late and alone, Johnson was visibly agitated. He turned pale and red. "Where's Martin?" he asked sharply.

"Oh. He couldn't come. He was making a telescope," she said, betrayed into the improbable truth.

"For Christ's sake! what am I supposed to do with these three tickets I bought?"

"You bought three tickets?"

"*Here!* Yes, you——" He gave the extra seat to one of the City College students who wait in the lobby for such emergencies. The young man had ferocious brows and dark-rimmed spectacles and was quite ugly.

Johnson could hardly contain his displeasure. Ordinarily he could not act rudely, even with strong provocation. But now, sandwiched between the stupid girl and the owlish young man, he bit his lips and did not enjoy the music. He toyed with the idea of asking City College to change seats with him——

"You know, it won't do," he said to her during the entr'acte. "When I say bring Martin, I mean bring Martin. You mustn't trifle with me."

"But why on earth?" she asked, bewildered, near tears. "What interest can you have?"

"What's that to you? For heaven's sake, girl, wouldn't you want to meet somebody if you were told he was beautiful and intelligent?"

She tried to change the subject. He wouldn't.

"Do you *like* your brother Martin?" he asked suspiciously.

"Oh yes, I am very fond of him."

"Well, that's good," thought Johnson, "at least she likes him and I like them both." He was not a vindictive person and, falling under the spell of the music, he soon began to be quite in love with brother Martin. Rigidly excluding from awareness the actual girl and the beetling brows on either side of him, he wandered into scraps of revery about chemical Affinities—he had been reading Goethe's novel. We call them valences. These days, of course, we have much more complex compounds—DNA —it comes in spirals.

"Will you please try not to mutter, sir, it's distracting," said the young man on his left. With a start Johnson came to himself and found that his right hand was clasped warmly and damply in Larissa's. "How do you like it?" he said, "I give him a ticket and he tells me not to mutter. . . . Where do you come from, City College?"

"Yes."

"I thought so." But this was too harsh, and he added, "It's O.K., I went there too."

The act ended, with loud applause. It was *Lucia*. She was fair to middling.

"Now tell me some more about Martin," said Johnson.

She told him an anecdote. Martin was at the window with his telescope and a man in an apartment across the court—they lived in Sunnyside, Borough of Queens— climbed out on the fire-escape in his bathrobe and shouted, "Get away, you peeping Tom, or I'll call a cop."

They both laughed. The strained relation was relaxed. Dimly Johnson registered that it would be hard to accompany to her door a girl who lived in Sunnyside, Borough of Queens.

"I thought you said he was just making a telescope," he said suspiciously. For the first time it occurred to him that the apparently simple girl was lying to him, just as he was trying not to lie to her.

"Oh. I think this is a bigger one—" she faltered.

Naturally! he thought—Jews were interested in mathematics, chess, and music. They were intellectually combative but winningly docile. He foresaw that, as usual, he would alleviate the guilt of his boy-loves by becoming a pedantic guide and Dutch Uncle, even though his role took all the sex out of it. Well, he knew little about mathematics and nothing about chess, but he did know a good deal about music. Christmas was coming up—he'd buy him Vivaldi's *Seasons* for a starter. Maybe, he thought in pain, he had better start from the bottom with excerpts from *Carmen*. Sunnyside.

"Is Martin really intelligent?" he asked anxiously.

"Oh yes—I mean—he is intellectual." She was not sure what any of this meant but she felt that this was what he wanted to hear; she had to make up for the frightening misunderstanding between them.

"Is he very very good-looking?" asked Johnson.

"Oh *yes!*"

He had a further question but did not know how to put it. He took a breath. "Does he have a big penis?" he asked, reddening, as though he were not a man of the world.

"I—I mean—I don't know," she said.

Women! They were intuitive, but they never knew the material facts.

When for the third time Larissa came to the appointment without Martin, Johnson thought, "That settles it, the boy does not exist.

"Look here, Sarah," he said quietly, "why are you lying to me? What's the matter with him this time?"

He looked at her sharply, almost for the first time. "She knows how to play me. Perhaps the girl is more intelligent than I give her credit for."

Larissa was breathless and almost in tears. This time she had come late because she dreaded the ordeal, and then she had had to run in order not to be late for it. "I'm so sorry—" she faltered, "I mean—yesterday he went away for two weeks to Lake Placid."

"Ah, ah," gasped Johnson, like a landed fish.

He could foretell the entire future. He would end up marrying her. She knew how to entice him in the preliminaries and then, when she suddenly relieved his anxiety

—for there would be no Martin—he would be left confronting *her,* and nothing to do but succumb.

But the real reason, this time, for the non-appearance of Martin was that his sister was ashamed to bring him. She began to feel that Johnson expected to meet Lord knows what, and that, in her eyes, was not Martin. Once he met Martin he would be so disappointed that he would not see *her* any more. The more she faced it, the less possible it became ever to bring Martin. She scrutinized her brother; it was not encouraging. Yet since she had to produce him in the end, she wished at least that he could be improved a little, coached a little. She gave herself two weeks.

"Who was Vivaldi?" she asked. Johnson had mentioned Vivaldi.

"He was an Italian composer, stupid," said Martin.

"Good!" she said, surprised. "Who was Heine?"

"He was a Jew."

She was astonished. "Who was Burckhardt?" she asked.

"What the hell do you want?" said Martin.

"How can you be so ignorant?" she cried passionately. "Aren't you ashamed?"

"What am I supposed to be, a cross-word puzzle?" said the gangling dark boy indignantly.

Johnson could not make out why, when he talked to her, she kept jotting down items on ends of paper, the backs of envelopes, and cramming them into her hand-bag. She was sloppy—but she did not smell. "What can she have to write so much?" he wondered. "Can she really be taking notes on what I say?" The idea mildly flattered him.

He contrived to get hold of her hand-bag. They were in a tea-room. "I have to 'phone," he said, and as he rose he picked up his book and her bag underneath. In the booth, he explored the multifarious recesses, the lip-sticks, keys, compacts, handkerchiefs, address-books, coins, combs, thread, needles, matchbooks, innumerable papers. A mirror fell on the floor and broke. "Bother!" A gentleman opened the door and saw him on his hands and knees covered with powder. "Damn!" he crammed everything back into the bag.

"How tall is Martin?" he asked vindictively.

"Five foot ten inches."

"Is he dark or fair?"

"Dark, of course. I've told you a hundred times."

"I thought you might have forgotten what you said. What color eyes did you say he had?"

"Why are you asking me all these questions?" said Martin to his sister. "What difference does it make if I know who Hannibal was? Anyway I did know that, I meant just what you said. So what if I am to meet this fellow Johnson? Who's he? Does he know baseball? So what difference does it make to him if I know Hannibal?"

"You ass! I don't want you to make a total ass of yourself. Here, I've got some new bibliography."

"What's that mean?" he said in a toneless voice.

"That's books for you to read."

Frederick the Great. Sappho. *The Dialogue on the Two Systems*. Clement of Alexandria. Boswell's *Life of Johnson*. *War and Peace*. Schmutsky. (Schmutsky was the painter who made his reputation by the retrospective exhibition, "Post-Impressionism from Cézanne to Schmutsky.—Joke by Meyer Schapiro.)

It was over. Johnson had to confess it, sadly, for he really wanted to be happy, just like anybody else. He looked at the girl—she had beautiful color—without interest. She had a sympathetic manner, she was not even hostile. But his work of art had died in his hands, he didn't care whether Martin existed or didn't exist. These things had to happen just when. Or why bother? As Horace pointed out long ago, an imitation is great, or it is nothing at all.

With a mighty kick he kicked the tin waste-basket into the next room, where it fell with a tin clatter. Larissa looked at him in stupefaction, then fear, for to her he was considerate and polite, though a little distant. The life streamed into his legs, first the right, then, flooding anger, into the left. It was Leonard he wanted to kick, or whoever else it was, long ago, who had cast a blight on everything beforehand. He went inside and carefully brought back the dented waste-basket to its place. He looked at Larissa but found that he could not stand the sight of her, she looked like a parody of Leonard—or whoever it was.

"Go away," he said, and gave her a push. "Just go away. Don't you understand? the sight of you makes me sick. Good bye."

He crammed his hat on his head and went out, leaving her alone in his apartment.

"Don't you want to see *Martin?*" she wailed. "He's coming back tomorrow."

"I *want* to see him!" cried Martin hotly. "You said I was, now you're trying to back out of it."

The boy had worked himself into a passion. His sister was cooler.

"Be a reasonable boy," she said. "What do you want to see him for? You know what a man looks like, don't you. A postman, a doorman. A man. A man like any other," she added sententiously.

"Then why can't I see him? Why?"

"You can't see him because. Just because."

"For Christ's sake!" he roared. "Then *what did you tell me for?*"

"Don't shout at me, Martin. Why I told you—that's my business. Supposing you knew, how would you be better off? Now there's a question. You answer me that question and I'll answer the other question."

Martin said nothing.

"Trouble with you, Martin," she pressed her advantage, "is you think everything people do has a reason. Sometimes people do things *without* a reason."

"Ah. Did he give you a stand-up?"

"The reason I said you were to see him," she said coldly, "was that he asked to see you."

"Cut the shit. Why can't I see him?"

"Why do you *want* to see him?"

"I can answer that," said Martin quietly. "I want to see

him because he takes an interest in me. Not like those
other dodoes you bring around who wait for me to fall
through the floor so they can get you on the couch and
maul you."

She tried to slap his face, but he cracked her hand
away with his hard forearm.

"You hurt me," she said.

"You said he'd teach me things," said Martin quietly.
"Do you think I like to sit here in Sunnyside with nothing
but watch TV?"

"You can't see him because I don't want you to."

"Aha! That's what I thought. You don't want me to see
him. Why? Out with it."

"Because."

"Don't be a fool, girl. I said out with it."

"Don't you dare call me a fool."

"I didn't call you a fool, I said don't *be* a fool. Out with
it."

"Well, don't you call me a fool."

"Did Johnson call you a fool? Is that why he stood you
up?"

"Do you think I'd tell you that? No. Johnson didn't
call me a fool."

"Why don't you want me to see him?"

She said nothing.

"Out with it," he said inexorably.

"If you must know, I'm looking out for your own interests, that's why. He's no good, that's why. I don't
want you to see him because he's dangerous."

"Ahahaha! so you don't want me to meet him because
he's dangerous. Why is he dangerous?"

"Will you stop repeating everything I say? What do
you think you are, a tape-recorder?"

"Why is he dangerous?"

"Why? why? Out with it!" she mimicked him. "I try to
do something for his own good, then he asks me why."

"Why is he dangerous?"

"MUST YOU KNOW EVERYTHING?"

"Why is he dangerous?"

"All right, you asked for it. He's dangerous because
he's a pederast."

"What's that mean?" asked Martin sharply.

"God, are you ignorant! That means he makes love to boys."

"Gee?"

1933-1968

THE BIRTHDAY CONCERT

When I had finished my part of the Brahms B-flat Sonata, —a work tired for us both, but we forced our feelings,— I quietly spread my folding chair in the wing and sat down to hear Herman perform Handel's E-minor Partita for violin unaccompanied. Quietly, because I knew what the performance would be; not without gnawing anxiety at heart, nevertheless, for my friend.

It was again his birthday concert. In the crowd were our many friends, of whom some—I saw Alvin in the front row of the balcony and Husky near Exit 10, staring fixedly, like myself—some had been present at the very first one of these concerts, when Herman was seventeen. He would be thirty. It was really the eve of his birthday, the idea being for him to play till nearly midnight, and then all of us would go to a restaurant or roadhouse, to celebrate the incoming day. Loud applause crowned every number; and the warm atmosphere of the lighted hall was a patchwork of the noise of handclapping and the sounds of his violin.

The louder the applause the sadder I became. There was no longer a moment of music, neither tone, rhythm, brilliance nor insight; only notes, bars, a thin technique and nerves. But on pitch. The applause was in honor of a memory. (As for me! the sadder I became the better I played, but I could not teach this to him.) Now, in the wing, during a moment of silence, while Herman raised his bow—a void moment in which one often sees the unvarnished truth—I realized bitterly that I was now a better musician than my friend—if it is even right to consider such talents as musical. He was done for, *fichu*; he had, as we say, "shot his bolt."

He started to play, a largo introduction, a quick movement. There was not one moment, I say, when the music was played from within.

I could remember a time when each note fell crowded with mind, as it had been written down; but now the several tones without meaning slipped into cadences without meaning, and these formed no whole.

"But sometimes when I am alone," Herman insisted to me, "sometimes there is one tone that is truly bowed. Here or there, through no doing of mine, one phrase comes to life and is crowded with the composer's mind. Then we slip back. No doing of mine, one way or the other."

At the concert, I could have wept at the hollow tone and the pitiful brilliance. Of course, there was a difference between *this* bad playing, which was a fall from perfection, and just ordinary playing. In his days of fire and form, when he was twenty-six and twenty-seven, Herman had refined from his execution—I remember how he did it, week by week—every last dross of personality, rhetoric, and technique, so that the natural music glowed with a strong and unwavering light, like a flawless candle. But now, therefore, when the music itself was gone, there was nothing material to fall back on. It was all framework, no content, either personal or musical. I was surprised that any sound came forth at all.

"You see, I have lost my touch." He tried to explain where the bowhand was at fault, and how the fingers of his left hand had for some reason become "too cautious." But the change was not in his hands, but in him; what he needed was not a violin lesson, but a revival of the spirit.

With a cadenza and a flourish, he closed the first movement. There was a volley of handclapping, at which he turned toward me in the wing with a wry smile on his face. Then at once, with his head averted from the audience, as if to conceal tears—which were not there, however, so far as I could see—he struck up the largo.

I followed on a miniature score: it was the same, a faultless reading and no music. We came to the bottom of the page—I turned.

Then, at the top of the next page, in the midst of a delicate phrase, was one tone, a B-flat—

As he had said: "Sometimes there is one note truly

bowed. Here or there, through no doing of mine, one tone comes to life and is crowded with mind—" I knew him well, and as soon as he touched this B-flat dotted quarter note, I looked up from the score.

Herman played this tone again, and again, a fourth time, a fifth time, a sixth, a seventh.

The song came to a stop, like a nicked phonograph record on the same groove. The audience looked up in astonishment. Those who had been tapping the time on the arms of their chairs, found themselves with finger frozen in the air, for the note was in the middle of a bar; those who had allowed their souls to wander off in an internal revery, found themselves *fixed*, like a butterfly on a pin.

Nothing could advance this whole situation—my stare, the violinist on the platform, the throng of people in the theatre, the social life of the Americans, the imminence of violence—onto its next movement.

This uneasy peace
could not cease;

we had no power
to break this endless hour by hour.

Herman, absorbed, out of his mind, played this B-flat dotted quarter note a tenth time, an eleventh time and a twelfth time. And in his mind and in mine too, and in the minds of Alvin and Husky out front, under the influence of this one note of true music, there revived all the great moments of music that our friend had ever brought us: the Chaconne, the Vivaldi Concerto in A-flat, the Sinfonia Concertante in E-flat, the "petite phrase," the cadenza of Beethoven's Concerto,—a world recovered from one memory, as Socrates promises Meno,

for as all nature is akin, and since the soul has learned all things, nothing prevents one, if he can recollect one single thing, from finding out all the rest—

all the rest! all blooming from this one quarter note and filling the air with choral sound,—forever and ever, from this crotchet.—

No wonder that our friend, lost to the occasion and to the fact of his birthday, played a thirteenth time, a fourteenth time, this one note that brought back to him, or rather brought us back to, the realms where we had been ceasing to live.

As he played a fifteenth and a sixteenth time—to him each time it seemed with more power and more glory, but it was already only a monotonous scraping—the audience began to murmur. Several persons rose.

On the seventeenth repetition the string snapped and Herman fell down in a faint.

They rang down the curtain and there was a scene of confusion backstage, reporters taking notes and admirers crowding round; Morton-Moses wanting to know whether or not to refund the money.

I advised him to. "One note of music, even though repeated 17 times, does not make a concert."

Afterwards, the three of us got Herman outside, into my car. He was pretty much recovered, and we started up Broadway just as if nothing much had happened, for inertia always takes us a few movements further on. I kept stepping on the gas, and the others sat silent in the rear; but Herman talked in jerky sentences.

"How would *you* like to feel you're losing power?"

"Oh, this is a good motor," I said by way of a joke. But I knew the feeling, going up a hill in some of the jalopies I have driven.

"No! I mean an electric current, a telephone—" as if the particular machine made any difference. "The connection is fading. You're far. Can you hear me, Abe?" he shouted. "Hello! It's cut off." He joggled the switch.

His left hand was shaking, in tremolo.

I stayed on Broadway as it became Route 9, the Albany Post Road, north through Riverdale and Yonkers. I was driving too fast.

"There's no connection. And that big audience— they're looking. So I remember the old days. But can feelings be forced? They're dead."

"Are they? It's more likely that they are busy *else-where*. You'll hear about it later."

"Aaah. You mean that I've drained off the power by my—excesses. Hello? hello? But anyway this isn't the rea-son—not only this reason. It wasn't only for *this* reason."

This was simply idiotic. There were no such excesses. I veered sharply up a side road. We had reached Harmon, two miles this side of Croton, and it was nearly midnight. We got out at Nikko's, a roadhouse at the end of the turning. The place was moderately filled with a weeknight crowd, about fifteen couples dancing to Cuban music. We sat down at a table to celebrate and we ordered Old Fashioned cocktails.

Herman began to cry and said: "You see, my birthday always comes in a noisy restaurant, or driving across the sleeping countryside in an automobile. Then I sit back, and my friends congratulate me."

At this, a church bell in the town of Harmon rang out midnight.

"Happy birthday, friend," I said to Herman, raising my Old Fashioned, and we all drank, including Herman.

The liquor seemed to do him good, for he said, in a decided tone quite new to him, hard with conclusions and decisions: "The great fact to remember is that it is not through our own doing! These inner changes, from childhood to youth, so on and so on—it is something that happens to us! as much given as anything else. It's impossible to spend your life as a virtuoso. Well! there are some who when their bolt is shot—"

I was startled, to hear from his mouth this same expression that I had myself used.

"—there are some who when their bolt is shot, still try, still try, still try, still try—try—" he faltered and we rose. But he *did* not say it again, and he did not fall down in a faint. He said: "Just as if nothing had happened, I mean as if their bolt *hadn't* been shot! But I, friends, shall look around—" he said it suavely and with a smile on his face, relieving our tension, lightening the atmosphere, just as if he were making an after-dinner speech.

He was like a dead man.

New York City
1936

A STATUE OF NESTOR

FOR SUSAN

Of all who sailed to Troy, only one has lived to die in a bed. It is Nestor; and now he is about to die, at home in Pylos with no untoward circumstance.

This quiet sentence makes itself known like a thunderbolt in the little world ringed by the horizon. This heavy sentence of death is heard by his friends with somber joy, for we (we all are his friends) have been waiting out our generation to hear it. Shall we not send a commission to witness Nestor's death and certify that there is no untoward circumstance? Then he shall have been the proof of our hope, that it is possible to live greatly and die in peace; for he at least committed it.

As Orpheus invented harmony and Theseus established the political laws, Nestor will be the norm of our generations; but they were not quite men, being godly hybrids, while Nestor is every way a man. Therefore the unobtrusive fact, that he is about to die, breaks on all the circumscribed world like the rumbling of thunder.

King Agamemnon came home to what he had hidden behind the palace front.

Queen Helen came home to the pool in Sparta and looked in it, she was a witch.

The character of Achilles was not to go there, yet in the end he perished in the butchery like Priam.

The giant Ajax went mad. And forever and ever Ulysses twisted his mind and, as poets have said, he cannot now remain but is drowning in a twisting wave.

So the vortex of violence has engulphed every soul that crossed to Troy. Only Nestor knows the right raft.

Perhaps the *fierce* joy of the friends of Nestor—all of us are his friends!—is that this living reproach to us will no longer *be* there. When he dies, we will say *Oof!* It is the kind of lightning that clears the atmosphere.

But there are persons in agony, driven by fates and furies, who cannot afford the luxury of cheap resentments and have come humbly and hungrily to Pylos to hear a useful word.

In the anteroom there is such a rout that you would think it was again the gluttonous suitors. Representatives of the cities are continually arriving, under commission to observe whether there is not an untoward circumstance that can be taken as even a symbolic or oracular violence. (I myself am one of these representatives.) Some are gathered in a knot about the physician, Machaon. Others are eating. Everywhere are hushed conversations, but a large crowd makes a buzz.

This crowd of the friends of Nestor wishes that Nestor would die *soon*, the better to avert any untoward circumstance.

Almost *we* are the untoward circumstance, by whom Nestor cannot die at his own time in peace.

"In the end he will *fail* to die and be rapt away like Oedipus."

"We'll be back next year."

"What role did he play at Troy? He was a kind of adviser."

"Yes, by that time he was already old. The time he fought was during the preceding generation, shoulder to shoulder with Pirithoüs."

"Nobody took his advice."

"He foresaw this. He gave the advice so they could rush to their doom with their eyes open and not be foolish as well as demented."

The rout is not disrespectful, but just as at a funeral a large crowd makes a buzz.

In this home there are four generations of Nestorides. The son Antilochus (some say there is no such person, for he died at Troy—this I must check), even in the time of Troy they called him "a second Nestor," when he won the chariot race. Anyway, he is nowhere to be seen.

But the grandson Neleus is a man in his early thirties like myself, and I think that I know what he is thinking, standing alone against a wall:

"Either these persons are fools, taken in by a public reputation; or, what is more likely, this is a public demonstration for a public reputation, and my home has become a place of fraud."

In thirty years the grandson of this famous wisdom has heard him say mostly commonplace things, sometimes grudgingly and hesitantly, sometimes in garrulous profusion. More rarely the old man made a violent paradox, as though he were trying to be witty. Once or twice, however, he said something that seemed to be the motto and oriflamme of a new age; then Neleus recognized with a thrill of pride the blow of the decayed power. But he cannot see (as I find it hard to see) that all these sayings might be equally true together.

He sees that his own father abdicated and ceased to be, as if swallowed up by the old serpent. (It is said that Antilochus died at Troy shielding the old man with his body.) The grandson lived as a child in a family whose hieratic forms he did not comprehend. (I had no father.)

Meantime there is a fourth generation, another Nestor, growing up and crowding him from below. And still the ancient serpent is not dead! Do we not have the right to resent this, that we are so soon being crowded out of life? He wants to shout, attracting all ears in the sudden silence, *"There are furies also in this house!"* He begins to say in a high and strange voice, "You say that there is nothing untoward—"

(Would this have been an untoward incident? No, this is the case in every house.)

But standing across in the doorway is Orestes the son of Clytemnestra, a young man like ourselves. With Nestoride discretion, we do not compare our situation with his, our potential furies with his actual furies. Is it living in the house of Nestor that makes just this difference? Abashed, we stifle the outcry and bow to grandfather's guest friend.

Now a quick silence falls, as when the light breeze suddenly departs and leaves the water glassy smooth. On the arm of the physician of Troy appears the old man Nestor. Let us see: no posture in the doorway, no anxious glance around. Good. But what! does he not even seem to shrug his shoulders at the peculiar scene? Is his gesture the commonplace, or the violent paradox, or the motto of the new age?

From time to time, in my notes, there is a blank.

Raising the cup of wine, he says in a clear tired voice the following prayer:

"To the Creator:

"And to Mother Earth and the Sky, not ringed by the horizon, they are the horizon:

"And to my great-great-grandparents Time and Flow, the Serpent swallowing his tail, and the Swallowing by the serpent of his tail. Men are free in the age of gold, and there is no threat of a change. He has a scythe to sever that duration. His children are being savagely devoured one by one:

"And to Compensation and the Bones and the Blood and Holiness and Heat and Nourishment and Vision:

"And to the Gods, who have authority in art and nature:

"And to the Giants in the earth and in the soul:

"And to the Heroes—(I myself was a comrade shoulder to shoulder with Theseus who slew the mixed man in the south):

"And to the Tragic Men, those who sailed with King Agamemnon and those who did not sail and also those who dwelt in Troy, for rage made no distinction of them all who acted in their own persons what they did not know they knew:

"And to their Furious Sons:

"—To them all I give thanks that I am what I am."

He poured the drink and without another word or sign (there is here a blank) he was moving on the lawn toward the sea, waiting always for Ulysses to come.

· · ·

An excited buzz rises among the glossarists:

"By Time and Flow I take it he means Saturn and Rhea; but what are the Bones, the Blood, etc.?"

"Iapetus and the original Ocean in our bodies, whereby we first jumped out on the land like frogs. By Compensation he means Themis. These are all the Titans."

"Easy for *him* to know where he is at!" cries one fellow in a loud and bitter voice. "In these few generations he can count back to his great-grandfather the Time. What about us who have lost the count, and all we know is that there was miscegenation on miscegenation?"

"Is the confusion his, my boy, or yours?"

In blank horror the young man Neleus has been staring at the ancient serpent looming before him, involving us all in his coils and placidly chewing his own tail in his egotistical mouth. He could hear nothing further than the threat: "The Serpent swallowing his tail, and the Swallowing by the serpent of his tail."

I fell to the ground, gasping "Air! air!"

They hasten to loosen his clothing.

—When we are lulled into awaking out of sleep (for there is a more regular rhythm than these nightmares), it is to look up, lying head in her lap, into a wondrous timeless face, time-ravaged, such a face as could be maiden, mother, queen,

Maiden Mother Queen
Goddess.

Ulysses

But the python Nestor slowly unwinding his haggard coils is sliding down to the sea. Shining, more brilliant than fire, each scale wide as a mirror framed in gilt and verdigris, in which a man might see himself.

The voice of Ulysses is gasping and wailing, "Poseidon! *Ai!* Poseidon—Poseidon—" The dragging weight of the water is falling back to the deep, but his claws are clutched in the weeds of the rocks.

He can no longer see the world as it appears, except a shiny world a man's length away, for the salt tears and the salt sweat blinds him; the brine of the exterior sea is dashed in his face as he wipes it; and a fourth kind of salty blindness is blood in the eyes. The shiny wall by day is streaked with rainbows, but by night it is a gulph of woe.

The music of the sea does not have the harmony of the tetrachord of Orpheus; nor would you distinguish out of it the pitch, the timbre, and the volume, the booming and hissing tones; but the beat is distinct.

This is the Dialogue of Ulysses and Nestor:

"Which gave the wiser advice at Troy?"

—Among the Greeks at Troy it was thought that Nestor had a honeyed tongue. All the while he was giving a dry recital of the facts of the case in the fewest possible words. And how can the nature of the case fail to charm? it has such order and plausibility; it is almost persuasive; it is so unburdened by the tiresome details of the expedient that it seems to fly; yet it has the curious, pleasant complexity of the irrelevant. Sometimes when Nestor spoke they broke into laughter, the laughter not of ridicule but of delight. He said what was, it was absurd.

—Captain Ulysses knew them one and all, and in a few blunt words beside the point he advised them according to what they did not as yet know they wanted. He called this his collection of rainbow tales. Nevertheless, in the comedy of the war, his advice was often good enough, because the adversaries shared with each other the same crazy ideas.

Ai! Ai! Poseidon—Poseidon— Wherever is a crevice the salt sea is flooding in. The ripples in their thousands are passing like a great thought over a great face.

This is more of the dialogue of Ulysses and Nestor:

"Which is the more violent man?"

—I violent? gulps the baleful Python. How can it be? I hold the opinion that 'everything is what it is and not another thing.' Therefore I address myself to each thing in itself . . . in turn . . . On this principle I have swallowed whole three generations of mortal men.

—I do not even address myself to things, insinuates the

Old Man of the Sea. I politely pass in between them, wherever is a crevice. I do not make a gory mess.

—Neither do I make a gory mess.

—Neither of us makes a gory mess.

Aiaiaiaiaiai.

The ripples are arrested, in a black frown. On the streaming swell (the waters are flowing in sheets down the mountainous swell), the man is eased, loosed from his despairing clutch of the weeds.

"Nestor! Father Nestor! help me. . . . *Ai* Poseidon—Poseidon—"

Oh, if that frightening Python also would uncoil his folds and continue on his way and slide into the boiling foam! But what did I expect? that it would *not* be monstrous to have descended into Hell with Theseus, and held the hand of raving Ajax, and to be a father to Orestes—and still live on?

The Theory of Non-Commitment

The dilemma of non-commitment is evident: that not to commit oneself to doing or not doing a thing is the same as committing oneself to not doing it, for it is not done. Either one commits himself to do the thing (and in fact does do it), or he has committed himself to its not being done, even though he has not committed himself to not do it.

Therefore the man who would make a non-commitment must do so positively. He must not merely refrain, but must invent new circumstances in the issue, a sharper form of the issue, so that even after he has not committed himself either to do or not do, and so faces the consequences of not doing, nevertheless the consequent issue is not settled after all, but *it* must still face the issue of whether or not he will commit himself. Thus if, as is often the case, a man is non-committal because he does not want the issue to be settled at this time or in this form, he does not retreat from it or merely look on, but advances to a quite different position from which, when all seems to be over and done, he is still forcing the issue essentially, and is non-committal. Certainly it requires a man of resources to invent the "new circumstances"; but it is just such a man who is dissatisfied in the first place with the issue as ordinarily presented. If he brings into the open the grounds of his dissatisfaction, he soon finds in them "new circumstances" and the principle of a new non-committal position. This, then, is *aggressive non-commitment*, which looks like a commitment not to do, yet *still* remains non-committally alive.

Contrary to this is the method which proceeds from an apparent commitment to do (or to not do), yet still is non-committal: this is the *limited commitment*. It is used by the non-committal man, dissatisfied, in the following cases: when it seems that nature or history cannot present the issue except in these unpromising alternatives (to me this seems unlikely); or when it is likely that the issue will clarify itself but he is not master enough of the situation to force it to do so by an aggressive non-commitment; or best, when he judges that the true issue is actually involved in the presented issue as in a matrix. Then, as the issue clarifies, he can still become non-committal. But the danger is that, though he commits himself with a limitation, the force of his commitment (to do or to not do) is positive and definitive, he becomes too involved. No; for the person of resources can occupy such a position by his limited commitment that unless the issue clarifies itself to his satisfaction the issue proves (by his doing) not to be committed after all. He can inhibit it.

If he has no resources, and can neither invent new circumstances nor occupy a potentially inhibiting position —how does such a person claim to be a non-committal man, and dare not to commit himself to issues like everybody else?

Thus, alternately, aggressively non-committing himself and committing himself with an inhibiting limitation, the non-committal man undergoes a life-gradual growth to his absolute commitment. He is Nestor.

Helen

Lulled forth from slumber by rhythm, the young man falls awake and opens wide his eyes to look into the face of Queen Helen.

His head is between her knees and she is stroking his forehead.

They are conversing in whispers. She is crooning "Lullee lullay," and her voice comes from that deep place where the nerves are knotted that, when you hear it, the apparent world is ringed in gold and the five senses are standing equally at their distances, in the air, at attention.

The persons in the room he sees, upward from below, large and clear as if they were at no distance; and he hears their conversation close to his ear. He is not out of this world.

But what are *they* whispering, the two? Mostly she is singing that new aubade: *Lullee*—

> lullee thou tiny little child,
> awake! lullee lullay.

And she says:

"Is it not unwise for Grandfather to piece out our world so, into those Titans and Gods, and Giants and Heroes, and the Tragic Men and their Furious Sons; and not say further that these are all the creatures of love that revives the grass?

"The easy flooding of longing needs no urging, it is itself the urging—little child, it has the forms of resentment, jealousy, murderous wrath; disgust, guilt, self-castigation; impotence, cruelty, scrupulousness, inconsequence, emptiness: all of these (I read them off at random in my heart) are forms of love. No matter where you longingly look about—turning to each thing after it has struck—you see the cause of your dismay, is love.

"But if you shut your eyes—lullee—you will see these things coming friendly toward you like the countryside whose trees are sprouting flowers, and the reappearance of the grass.

"Don't cry, little child, don't cry, and I shall tell you what I have seen: I have seen Tantalus eating grapes, and the daughters of Danaus easily bringing the water!

"Do you think it is a hard thing to stretch out a hand? See, stretch out to me your hand. So. And cannot great King Tantalus stretch out his hand and eat?

"I have seen a lover wish her beloved well and speak to him kindly and with regard for him, and without thinking of his death, and take delight in their pleasures together without fear and be confident of herself, easy at heart, and full of thoughts, and congratulating herself on her good fortune, and judging rightly—all these are the forms of love. Do you think it is hard for a lover to wish well to a beloved?"

So whispers Queen Helen, stroking his forehead, his head between her knees, stroking his forehead, and lulling him forth from slumber by rhythm—He falls awake.

He falls awake, and it is the witch Phorkyas, the time-ravaged lust, of whom they cried out in despair: "Let her go! let her *go!*" She has come here.

Orestes

"You do not see them, but I see them."

It is the saying of Orestes when his furies stir and wake. I do not think it is by arrogance that he distinguishes himself from us. But at the risk of saying what is peculiar, he is making an effort, he is making an effort to speak according to common notions. The next moment he cannot make this effort and he sadly calls out, not in English.

As when a demented man, who sees every person as a hound-dog, comes to the physician and tries to explain to him his hallucination, but the physician is sitting in front of him a hound-dog: he cannot help but call out.

I do not think it is by any arrogance that he distinguishes himself from us. We in turn, stupefied to see how he is, do not compare to it our life-gradual growth into fury. We also falter back a step.—"Perhaps I ought to try to convince him that nothing is there," says the very person at whom Orestes is looking with peculiar horror.

"*I* see them," says the old man Nestor (it seems to me that there is arrogance in his voice), "for there are Furies also in my house.

"*Good* dogs—*down*, lady! down, miss! *down*, now. There's good dogs."

With a wink he says, out of the corner of his mouth, "I'm a good caller. Sometimes I dance along with 'em.—" He falters back a step. *Aiii!*

"*Down*, miss; DOWN!—

"Why not? Everything—" he is gasping—"is what it is"—in a voice of anguish—"and not another thing."

These wails and gasps he is now accompanying by a regular beat of his right foot on the fourth count: 1 2 3 4. But when he comes to dance himself, it will be in the self-contained abandon of choriambs.

The figure he is calling is the Gracious Host Speeding His Guests (as if we were taking our departure and not he):

> "Again soon! friends! let us see you,
>   calm in our house the furies around you,
>   make one of our days happy with you
>   again and soon!—

"There's good dogs. There, there—lullee. Orestes?"
"Sir?"

> "Our prowling silent furies play
>   with your ferocious dogs away.
>   Let us renew the holiday
>   again and soon.

"Yes, sir."

> "We'll teach by practices of order
>   these dogs to dance outside the border,
>   and speak of peace instead of murder
>   again and soon.

"Orestes?"
"Sir?"
"*Give* me your dogs.—Come, yelpers. What! 's there not flesh in me enough to make one bite? I'll dance with ye. Why not? Everything is what it is."

He calls savagely:

"We'll fiercely dance the dance together
    of the men and dogs in gather
    that formerly fled one another!"

And now Nestor dances with the dogs. He is dancing the dance of the Hounds and the Man. This sight most of us do not want to see. We turn our eyes to the wall. Some of us hide our faces in our cloaks. One or two of us are looking humbly and hungrily on.

These yelps and snarls—these commitments—are not English. What does it mean?

It means that the past with its curse is still blessed.

Therefore I cling like death to what I might forget. It has brought me at last to not less than I am.

The tiredness slips from my shoulders like thunder.

It means that the past with its curse is still blessed and has brought me at last to not less than I am. The tiredness slips from my shoulders like thunder.

"What is it with you?" he says to us, "why am I calling the figures if so few are willing to join in? If you will not dance socially with my furies, why have you come so far to the deathbed of old Nestor?" This quiet sentence—is pounding in every heart like the rumble of thunder.

"To the Creator and his commitment: and to my Fury-Dogs: and to Courage."

When I consider how again again and again I have, with my strongest will and my best ingenuity, maneuvered myself into the same impasse, then I say, "I know this place; why do I not consider it beforehand and cure the error that will bring me here again and again until it is too late?" But this correction, to be sure, is just what I cannot make.

If *once,* with manly courage and clear principle, I should face my fear through and act my role out, if not with faith at least with art! then perhaps I could be done with the repetition. But I cannot propose to myself some other way than the same temptation day by day unvarying that is all my resources. The way is the difficult ease.

Logia of Nestor

I.

"He wishes to speak to his family." The physician lays a finger across our lips, for there is little breath left in Nestor.

Nestor says to them, "Goodbye to you, little Likely. Let's play the game of statues."

The small child does not make a sound when he sits back motionless, and we also do not.

Nestor said: "In my household, if for a day I was perfectly good and easy, then insensibly but swiftly this easiness turned into a stone statue."

He said: "To a young man, to be true to himself is the way of difficult ease; afterward it is easy but it is not the way."

The Master said: "During the first generation I committed myself, during the second I was non-committal, during the third I made limited commitments."

Coming to Achilles' tent he found him seated on a stone staring out to sea, and he said: "If you are waiting for remorse or any other feeling to stir in somebody else's heart, you must choose a comfortable seat; remember, he is occupied, you are not; your long time is not the same as his long time."

Of Ulysses Nestor said: "He is reasonable in everything but desire; he is quick at attaining everything but his ends; he is resigned to everything but living on a little."

During the butchery after the fall of the city, Nestor said: "This is what no one wills and all desire."

He used to say: "To have the useful is good, to have the needful is best."

Said: "The word that heals as it violates."

The Master was an observer of natural things and noticing the parallax of moving things he remarked: "The nearground backward flies, but the background onward, unless farther back you take a grander background to refer to. To see all move look to the sky."—This is why, pretending to be garrulous, he used to mention Theseus and Pirithoüs.

II.

The Master said: "Clear to loneliness on his hilltop ringed by the hills shines the way of difficult ease! Among the people he does not forget it, but his divided heart is darkly boiling: Therefore he cannot take the wandering step ordained with the beginning of the world, nor stretch the hand whereby the heavy things fall of their own weight, nor speak the word that heals as it violates."

He asked: "To use the power by which each thing is what it is, stored there from the beginning of the world, is this the way?

"What is the way?" said the Master. "During the first generation I learned to be true to myself; during the second generation I achieved immortality; during the third generation I lived at home;—*still* I have not found the way." Asked concerning immortality, the Master replied: "It is to draw on the I-creating energy." Asked concerning living at home, he replied: "It is the art of dancing with one's furies."

It is said that when he exclaimed, "*Still* I have not found the way!" he became invisible in the room; and at this moment he was riding the whirlwind. Most often he was inconspicuous where he sat, and silent and light as the breeze when he moved, for his behavior was without indecisive gestures and divided intentions.

III.

It is said that the Master assumed many forms. In the form of a python he ringed the horizon with his tail in his mouth.

The Master said: "What is the use of dancing? I should have lived when several suns sailed through heaven, before he swallowed them down; then there was light enough in the world and it was possible to judge by shadows. When the mountains had not settled it was possible by art to bring a heavy body down. When the Gorgons were wailing, there was a use in honeyed speech. What is the use of balance when all is flattened out? What is the use of dancing?"

He used to say: "Each moment is the end result."

At Troy when the Ethiop Memnon pressed him close and Antilochus shielded him with his body, it is said that Nestor revived him from the dead lest there be an imperfection in his own household.

The Master said: "What is the use of dancing? It is no longer the way."

It is said that he could make the branches blossom before one's eyes.

He used to say: "The word that heals as it violates."

Finished at Quaker Hill
1939-1944

THE COMMODITY
EMBODIED IN BREAD

　　　　　　　※　　A commodity is therefore a mysterious
　　　　　　　thing simply because—

　　　　　　　　　　　　　　　　CAPITAL, BOOK I, I, 4

FOR BEN

At the super market, a certain prospective purchaser was
frantic, pale and flushing by turns, and alternately
clutching to himself and holding out a two-dollar bill,
which everyone knows to be unlucky. It was Mr. Impetigo! the same as once bought a dozen gross of scissors
to benefit by the wholesale price, and so always had many
scissors lying around. He was thrifty on a lavish scale. But
today he wanted only a single metal stew pot.

The trouble was—it was really in Impetigo's bad education, his aggressive sociology—but the *proximate* trouble was that a little sprocket seemed to have been dislo-
cated in the machinery of the Economy. The Aluminum
Company of America (*Alcoa*) had just advertised new
kitchenware: "these utensils will wear forever"; "they will
shine on the wall"; "no dirt in the curves of an aluminum pot." The advertisement ran a page in aluminum
paint in *The Saturday Evening Post*; and it aroused in
Impetigo's breast—as in whose not?—a strong desire to
purchase such a pot.

On the *same Tuesday,* however, the Company withdrew all this line from production, distribution, and sale.
This was because it was essential to set this metal aside
for the National Defense.

Here, then, was the *zealous* Mr. Impetigo in a moment of frustration—

He cried, "I want the pot with the Titegrip cover—"

The counter girl said, "The Boy Scouts will collect your aluminum on the Fourth of July."

But this actual frustration was not what was making Impetigo so frantic, bringing him to the edge of what is called a "nervous breakdown." After all, he really needed the stewing pot, and actual impasses lead at worst to physical, not mental, disorders. Rather, it was the horrors of the imagination! Mr. Impetigo did not drive, but he knew well that the night service at Texaco Gasoline Stations is a refreshing pause for the motorist who, after weary riding through the rain, can *count on* a cheerful greeting. But the fact *also* was that it was forbidden to sell gasoline after sunset and every station was closed and dark. Now imagine—one need not imagine it, it was in a memorable picture—the anxious motorist on the road, his lights glaring in the pelting rain; but he thinks that *round the next turn* (as the ad said) there will be comfort, ha—And *there would be no comfort!*

Mr. Impetigo was an economist. On the one hand he saw with satisfaction that the advertising was becoming keener: the people were responding to it with enthusiasm; there was nothing that everybody did not want and indeed did not absolutely need to have. What a flow of the Commodities this promised! On the other hand, he saw with dismay that mere money was inadequate.

The face of the economist went white—

II.

It is a pleasure to turn from this little frenzy to the serene and cheerful confidence of Mr. Tobias Thomas, who was also at the Market on this Tuesday evening.

With a smile of *amusement* Tobias watched the anxiety of Impetigo under his Panama hat.

"Give me a loaf of bread," he said to the girl with easy assurance.

"Here it is, it is eleven cents," said the blonde merchant,

producing from the shelf the shining waxen wrapper given form and body by the doughy mass within.

"Is it eleven cents?" asked Tobias, knowing it well, but drawing out even this preliminary with a certain piety.

"Eleven cents."

"*Here* is the money!" said the man quietly, and laid down a dime and a cent on the counter.

Obviously this act, of Exchange, had a certain sacramental character—But no! for look, instead of resting in the moment, or expressing any ecstasy whatsoever, Tobias leaned confidentially across the counter and said in a low voice: "Now, Miss, supposing I wanted to change this bread, eh? Supposing my wife wanted a different brand?"—

This was apparently absurd! The package was Silver-Sup, the same as he bought every day, and that was advertised on the radio by a famous horse. There was no doubt that this was the package.

"You may bring it back if you haven't broken the wrapper," said the businesslike girl.

Ah! Now Toby took up his purchase, whose waxen wrapper, stamped with the name Silver-Sup Silver-Sup and an equine design, was secondarily protected in a manila bag; and he left the Market.

The reader would have thought—is it not so?—that the moment when the man Bought and Paid For the Commodity was the pregnant moment: the moment charged with invisible power to move and keep in motion the two billion human inhabitants of the world and many dumb beasts; to call into being their tools, conveyances, and—in imitation of the First Day itself—their lights. This was indeed a moment! it rested on a mystery. Yet Tobias, though assuming, as we have seen, a decent demeanor in the face of the Exchange, was an orthodox believer and reserved his *unlimited* awe for the consummation of the mystery itself, the breaking of the wrapper.

There is a form of heresy—perhaps Mr. Impetigo was such a heretic—that rests its faith *in* circulation rather than *by* circulation. Fascinated by the rapid, the accelerating, exchanges—a study which could indeed distract even an acute mind with its intricacy—these persons vainly imagine that such quasi-visible goings-on are the force which keeps us all as we are and which therefore merits our *deepest* meditation. Once I described a hero of this heresy of Exchangism, the Eliphaz, who sought to turn all his property into money and wrote down his abomination in the *Book of Endlessly Accumulating Zeroes Without an Integer*. But in the end, these persons are Money-changers.

The essential mystery is simple. It does not require of us subtility, like that of Mr. Impetigo, nor heroic inventiveness, like the Eliphaz; but it is for ordinary persons.

On the way home, Tobias once opened the mouth of the manila bag and looked inside. The brown bag had absolutely no primary significance; it was even given away gratis to all who participated in the social acts. There was none too poor to be given a paper bag. The transcendent wrapper was the wrapper of the commodity itself.

Leaning in the doorway of the Apartment house and smoking a pipe in the sunset, Toby saw G. A. Jensen, the Scandinavian janitor with his walrus mustaches. The two exchanged a cheerful greeting. "Good evening," they said. Tobias, the tenant, liked Gustavus Adolphus, who serviced the building and analyzed the Garbage.

But if he knew the truth he might have been disturbed, for the fact was that the Swede was a natural philosopher; with little or no belief whatsoever.

The Apartment house—so named because all the units were enclosed apart—was an imposing structure of six stories with four Apartments on each. The stories were designated by numerals, the Apartments on each by the letters A, B, C, D.

Tobias dwelt with his family in Apartment 3 C in the rear.

These Apartments were rented on the Market, and each painted afresh for its new tenants. When the Lease was signed, they moved in; they scratched the paint and the Apartment was then considered out of circulation.

Round the table of Tobias Thomas, besides the master and his wife, were the three children it was necessary for each pair to beget, taking account of accidents.

The eldest, John, understood that when the hermetically sealed package is opened, the goods is out of circulation.

The middle child, June, knew that the package was bought for money at the Market.

The youngest was too small to have any understanding, but shouted "bru-le-bullah! bru-le-bullah!" meaning "bread and butter."

Mimi Caffrey Thomas, the wife of Tobias, prepared a shining white platter, with a border of gilt panels containing carmine roses with pale green leaves, to receive decently the whited and rather worthless body of the Commodity after it was taken out of circulation.

Tobias raised aloft the Bread.

—At this reach of inwardness, it is necessary to observe verbal niceties. When I speak of the Bread with a majuscule B, it is the Bread par excellence (*eminenter*) that stood on the counter. There is no doubt that this was the same Bread that Tobias now held in his two hands; for *all* of us may, with our animal hands, *lay hold* on the Commodity in some shape or other. At the same time we must speak, with a b-minuscule, of bread as mere bread. This is to speak physically (*naturaliter*), but there is no help for it, for in the end all language has this natural origin. This bread is, of course, worthless.

Ought we then to refer to the physical bread perhaps as "bread," in quotation marks? No! this arrogance, which *seems* to free our society from material bonds, in reality robs from us the wonder and the glory of our existence, which is just that *we,* as we are, not "we" in quotation marks, somehow do lay hold of the Bread. It seems innocent to say "bread" in quotation marks: it is Docetism. But follow it through! and it is *Exchangism* and the doctrine of the *Book of Endless Zeroes Without an Integer*. It is frenzy and no peace.

In the end we must keep steadily in mind the words of Marx: "The Commodity is therefore a *mysterious* thing."

Again he says: "When it steps forth—" he is referring to the physical table, the physical bread—"when it steps forth as a Commodity, it is changed into something transcendent.

"The existence of the things *qua* Commodities . . .

has absolutely no connection with their physical proper-
ties and with the material relations rising therefrom."

Tobias tore the wrapper of the loaf of bread, and the
exchange-value departed from the Commodity.

This sacrament—this service—this sacrifice of the real
being of the Commodity—*sealed* and *revivified* the identification of Tobias and his family with the unity of the
imperial Economy.

So long as every one of us can partake of this death,
earning by arduous works the *fact* that the Commodity is destroyed for us, the Economy is secure and will not
degenerate into chaos. The exchange-value has vanished!
The system of exchange is reborn! By this ever renewed
fact the several billions of the world find occupation for
their time and the order of the classes is maintained.

Let me repeat it: the exchange-value departs, and at
this same instant, the Exchange value is potentially given
again.

In this simple service the family found peace, having
bought and in the relevant sense consumed. How different this is from the torment of the Impetigos and the
Eliphazes, raging in the Market and their hearts pounding at the late Figures, as if this were the only service!
But they do not put their trust in the system.

The Eliphaz, intent on changing all the capital into interest, regarded the ultimate consumption, of which we
have just seen an exemplary observance, as the original
sin! In his delusion, he thought that he could divest
himself of the creative physicality of being human.

It was seven P.M., and over the radio sounded the loud
whinny of the famous horse himself, whose name was
Silver.

The buzzer of the dumbwaiter rang, for the Garbage;
and the mother rose to put on the day's refuse, including
the waxen wrapper which was now, of course, an insig-
nificant husk.

"Garbage!" sang up the voice of Gustavus Adolphus through the long shaft. The buzzers were sounding also in 1 C, 2 C, 4 C, 5 C, 6 C.

The small child was greedily stuffing a slice of the white bread into its mouth, and Tobias, with fatherly indulgence, was buttering another slice to follow that.

Perhaps I can say something of this physical bread: It had the potential *virtue* of being quantifiable, in pounds and ounces, for the estimation of the Price. Further, it had the convenience (*convenientia*) of being malleable in lumps or loaves, for the purpose of purchase across the Counter and conveyance. It was destructible, tending to harden, rot, or be devoured, so that it presented no temptation (*scandalum*) to Hoarding. At the same time it was rare, so that unlike the air or earth of which it was composed, it offered an incentive (*fundamentum spei*) to be made the embodiment of the Commodity.

Gustavus Adolphus Jensen was a Garbage Analyst.

This science, sorting out the elements into a battery of cans, he pursued partly for the sake of the Economy, reclaiming the precious foils and metals, and the fats and the bones. But mostly he studied the Garbage just to pry and to know.

This, like all learning, gave him *power* over every single Apartment.

He was a natural philosopher and did not judge the bread in terms of its sociological virtues. But not believing this, he fell into superstitions of his own: for instance, he was a believer in the Vitamins.

A little Swede with walrus mustaches, he stood beneath a feeble light in the basement, cautious, often using a tongs or tweezers. Slit the manila bags up their backs, picked a pair of spectacles from among the grounds and eggshells, and drew off the serums in syringes. The midges flew toward the light, and Gustav had a little monkey who, curling her tail round a pipe, delighted in snatching the insects from the air.

These were the revealing remnants of private lives.

Sometimes in the Garbage of 1 C he found her golden wedding ring, which he discreetly placed in the mail box.

2 C *never sent down any Garbage at all.* But it was only an Exchangist, intent on turning *all* his property into fungible goods and storing it up against the Day.

Every evening Gustav shook his head disapprovingly when he found the wrapper stamped Silver-Sup Silver-Sup. It was his belief that 3 C would be wiser to buy instead the ochre wrapper of Lugan's Gluten, on which was plainly stamped the formula "1200 units vit. B1, USP."

—But the great time was Monday morning when descended bales and bales of the *Sunday Times* and nothing else besides!

The monkey had the face of a malicious old person, alert and lively without any curiosity. Sometimes she stood with her long tail drooped over one arm, like the train of a dress. At other times she arranged her tail in a perfect circle on the floor and squatted in the middle of it.

New York City
1941

THE ARCHITECT
FROM NEW YORK

FOR PERCY

I.

The town, he noted, was founded in the 17th century and grew rapidly till it slowed down; but it continued to grow slowly and became a substantial center in the valley. Since 1935 it was again growing rapidly. The Berkshires were flaming red and yellow, like a Roman triumph. As the train pulled in, the architect, without his roll and brief case, felt the excitement he had felt from a child whenever he came to a new place. To take it in! Now he did it with a practiced eye—nobody in America knew more about it. There were rarely any surprises, nothing he had not predicted from a few notes of history and studying a few statistics. Even so, if he felt well, as he did sometimes, his wondering excitement might last for a couple of hours; for there is a difference between knowing all about some one and actually meeting her. This evening he felt well and glad to be out of New York. He was Harry Hodges, and here was she, the town.

Low on the horizon the October sun poured through the big trees. There were still big trees even down at the station. Of course in such magical light any place looked lovely, strange. He was pleased that he had a couple of free hours to look and have dinner, alone. He was to meet the building committee at 8:30. Daylight Saving Time, thought Harry, was a good idea because the clear day of dusk was strange. (But when he returned with his roll and his brief case—for they would accept his terms, they always did; and he would take the job, he always did —nothing would be strange, except the art.)

By god, the town had a shape! Harry's breathless relief was like an adolescent's when the blind date turns out to be pretty. A quarter of a mile from the station was a fine green square, bordered by the usual remarkable big maples, with the wooden bandstand well placed off center, the lawn poorly kept. And there was an absurdly small iron fountain, like a prim belle, that—what a contrast to Italy!—had in it all a world of New England shame and sweetness; as if it were sinful to lavish wealth on useless decoration, yet God thought that a pool was proper and there is many such a living eye in Scripture. Harry doubted that any brasses blared from that bandstand any more on Saturday nights in summer; but it was likely still gay and busy on July Fourth and perhaps on the anniversary of Lexington.

It was quite as usual for a New England town like this to have a shape and to have this shape. Why was our friend so moved by it? It was that he had been traveling too much abroad, where *every* town, whether in France or Italy, or Ireland, or even Latin America, had a shape that you could grasp and read off the social history. When you left, you knew that you had been somewhere. But returning home, he would go to our American towns, in the South or Middle West—for his churches had won a peculiar reputation as something "special," like Sunday itself, and he was asked to build in all parts; and then he was struck with dismay to see how we have neglected ourselves. The filling stations, the five and ten, the diner, not so much poorly located as with never a thought of location; and the shameful immodesty of the billboards and the neon. He sometimes became so down in the mouth that he could not eat.

He was hungry. He cut across the green toward a high veranda that must once have been "the" hotel, though certainly no longer the biggest and best in a town of this size. And while he walked across that green, in Harry Hodges' breast welled up his plain duty and made him choke, and his ears were aflame. He was bursting with pride. *He,* Harry Hodges, would see to it that the Middle

Western towns of America got a shape. If not he, who?
(What shape?) He ought to; he was *going* to! He had
energy, he swung weight, he had the means of the American Institute of Architects. His countrymen would make
him a statue in the park. . . . On the left was a statue of
James Warren.

Harry's step was light but lagging in meditation, as he
cut under the maples across the ragged lawn toward dinner, while the big sun was touching the horizon and flaming in the glass windows.

II.

Surprisingly, in the shadows he was confronted by a monumental building on his right, that he had not noticed although it dominated the New England square, as it
should, for it was a church. The church had scale. It was
small and looked big.

Despite its absurd premise of being "Gothic," the architect could not resist a smile of approval. Maybe it was
only the dusk and the magical clear air but, really, the
church was very good. Maybe it was that it was surprisingly Gothic of 1875 and quite out of place; and of course
it was not out of place at all, and certainly not Gothic at
all, but the yearning of an individual Romantic for some
richness and color in New England 1875. Who? For a
moment Harry racked his brain for the architect's name.
He was annoyed, for it was a famous name that he knew
perfectly well. He paused and became aware that he was
smiling with recognition, and with unembarrassed formal-
ity he nodded his head to the other master. And why
shouldn't he go in and visit, since he had come?

This was odd to do, in America. When we are in
Europe, we walk into every little church, partly because
we're there for that, but partly because we know that *in*
there, however humble the building, we are likely to be
astounded by some imperishable gesture of spirit, an al-
tarpiece, a window, a sepulchral effigy. We come on
Moses in San Pietro in Vincoli and say, "For heaven's
sake!" In our country, we have not had so many cen-

turies to scatter human treasures around, nor, in the time we have had, have we given our genius lavishly to this.

The pointed half-shutters of a side entrance were flung wide, like cardboard angel's wings, and Harry entered.

To his astonishment, the last rays of sunlight flamed into his eyes through a window of Charley Tiffany's, made long ago when that artist was first inventing the glass and was inspired by the angel pre-Raphael. The sheep in the picture were comical and Jacob looked like a divine oaf, and the beads of the border were gurgling and shouting in the light like a one-year-old for joy. The glass window was heavenly innocent as, in that period, was possible *only* in America. Harry was unable even to smile, for his eyes misted over. He blinked them. The sun set and the twilight came rapidly on.

Naturally a roomful of Charley Tiffany's early work, before he became a manufacturer and a patron of the arts, was a rare experience. Even in the rapid gloaming the glass gave off color. Electric lights went on; and as he unhurriedly went up one aisle and down the other, studying the pictures, Harry was like that fellow who lay down just to take a nap but fell asleep; he had come in just to have a look, but he became absorbed in what he saw.

Who? Who? He kept trying to recall the name of the architect. Nixon? Roberts? He knew that it was the master himself and not a disciple, for it had the original definition: the arbitrary Gothic turning at once into a robust Romanesque, full of feeling, and discovering in the stone Romanesque a new Romanesque of masonry that would soon appear, in vast spans, in the secular buildings of Louis Sullivan and Adler. The onset of modern construction. 1875—certainly around 1875—he wouldn't be off by five years; but what the devil *was* the fellow's name? Nixon? Robertson? Hendrickson? Harrison? (He winced at the thought of Harrison.) Nixon was the Vice-President.

Somebody's *son,* that was for sure. Everybody was.

The architect touched the granite with his hand.

Panicky he consulted his watch. 8:30 on the dot! His dutiful unconscious kept good time. He fled from the building, even though he would hardly be late. Outside it was dark. He asked his direction from the first passerby.

He was not going to have any supper, and he realized that he was ravenous.

III.

The rectory, where they held the meeting, was on Duane, off the business street, in a dark-red brick building with gables, in an ambiguous neighborhood. (Negroes were coming in.) The committee was all assembled in the parlor and was indeed a little anxious, as provincial people are, whether the great man from New York might not show at all. 8:35. But the doorbell jangled, the minister went to welcome him, and the architect came in hatless and breathless. They recognized him from his pictures in *Life,* and everybody stood up for the handshaking.

"That's a *noble* pile there on the square!" he burst out oddly, without waiting to be introduced. "That's why I'm late. I went in to look around and—it was 8:30!"

"Not late at all, not at all!" protested the minister. "The others just got here."

"I was *surprised* to find a building like that in the town!" cried Harry, gasping.

"I want you to meet Mr. Foster," said the minister, "the chairman of our committee. Mr. and Mrs. Foster."

"The green is nice too; even better if it's kept ragged," said Harry.

"Pleased. Did you come up on the 8:12?" said Foster. He had a rasping voice. "That one is always late. Why didn't you tell him to take the express?"

"But I did recommend the 6:30," protested the minister. "This is Dr. Alexander."

"Pleased, I'm sure," said the architect. "No, I did take the early train, but I got lost—"

"Mr. Tom Hawthorne," said the minister. "He's descended from the novelist's father's brother—I tell you so you won't ask, ha."

"Are you!" said the architect. "Let me tell you right now, if you people are going to put up a church here, you'll have to go far to compete with a building like that, put up in the dark ages after the Civil War. I'm not sure I can match it," he said modestly.

"And Mr. and Mrs. Parsons," said the minister.

"I *am* willing to try," said the architect and held out his hand.

He detested these committee meetings that he ought, with his sociable disposition, to have enjoyed; for art is lonely and these folk were collaborators. But the bother was that they were not collaborators, they were not peers; they had no confidence in what they wanted and needed, so they didn't talk up. They wanted to be bowled over by him, and then to leave everything in his hands, including *telling* them what they wanted and needed. They didn't take themselves seriously. But he had found from unhappy experience that if he took them seriously and tried to draw them out, then they walked roughshod over him and intervened in artistic matters in which they had no competence. So instead he dictated and demanded, which he hated. It isolated him. He felt unsteady on his eminence.

"Shall we sit down and get started?" said the minister briskly. "Does any one want a liquid refreshment?"

"God!" persisted Harry, as he sat down, "my walking cold into a strange building and seeing twelve windows of Charley Tiffany's! Next time I'll bring a photographer and you'll have them in color in the *Forum*."

He was persisting in these remarks about the church on the green partly because he *was* still there, having left so rudely; but partly also to create the tone for the meeting, cultural *and* informal, giving himself very much the advantage. This procedure was dishonest and he knew it, yet here was no help for it, for it was how he was, familiar with the muse, burning for fame, and needing to get the upper hand so that he could do what he wanted. There was no way to be honest with people. He used words like "noble pile" because they did move him and he really wanted English to be like that; but he knew that they had an odd effect and he capitalized on it.

The doctor had been the only one to listen to a word he said anyway. "What building is it that you're talking about, Mr. Hodges?" he asked sociably.

"Please call me Harry," he said. This was not to be pally, but because he was embarrassed by being called mister. He looked at the doctor in blank surprise. "Is there another building in this town?" he asked unbelievingly.

"I'm sure I don't know anything about it," retreated the doctor. "Only, you said you were admiring some building—"

There was something in the tone and countenance of the famous guest that made everybody suddenly pay attention.

"I mean the church, of course," said Harry in the silence. "The big gray one on the green."

"*Our* church?" cried Mrs. Foster faintly.

"*Your* church?" said the architect. His face fell. Something was wrong. "I went in on the way here from the station. That's why I'm late."

"Not late at all!" cried the minister. "Why do you keep saying you're late? Naturally!" he exclaimed, rubbing his hands, "you dropped in on our old church to see. What could be more natural?"

"But—" said the architect.

"He means the Monster," said Mrs. Foster, who understood what was the matter.

"Oh no, he can't mean the Monster," said Mr. Parsons.

"Yes, he means the Monster," said Dr. Alexander.

"Not the *Monster?!*" almost screamed Mrs. Parsons.

"Well!" said the minister jovially, "he's got to see it sometime! We can't keep our old building hidden from our new architect forever, can we?" This struck him as a jolly idea, of concealing a large church on a public square, like stealing a grand piano, and he gave it a good chuckle. "Ha! ha! So you see, sir," he said, "why we want to get rid of that one and build something new and modern and fitting the worship of God. That's what *you're* here for. We held a meeting. We'll get Harry Hodges. Who else? The best, sir. They call it the Monster."

For a long moment the architect had not a blessed word to say. He wore a feeble smile. He was at a loss.

"Tell me," he said finally, "do you have your announcement out in front there on the green? I mean the name of your congregation and pastor and so forth."

The minister reddened. "Of course," he said sharply. The question did seem to him in poor taste. Joking aside, it *was* rude to ask if they kept their name hidden. After all, there was nothing shameful; they had not built the church, it was a hundred years old. He decided that it was simply a poor joke, nothing offensive. "Prescott Green Congregational Church. D. T. Wieck, D.D., Pastor," he said proudly. "Sunday October 4, *The Saving Power of Prayer*. Right out on the lawn and tall as a man!"

The architect closed his eyes. "I saw that sign," he said. "If I close my eyes, I can read it off right now, *The Saving Power of Prayer*. October 11, *Hope*. That's right, isn't it? I saw it and knew it was your church, and that that was the church I came up here to replace. But I never did see it and I walked in. . . . Tell me, who built it?"

"I couldn't give you a clue," said the minister.

"A chap named Richardson," said the doctor, who knew about such things.

"Yes, Henry Richardson," muttered Harry. "H. H. Richardson—H.H.—" And there, to their amazement and somewhat alarm, except that they didn't know what to expect from a famous artist from New York, Harry Hodges turned white and fell back in his chair and almost fainted away, as the full force of his lapse of memory, of his self-betrayal by his own unconscious, smote him between the eyes. He even understood the details. The "Richard" in the name he had forgotten was King Richard Second deposed by Harry, for he had seen Shakespeare's play the very evening before. And H. H. Richard*son* was—Harry Hodges, murderous son. This was the simple personal guilt. But underlying these personal motives, and far more important and personally terrible than any personal motives, was the social fact that we in America are forever in a state of ruthless change. Monumental works, built of materials that should last two thousand years, will be demolished in one generation, and with them the builder's name. And yes! by a fatality, it is precisely the loveliest and the best that must be destroyed the soonest and the most ruthlessly, as if God had a hatred of excellence. Who can build in stone under these conditions?

Such was the *fact* of the architect from New York as he

cringed in the chair before them, with his mouth open, and his chin on his breastbone.

"Gentlemen! and ladies," said Harry drily, recovering his wits. "My considered advice is that you stick with that fine edifice of Richardson's on the green." Edifice was another of his words. "Learn to like it. You'll thank me. I'm saving you money and trouble. Let me tell you—I know—the Tiffany stained glass alone would warrant preserving the building as a national monument, even if the building were mediocre. But in fact the whole is high minor art of the first rank, and I'd be proud to do as well."

As he said it, Harry already wondered how much of his enthusiasm did arise from the magical light of sunset and the manic aftermath of deposing papa.

"The stained glass. He's talking about the windows," cried Mrs. Foster faintly.

"The sheep, it's too much!" said Mrs. Parsons and got up hastily and left the room.

IV.

There ensued a peculiar debate between Parson Wieck and the architect from New York.

The minister was thrown into confusion by Harry's praising the old-fashioned building, for he had been the moving spirit in inviting him up. What was happening?

Wieck was a large fair-haired man with a good voice, a fair education, and a gift for creating a friendly atmosphere. He was an adequate pastor of the flock, but he was not quite grown-up. The little boy in him was always trying to say the right, the mature, the sophisticated thing that would show how precocious he was. This had gotten him handsomely through the seminary to a wealthy pulpit and prestige in the synod. But since, after all, he didn't understand what he was talking about, whether about psychoanalysis or crisis theology, ever and anon he was left high and dry. The irony was that deep down he did have a puritan abhorrence for the church on the green because it was ornate and catholic—his feeling for a bare functionalism was genuine enough—but this he

could no longer remember, and he would have been
ashamed to say it.

Harry had not yet made up his mind whether to accept the job or reject it. After all, Henry Richardson
was dead and life must go on. Why shouldn't these folk
have their way? Yet he found it hard to take their esthetic
judgment at face value. What did they *really* have against
the building? He asked them. What really did they have
against the building? Had they outgrown it? Didn't it
function any more? Had the neighborhood degenerated
(become Negro)? Why couldn't they sell and find an
equivalent site and move? Maybe the town could have *two*
interesting churches! With this happy inspiration, Henry
Richardson got a new lease on life.

But instead of an answer to his pressing questions,
Harry was treated to the pastor's lecture on organic architecture! The trouble with this four-bit lecture on honest form and function, however, was that it had long ago
been delivered by Henry Richardson who learned it from
Ruskin and others; and Richardson had taught it to Louis
Sullivan; and Sullivan had taught it to Frank Lloyd
Wright; and Wright had taught it to Harry Hodges. And
when he was himself a younger man, Harry had broad-
cast it far and wide, in his classes at Harvard and in the
architectural journals, until it penetrated even the Sunday
papers and the radio and finally became the mature and
"tough" wisdom of Pastor David Wieck. And now curiously, the moral of this lecture on the American style had
gotten to be the necessity of knocking down Henry
Richardson's ornamental church, the Monster.

But Harry loved decoration. He didn't think the
church was a monster at all. In principle it was as absurd
as you pleased, but things were not so simple. There was a
man there.

Listening to his own opinions played back to him on a
poor tape, Harry was less and less convinced. "How much
money do you have in your building fund?" he asked suddenly. "Can you *afford* a new building?"

"$238,420," said Mr. Parsons, who was chairman of
Funds for the new Building.

"There you are!" crowed Harry triumphantly. "You
don't begin to have enough money for what you want! At

present prices I couldn't promise you what you ask for less than a million and a half megabucks, plus my fee." And he spread out his hands graciously, as if that settled the problem to everybody's satisfaction.

"Not so fast, young man," said Mr. Foster, with a voice rasping like iron. They were the first words he had uttered in the discussion. "We have the heaviest endowed congregation in New England, and *we* shall take care of the finances."

As if shot, Harry turned to this new voice and flushed. He recognized the boss. "Cut the shit," he said brutally, dropping his guard in order to throw his punch. *"Why?"* he said menacingly, "why do you mean to tear down that fine building and build elsewhere?" But as soon as he heard that voice, he had known the truth.

Mr. Foster bared his teeth in a yellow smile.

V.

"It's none of your business, young man," said Mr. Foster. "But since you ask me, I'll tell you."

Harry knew him well—he had sat with him on twenty committees—the aged American businessman who has worked hard and skillfully and has retired rich and prestigious. Now at leisure he gives his time to serving the community, in philanthropies and churches and schools. He is well trained for this, he has connections, he knows administration, public relations, fund-raising by horse-trading and covert blackmail; and he can give himself to these enterprises with a ferocity that is not possible any more, without landing in jail, to private persons not working in a good cause. A man like that is free for the first time in his life and he rides high.

"I suppose you've sold the property already," said Harry.

"You are right."

"Well, if you have you have. What's all this palaver about?"

"We didn't start any palaver. You mistake yourself. We asked you up here to design us a new set of buildings in Dorchester Heights. Are you interested or not? If you

are interested, what are your terms—for a set of preliminary drawings? But you—is it your custom, young man, to teach your clients their own business?"   .

"Yes, it is," said Harry. "What else did you sell?"

"Really!" exclaimed the chairman. "Really! This is an *odd* way to do business. I'm not sure I see the necessity for it." He was, rather naively, taken aback that the architect had an acumen that among his business colleagues he would have taken for granted.

"Did you, then, sell out the Green?" asked Harry with a melancholy pleasure.

Foster tapped his fountain pen angrily. "*Quite* uncalled for!" he said. "Quite uncalled for!" He flushed. "Sell out?! Really, Mr. Hodges! We have had title to Prescott Green since 1754—*isn't* that long enough? Now we can put the investment to better use. An enlarged school. A psychiatric clinic—" He was somewhat honestly indignant, for he did not weigh the values like the other man. "Explain yourself, sir! what do you mean, sell out? There are other uses for money than to tend a field of weeds." His face was purple.

"Please, Humphrey," said Mrs. Foster, taking her husband's hand.

"Yes, a psychiatric clinic," said Pastor Wieck. There was a chance of an added melon from the National Institute of Mental Health.

"Shall I get you a glass of water?" said Mrs. Foster. "Doris, get him a glass of water. Please, Mr. Hodges—"

Harry had finally closed his notebook with a snap and put it in his pocket. Nevertheless! he could not forbear pursuing, with a melancholy rapture, his vindictive examination, not otherwise than a jealous husband continues to torment her, and himself, even after he has found out the truth. "What is to become of the hotel on the Green, Mr. Foster?" he asked, closing his eyes to review the scene of the *flagrans delictus*. "The hotel, Mr. Foster, the library, the statue of James Warren, that building on the south side with the flag—is it the Grange?"

"*I* don't know what's to become of the Hotel Prescott, I'm sure!" cried Mr. Foster. "Is the town never to grow?"

"*Mr.* Hodges! Don't agitate him!" pleaded Mrs. Foster.

"It *is* a handsome parcel of real estate!" continued

Harry inexorably. "You certainly *have* been heavily endowed. There'll be a new Statler Hotel, a supermarket, a very *grand* cinema—and—the promoter is P. W. Finch, Incorporated," he said positively.

Now how in the devil did he know that? wondered Foster. It was *absolutely* confidential. It was this fearful doubt, of how far this diabolic man's knowledge extended, and what he was merely guessing at as an expert, that was choking the old man and making it hard for him to breathe, not otherwise than the wife in the situation chokes up and becomes dumb, as the evidence turns up, and who knows what further will turn up?

But Harry was no longer fighting for Henry Richardson. He was fighting for his own immortality, and losing badly in the contest. Just as the statues went down on the Green. Who cared about James Warren? (Who *was* James Warren?) With a stammer of embarrassment he was fighting for his country, and losing badly. Even so! though he was losing, there was something in him indestructible and he knew it. The art was indestructible. The idea of his country was indestructible. He himself didn't come from these hills but from the Hudson Valley on the other side of the border, near Red Hook, where they have thrown the new Rip Van Winkle Bridge across to Kingston.

"Is the town never to grow?" he repeated the other's remark thickly. "Mr. Foster, what will be the shape of the new town?"

"The shape! the shape!" spluttered Foster, and fell to the ground with a stroke. For it was not with impunity that a businessman in his late sixties meddled in serving his community.

Even while the man was falling down, Harry was quickly calculating: "They'll now go to Robbins and Peters to do the job. But I'll get to them first and make them see it our way. At least I'll try."

THE MEAN, THE MAXIMUM, AND THE MINIMUM

✳ —"The maximum, the mean, and the minimum are all good wisdom and destroy us without sin!"

I.

Pay-day, three young householders find that last month cost them only $42.50 each, for rent, food, etc. We say "only" because this was an amount they were easily used to, but there is a mean in your life too.

The doorbell rings. Enter Normal and Robber and sit down without taking off their hats. Now there are five and Loose says: "Five of us could live like kings on ten dollars a week." Normal cries: "If I could get out of business, it would be Utopia!"—he is a little salesman in the commercial world that tends always to the Extreme. Liv says: "We could play ball every clear day from April to October."

They are fascinated by the question of the Utopian life: to heighten by art, by juster proportions, an almost possible existence. What their life would be if they could pool just a few dividends!

Normal takes off his hat and opens the top button of his trousers; but Robber keeps his hat on because he has a date.

Liv's little brother is standing in the doorway secretly grinning.

They start with clothes: It isn't necessary to wear a tie; there are no buttons to lose on a pullover sweater;

moccasins have no heels; and corduroy pants last forever. Robber looks distastefully at Liv's filthy yellow corduroy pants, gaping at the fly and ripped symmetrically at the knees. Liv wears these for a purpose of his own, though he can afford better.

"It might be better to live in sunny Italy," says Henry Faust. "No, there's no big-league ball. Cincinnati's warm, but the Reds stink on ice."

"It's practical!" Normal insists passionately; "you don't take it seriously, but I take it seriously. Where there are so many billions of dollars in Chicago, couldn't you come into ten dollars a week? But when you try to *earn* it, you soon have to try to make eighteen dollars or you're out. Once I thought if I had ten dollars a week, I'd be independent; I wouldn't know what to spend it on. By the time I was making eighteen dollars a week I was thinking in terms of thirty-five dollars."

"Where do you stop?"

"The only thing is to go back to what you wanted when you began."

"Ha!" thinks Liv's little brother in the doorway grinning, "that's what *he* thinks!"

"—a little regular income; the main thing is to be regular, so you know where you stand. I'd be satisfied with eight dollars."

"If there was ten of us, we could live on five dollars."

"There you go multiplying. Where do you stop?"

Liv has planned out the daily routine: "Our daily routine could be as follows: in the morning a game of ball. I could be captain of one team and Norm of the other. After lunch some reading. . . ."

He slips into the routine of a boys' camp he went to, and these are his juster proportions. It was there he first wore yellow pants.

". . . In the afternoon a little scrub-ball until the big game about four. At night you sit around and talk just like we're doing now. Every Sunday we go to see the Cubs or White Sox, whichever is at home." "I think we ought to do a little socially useful work just to make you feel right," says Normal; "two nights a week I'm willing to canvass for Labor's Non-Partisan League."

Robber gets to his feet. "What about women?"

"I knew you'd start that!" Normal cries. There follow several dirty jokes. Anyway some women have sense and might even become Utopians. "Oh-oh, trouble."

"Generally speaking," says Liv, "to be honest with ourselves, we go with girls just for screwing and not for companionship or talking, and they can't play ball."

"Well, Abyssinia," says Robber, "I have a date."

"Oh, wait awhile," says Loose, "and I'll drive you."

Now Robber and the nameless little brother are standing in the doorway. In this pause—

In this pause, the formalities of baseball strike them with force: "When the outfielders swing to the right, when the left-hander comes to bat—" "Nobody looks so good as a self-possessed catcher who holds the runners close." "What about the centerfielder starts at the crack o' the bat and takes the ball moving without a hurry,— Tris Speaker, the Gray Eagle."

"Last week he fell off his roof drunk and broke his head," says Liv's little brother.

"If you're talking about individuals, what about the Babe striking out?" "Herb Pennock, the Silver Fox of Kennett Square, stalling for the rain."

"The hit and run."

"The double-steal."

"The home-run that breaks up the ball game."

Both extremes possible within the rules.

"But the trouble with *our* game," says Norm and the tears start into his eyes, "is that nobody can play it; nobody but us five can get off from work; no matter how hard you try you can't escape it."

"Maybe we could organize them as Utopians. We could have a number of separate units."

"No no no. You can't find more than half a dozen who are willing to be reasonable. I see it in business every day."

"To you," says Robber, "it's reasonable; to me it stinks. I don't want to miss a thing."

"When they begin to talk baseball," thinks Loose, "I get bored stiff."

THE GOLDEN MEAN

The Golden Mean is to have just so much there as a person is adequate to, to turn to it his full attention; this isn't much, but it's something. Not too small to do the job, but not a bit bigger.

HOW THE MEAN SERVES GOD

To know where one is, proportioning the self and the objects of desire, is prayer. Measure is the same as saying Grace.

HOW THE MEAN IS BOTH THE MINIMUM
AND THE MAXIMUM

Through the Mean we avoid the importunities of lust, which denial would make rage only the more, exposing us to impulses and accidents. Thus it is through the Mean that we attain the Minimum. Conversely, the Mean reconciles warring opposites and avoids waste. Thus it is through the Mean that we attain the Maximum.

Loose and Robber take their leave. "Loose, take me along!" screams Liv's little brother, vanishing downstairs after them. "Hey, where do you think you're going?" Liv calls after him.

Norm says, "Robber's against Utopia."

"Yes, and he'll soon talk Lew out of it; that leaves only three."

"I didn't think your little brother was very much impressed either," say Henry Faust, "if you noticed him standing there laughing in his sleeve."

II.

Liv's little brother has them let him off in the Loop. They can't understand what the twelve-year-old boy can be after there, so late at night. But he goes straight to the great Department Store.

Here he knows the Night-Watchman, and for the price of some trivial intimacies, he is free to play in the great store. Besides, the Watchman has a fourteen-year-old daughter whom the boy is hot for.

Everything is in the great Department Store! to be got by the infinite power of money, which is exchangeable for all things and proportioned to the infinite appetite. The Department of Canned Fruits! the Department of Polymorphous Love! Little brother puts on a pair of roller-skates, to move more swiftly from pleasure to pleasure.

Charlie Chaplin, in *Modern Times,* portrayed a Department Store as earthly paradise; he skates about the store like a graceful comic angel; in one scene he balances blindfold on the edge of an abyss, a comic angel. It *is* comic to have everything pell-mell, like Adam in the garden: for instance, an elephant with a writhing proboscis.

Like a giant, little Roy sits with legs outstretched—the wheels still spinning on his feet, like the fluttering ankle-wings of Hermes—on the floor among the toys in the Toy Department. Here's a toy farm, a house, a barn, orchard-trees and animals. Put the man and his wife together in bed, take the cow from the field and put her in the barn; and dim the light: it is Night. Here is an illuminated electric locomotive clattering on the rails. Here is a little War.

Huge Roy plays with our machines, with a derrick, an alcohol steam engine. Here's a whole town; pell-mell he scatters the houses, motorcars and men and women about him on the floor. And here is a War, with tiny cannon that fire through the empty store a loud report.

Here are the undistributed letters of a game of anagrams, the players of which betray themselves in the words they create. And here is a War.

—Sailing on one foot with the other comically lifted behind, soaring with wide-stretched arms and baggy sleeves, speeding from pleasure to pleasure, comes our Charlie Chaplin, and when he does so, no one can hold back joy and grief.—

On the fourth floor is the Furniture Department. In a silk-furnished ebony Empire bed in the form of a Sphinx, is sleeping the Night-Watchman's daughter. Roy kicks

off his wheeled shoes. He loosens his belt and his trousers
fall to the floor. Already his little penis is erect, like an
inquisitive little animal.

Each of the polymorphous acts of love strives to the
maximum; if a boy is well-educated by early corruption,
they do not give way to each other. Each kind of pleasure, struggling to be more, passes into uncontrollable
excess. The little body is afire, and now is the time for
flaming thoughts. To play with the toys until an orgasm
of technology. To scramble the words to a moment of
meaningless poetry.

THE MAXIMUM

To *have* each thing, to *turn* the attention to each thing,
into each thing—is the Maximum. It is always in excess,
for there is no room in the soul for a comparative measure.

Excess is the only prayer, because this is the thing that
is given to us and not made by us; as it is said, "The earth
is the *Lord's* and the fulness thereof."

Thus, it is through the Maximum that we escape our
too dear selves and so enjoy the Minimum.

The little boy is asleep, has escaped from the lusts of
his dear body and soul. His body is sore but has a strong
and sweet sensation. But it was necessary to undergo
many arduous joys of the intelligence and lust to come at
last to this home most have lost, on the very edge of death.

Six o'clock in the morning! With a loud clangor of the
burglar alarm the Watchman wakes the two children.
Everywhere into the store creeps the daylight. And already—how soon!—as he takes the iron wheels from his
shoes, the boy is laughing in his sleeve all day.

III.

Wanting to do without—perhaps as a method of punishment, and disgusted and weary with the continual consumption of goods in which he and every one else were
consuming their lives, and not without a little envy of

the rich, and also because he thought it was right to add this particular force to the general social conflict— Henry founded the National Industrial Boycott, an organization to destroy the bourgeois structure of society. The plan (a classical one, dating at least as far back as the *Fable of the Bees*) was to buy and consume as little as possible, the Minimum, and to spread this resolve as widely as possible. Then, since the productive system was geared not to necessities but to widely advertised superfluities, it would soon crack wide open.

To hear it *crack!* Henry confessed to himself that he had a lust for this particular sound.

A critical friend said: "Even granting, what is absurd, that you could get a following with this scheme, can't you see that it's not capital that will be hurt first, but labor? You might as well recommend a war."

"Yes, a war of attrition, minus the violence."

"You mean: all the poor people are to starve by principle as well as necessity."

Not answering, Henry cried: "All the same! If we don't all learn how much they have bullied us into needing, we'll still have subways in the Socialist republic."

He took to wearing one suit and to living on the diet figured out by the experts of the Relief.

He was a 1940 urban Thoreau, but omitted the idea of individual independence which to the transcendentalists had seemed the highest good, but to Henry pure egotism. "I wonder what deep desire to see their fellow-citizens deprived inspired *them?*" he asked himself; and with nervous joy read Hawthorne's biting observations on Brook Farm; "yet Hawthorne was the nihilist of them all, too Calvinist to approve even of privation!"

DOING WITHOUT

Nevertheless, N.I.B. gained a little headway and they began to *nibble*, as they boasted, at the economy. Several thousand bourgeois Americans, who were sympathetic to any effort to destroy the existence for which all had the deepest unconscious disgust, decided to keep their 1939 automobiles for another season. These cars, built to last one year and be traded in, broke down; whereupon

the manufacturers, by way of counter-propaganda, in-
structed their mechanics to be insulting to those who
drove in for repairs, and to be "out of stock" on old parts.
They waged a safety-campaign in the state legislatures.
There was a certain amount of chaos: fly-by-night mechanics set up shop; some drivers, having used the bus
once or twice, neglected their cars altogether.

Among these same people, there spread a movement
to read the books on their book-shelves instead of buying
new fiction. All were amazed to discover the pages of
Anthony Trollope, unopened; and soon there was much
lay literary criticism, contrasting in "meatiness" the 19th-
century masters and the 20th, represented by Margaret
Ayer Barnes. Clifton Fadiman loyally championed the
moderns, but lost his job anyway, since the publishing
business was so leaky that it couldn't survive even this
tempest.

But there were a few poor people who for a time were
freed by the suggestion not to want certain things obviously desirable. They experienced an enormous relief of
competitive tension—a relief almost like that of evan-
gelism. But these people were not large consumers in
any case; nor could they transmit their free feeling to
their children, but rather an even stronger cupidity, which
comes of being deprived of what one sees all about.

In the end all lapsed from N.I.B., perhaps even into
excesses that they had never before practiced. Perhaps
also this was the measure of success desired by Henry.

He complained bitterly: "Once they have experienced
a sensation, all—all except myself—find it impossible not
to have this routine as well as all the rest. How can you
hope for political reform with such people?"

His friend said: "On the contrary, yours is the self-
defeating plan. Why do you want to overturn the state?
Because the people have too little; and to accomplish this
you teach them to want even less. On the contrary, the
great hope for change is just to demand *more;* this is
what the profit system can't survive. It's called Rising
Aspirations."

Henry said: "Do you think that the way to the Maximum of pleasure is not always through the Minimum? Let me tell you a parable.—

"There was a Zwinglian minister during the Reformation who decided to dismantle his church. (Indeed he determined to tear down the building.) And first he dismissed the choir and took off his vestments, and stripped the altar, and took down the paintings, and burned the illuminated manuscripts. With a sinking heart, he thought of dispensing with the organ; he recoiled from it, but since the Holy Ghost had once put the idea in his head, he had them take out the organ also. In anguish he shattered the pictorial windows with stones; at first he said he would replace them with plain glass, but now that there were not even windows, why go back? Instead, he secretly decided to push down the walls! He was afraid to announce this to the grumbling congregation, but waited until a Sunday, when all were within the church and could not see what was taking place outside; and he ascended the pulpit to preach. Then his workmen, not profaning the day with this destructive work—for the *Lord* said, Make No Graven Image—proceeded, amid loud noises, to tear down the edifice. Bricks and plaster fell on the worshipers. The walls toppled, the frame rent and collapsed amid shrieks; there was a loud *Crack!* And there, roundabout, were the broad fields and the orchard trees, the village, the clouds and the sun. . . ."

"Very pretty," said Henry's friend. "You remind me of a celebrated argument of the philosopher MacTaggart on survival after death. The fact that all experience is sensory and that the sense organs decay, says he, is no proof that there could not be experience after death; for this is like saying that we cannot see without windows just because a person inside a house cannot see except through windows. Rather, MacTaggart asks, who knows what our experience will be like when once we have got rid of these sense-organs?"

"Do you think that is such a stupid argument?" said Henry, laughing up his sleeve.

Chicago
1939

A SENIOR CONCERT
OF THE HIGH SCHOOL
OF MUSIC AND ART

It's a big orchestra of empty chairs, with their stands, lights, and music-sheets. Eighty-five places. Only the drummer is there, a slight bespectacled boy with colorless hair; when he bends his ear close to the kettledrums, he is lost in the equipment. He has stage fright and is nervously banging away bang! bong! dominant and tonic. Other players are appearing at their stands, trying to look business-like. A young miss, quite a young lady with a turquoise blouse and a skirt of flaring orange, is screwing together with quick twists the three pieces of her silver flute.

The kids have collected too early, to warm up their instruments. They have stage fright and each is private. Each kid is practicing his own phrase fortissimo, the din is fierce. Each kid heedless of the others and of the audience that has begun straggling in, mostly parents.

You expect them to start pacing up and down, bursting into a sprint down the field, to heave a lead shot erratically in a thoughtless direction and knock somebody's head off, while the sun floods down unstinting light from the royal blue.

Now thirty or forty of them have gathered and seem to be practicing. But if you look at the program—the phrases they are loudly playing have nothing to do with the concert to come. Each kid is seeking safety in his "own" music, the way musical adolescents—and these adolescents are very musical—hear with fanatical rapture the harmony that was invented especially for oneself, no one else in all the generations ever "really" understood it. Also, without any stage fright in his isolated daydream, each is performing brilliantly on a bright stage to a vast audience, with universal admiration, triumphant over envious enemies who are magnanimously forgiven.

One lad with a brass trumpet is exclaiming *Freedom! Freedom!* from *Fidelio*. And another with an ear-splitting horn is boasting that he is Siegfried.

It is not embarrassing because they are not embarrassed; one is abashed for them, they are so young and exposed; but they are not abashed.

A slide trombone has a hat over his bell, and he is taking with an arrogant posture the chorus of a Dixie blues, but when he ends with a flourish, crazy, man! and gives it to his buddy—alas! the clarinet is brooding with the aged Brahms who has been reading Sophocles. Unconscious of everything, the young lady with the silver flute is discoursing earnestly with the Blessed Spirits. And the little drummer is banging away at the march from the *Symphonie Pathétique,* streamed round by the flapping banners of the United Nations and bawling out the melody. But you cannot hear anything in the din.

Next moment, silence. The house is full, the kids are poised, their conductor has stepped onto the podium and raps. The stage-curtain parts revealing the choir—so *there* are the rest of the seniors!—and they have begun *Wachet auf!*

The orchestra has begun to play and I am blind with tears.

But what's to weep about any of this? Naturally they play well, they are very musical kids. Naturally they play well together, they are well rehearsed and they know one another. The conducting is simple and sensible, firm on the broad lines and with obvious dynamics. There is plenty of spirit, it is *animal* spirit. The nobility—there is nobility—comes from the pride and aspiration of many poor cultured homes. All this is natural and to be expected; why then should tears be streaming down my cheeks and I cannot see anything but a bright sheet of light?

Because it is our orchestra.

Always it is absence and loss that we weep for; when we seem to be weeping for joy, we are weeping for paradise lost. And the case is—as I look about in our community and remember the longing of our lives and the frustration of our longing—the case is that we do not have any orchestra. This is a truth too bitter to live with and we usually dismiss it and keep our faces set as best we can.

Here is our orchestra! It is playing *Wachet auf!* Our choir is taking it up. With the opening of this new possibility, at once the old tears well. Our mouths are open, breathing in and out.

This orchestra is proud of its orchestra. The adolescents take it for granted that they can rely on one another.

I sympathize with the conductor who is a man of my own age. He is smirking and continually breaking into smiles and grins. Each time they have traversed a hard passage, he breaks into a broad grin as if to say, "Listen, hey? the way they got through that! I told you they could! I promised you they would!" But the young people are playing right on. They are neither smirking nor nervous nor grimly determined, just matter-of-factly playing the music that they think is just beautiful, and indeed it is very grand and beautiful. They are attentive to the music, but they are also damned proud of their orchestra.

The girls' voices ring out loud and bright. The young tenors and basses do not have an equal weight; you would say that the young men are not confident, they are afraid their voices will break. Boys! risk it! give forth! (the conductor is pleading with his shaking left hand)— what is the use of young male voices if they do not shout out loud and clear? That's better. It doesn't matter if a few break down when there are so many brothers supporting.

We are towards the end of May. The school concert is part of the commencement exercises, a demonstration of the work of the year, of the four years. *Wann Kommst du, mein Heil?* This is not the "own" music of any of those kids, I suppose, but they have chosen it for us, and do they not take it well upon themselves! They are reconciled to us (us at our best, to be sure); they agree to continue. It is their commencement. I wish that they were in fact beginning into such a community as they seem so well able to take upon themselves.

The scene is clear and sharp. *"Thou art That!"* What does it mean? The immortal humanity. Each one stands as a witness.

As sometimes happens when you have been surprisingly moved and are thereby *in* the scene, some object spontaneously brightens and stands out from the background; first one, then another, then another. A spotlight is falling across one face, another face is shining out of an unique shadow. Like those group photographs in the biographies of famous men, where the face of the hero as a boy seems to shine out from the group, destined for his career, although when the picture was taken all the faces were equal.

Before, they were all isolated in their jarring soliloquies, pathetic, violent, promissory adolescents. But they have become a community. And now one, two, and three heads loom alone—doomed to it—as witnesses of immortal humanity.

So geh herein zu mir. The red-headed boy in the shaft of light has been doomed to sing in a new way; you can see the guilt and suffering of his absolute break with the generations on his stubborn and imploring face. He is begging for us to listen to him, but stubborn to persist in his way whether we will or not. And why should we pay attention to him when he has broken with us? But also both he and we know that there has been no break at all; we are laughing about it underneath, at the same time as we are set on making one another very unhappy.

Notice, too, the face of that serious little girl in the shadow. She is cursed with an eerie and unerring intuition that frightens her teachers and makes her classmates freeze. In self-protection and protection of the others, she hides her truth behind clever words, she is a smart aleck. No one likes her, but every one is going to need her. She weeps a good deal because the boys do not make love to her and the girls don't invite her to their parties. She would like to be like the others, but she cannot, by willing it, be stupider than she is.

That dark lad in the choir whose voice, among so many, rings pure and clear right to my ears: why is he frowning? He is a forlorn angel. He is not one of the fallen angels, for he has a passport into paradise; but he seems to be lost in a woods, his wings bedraggled. His trouble is that he persists in wanting to bring us home to paradise with him, and we will not go along. He invites us, we start to go with him, and he is elated; then he finds we have deserted him, and he frowns. He has courage.

Creator spirit, prosper us. *Gloria!* they are thundering the chorale.

New York City
c. 1957

THE DEATH OF AESCULAPIUS

I.

These are my memories of the death of Aesculapius our
teacher.

When Diana the virgin huntress came keening, tearing
her hair for Hippolytus, "You virgin!" said our teacher
with icy contempt. "How do you dare ask for help from
a physician, from nature? Yet come," he said to us, "since
we have sworn the oath."

When our teacher Aesculapius demonstrated the
corpse of Hippolytus he was filled with passionate resentment. When we asked why he was angry, he lied and said,
"I am not angry."

He said, "Since this is an unfinished situation, I shall
revive Hippolytus. (But me, me I cannot revive.)"

He began as always with a description, absorbing soul
from the environment. "You see, the day along the shore
is bright. The regular waves are falling no louder than a
conversational voice, and the offshore islands are showing in detail. In a billow of sand, here is the billow, the
young horseman has come up the beach; he looses an arrow at the starting goose and misses. Here is the arrow.
There is the goose in heaven. Where is the horse? There
in the dunes. Why has he missed? Because he is disturbed,
and his habit has been to hunt the game calmly, the
attentiveness pouring from his eyes and from his hands
that do not miss. Such is the so-called chaste love of Diana." But when Aesculapius mentioned Diana the virgin
his voice was icy with contempt.

"Look! Quick as it rose the extraordinary storm named
Neptune has given way to fair sky and pink clouds. Leaving like a mangled lizard the body of this huntsman small
on the beach. Wet sand inside the clothes and in his hair."

Great Aesculapius knelt—we stood around. With his clairvoyant gaze he demonstrated the corpse: clairvoyant but that always proved to be nothing but immediate inference from natural signs; or not even inference but directly reading it off, for he was there, saying, "But you are *still* doing it! You are doing it right now!"

He said, "This used to be Hippolytus the son of Theseus. Falsely accused; he never felt anything for the woman. He never had such thoughts at all. But *why* did he not?" asked the physician sharply. "If he had thought more of living, he would be still alive."

He turned to us simply, as if he had lost interest in the body. "This is not a profitable question. Let us rather ask: *how* did he not?" Surprisingly our teacher's face was contorted with resentment. "All right, let me reconstruct the scene. He is standing in her presence provocatively, his head high and laughing in her face, here is the laugh, his pelvis forward, and sometimes he lightly fingers his penis without a thought. Phaedra stares at him, but he responds to her gaze not by recognizing it for what it is, but by becoming all the more animated and cocky. His forehead is too immobile. Such is the provocation practiced by young huntsmen who have no thoughts of love, either to suffer it or arouse it. Learn to notice this. What they do not express they exhibit. There is absolutely no one who has nothing to do with love.

"He is standing near her and feels he is looked at, but he never comes any nearer. But she stammers and staggers. Next moment, as if there were no such thing, he leaves without a word to shoot arrows at a stag and thrust his spear into the boar. It is hot with *these* things that he confronts the daughter of the mother who fucked the Bull in the machine."

When he reconstructed this scene, Aesculapius wept. He often wept, it was a way he had of washing his eyes bright.

"The wrath of Theseus," he used to say, "was the pathetic expedient of a man who has neglected a family obligation he does not care for, and he casts the reproach wherever he can. So he calls up the Storm."

We see now how the sea became sullen. In his dejection Hippolytus was crouched on the beach like a scared lizard that changes color. He was turning livid like the open space between the black clouds and the black water. The world had a mouth gaping with fear, and on its brow perplexed wrinkles. The waves were shouting, the air holding its breath. Darkness fell. The lizard turned blue-black. At last Zephyr let out his shriek of fright and the horses of Neptune have leapt onto the beach and trampled the youth.

Theseus wept: "I am an unhappy man. My father Neptune gave me three wishes and I have squandered them all to my disadvantage. Following Pirithoüs, I wished myself across the Styx in Hell. I did not rescue Pirithoüs but I found myself trapped among the dead. I wished to be back in the world and I came home and wished for the death of Hippolytus. And now my son is dead."

He is weeping bitterly for Pirithoüs and the hunting of the Calydonian boar. "I slew Hippolytus because I was unable to rescue Pirithoüs." He is in despair and he will do himself an injury. Nevertheless he has relented toward himself, because he foreknows that it is necessary for him to act out such wasted wishes, to go to Hell and back and destroy his most beloved son, in order to be rid, in order to become the lawgiver of Athens.

Theseus and our master sailed together on the *Argo*.

II.

Our teacher Aesculapius, he knew of these things, as he stood beside the jetsam body that had wet sand inside the clothes and in the hair. Briefly he described to us the essentials: the young man thoughtlessly provocative, a servant of the virgin Diana; the Venus-sick daughter of Pasiphaë; and the head of the Hero aching with the crown of immortality of which, however, he would not foreswear a single jewel.

Our master said: "It is senseless. I deny it. No such thing occurred. I deny it."

He told us this even as he was carefully undressing the corpse. He said, "There is no such thing."

We asked, "How is this? Do you deny it because it is senseless? Are we to understand that the past makes no sense?"

"No. The past always makes sense. What has occurred is, in so far, necessary; how could you live otherwise? But not this. It is senseless *because* I deny it."

We insisted: "Then why are you so angry about nothing?"

"I? I am not angry. Don't bother me, you are interrupting our conversation."

And indeed, he was all at once attending to the body with those eyes of his and his baby-panting breath as you attend to a second person, saying "You." He brushed us aside, us and our questions, as though we were discourteously interrupting a conversation he was having.

But with whom? Was *that* Hippolytus the huntsman? That thing couldn't hear. It could not, it did not, counteract the ground-force alternately to the left and right and run? That ankle, I thought, could not vault onto any horse; was that an ankle?

The horse was standing quietly among us, nuzzling at me, and I laid my arm lovingly and admiringly across her neck, for she was alive. We were both alive. With her animal flair she knew better than our teacher what the case was, and she was looking for a new rider.

"Lead that disgusting animal away," snapped Aesculapius, clairvoyantly observing us with the back of his head. I blushed with hot shame from head to foot.

My teacher rose and turned and lightly touched my shoulders with his palms, and—how shall I say?—he took my blushing and held it before him in space.

Nevertheless, as when a hungry hawk falls suddenly from the sky and strikes, and the lizard lies mangled, but the fluttering bird has not yet picked up his food to fly away with strong strokes, so that body lay worthless on the sand.

"Hippolytus!" whispered the physician, and our hairs stood on end. He was like a fluttering hawk.

He began, while he worked, to carry on a whispered conversation with the corpse, in a familiar vein. The conversation was one-sided. Some of what we overheard was the dirty humor of the Argonauts; he began to tell over, like an old fool, his hoary anecdote about the women of Lemnos. We were embarrassed to crowd closer to listen, embarrassed for him. We were embarrassed for him and nevertheless our hairs stood on end! (How was that?) Meantime, almost stealthily, he kept applying here and there a subtile pressure of his thumbs and fingers like a shrewd whore making love to an unresponsive client.

Our general impression was that he was babbling and carrying on not so much to exert any magical influence on that carrion as to convince himself of his own denial that it was dead. To say it crudely, he was wilfully becoming demented, as I have seen the Bacchae.

He was making love to something that had been not only disgustingly a virgin but was now not even alive. When he began to giggle it was beyond anything.

Once again he read our thoughts, as he could, and he said cuttingly over his shoulder: "What you are doing I don't know. As for me, I'm not playing games. Do you think I would deny the evidence of my senses if the non-existence of the fact were not necessary for me? Do you think I would be exerting an effort if I did not hope for success?"

We wished that the earth would swallow us up.

—Savior Twins! and Phoebus the Destroyer! and Aesculapius father of the Asclepiads! under his hands gentle but firm the ribs were breathing, the flesh flushed with color and stood erect, and Hippolytus opened his eyes.

III.

"Thief!"

It was the king of Hell stood there and said, "Thief!"

"I deny it!" said our physician. "If he had been dead, how is he now alive?"

As for us, we had fallen to the ground and wrapped our cloaks over our heads. (I peered out.)

Aesculapius was green with fear, like the underside of a leaf. That first sentence he had said manly enough; but now his voice stuck in his throat and it came forth, when it came, from the tomb. Yet he stood confronting Pluto; but his knees were knocking and his teeth were chattering.

The god had not yet fully appeared, and we projected into his space each one his own bad dream.

"I know you," said Aesculapius who saw him clearer, "and I am afraid. I do not run away like a live animal only because of these sons who expect of me otherwise. (In so far, I am making a mistake, but I must.)"

"Now five or six times," said the king of Hell, "you have stolen the dead. You brought back Lycurgus and Capaneus and two or three others. Shall Hell be despoiled altogether by you and yours, for we know you train up others? My brother Neptune destroyed Hippolytus; he came to us to send the storm and seal the sentence."

Oh! a fine band of brothers! a fine band of brothers! Pluto, Neptune, and Jupiter, and the cannibal their father! A tide of resentment flowed hotly into our cheeks and from that moment on we have ceased to shudder forever.

"I deny it!" said Aesculapius our spokesman. "There was no such thing as you say. It did not occur." And to our astonishment and glory he found the words for us and cried out, *"Here* you see him! it is Hippolytus. Sit up, boy."

But Hippolytus was pale and faint, and could not.

"Support him!" said the physician.

Willingly two of us supported the young man to his feet. He grew alive under our hands, though he was moaning with pain. Our eyes were blazing with audacity. Our leader was drunken with defiance. We no longer knew what we were doing, nor cared.

The god, of course, was not taken aback. They are what they are. The question is always how we are to cope with that.

Hippolytus, as he stood there supported by us, was not at his best, he was not wearing any laurel wreath, yet he was a very adequate specimen of a living man.

We were frantic with pride.

"So?" said the king of Hell, "you deny it? You deny also, no doubt, the order of natural consequences! A foolish man, a vicious woman, and a callow boy: henceforth, no doubt, one thing is not supposed to lead to another.

So say the sons of Aesculapius! Are *you* the ordainer of the heavens and the earth?"

"No, God forbid," said Aesculapius, "God forbid that I should deny the order of consequences, by which alone we have a world not only to our disaster but to our advantage. But am I to take every senseless error or impulse of lust as a fatality? The natural consequences, as you call them, are often only passing symptoms, warnings for our guidance; and these have been given over to the skill of me and mine!"

He spoke it with breath-taking assurance. One could not resist a bleak smile in the very teeth of the god. Yet, to be truthful, it was all a pack of lies, for we *do* steal the dead, whenever we can, and whatever the circumstances!

IV.

Turning away from our conversation with a gesture of dismissal, Pluto lifted his fists to heaven.

The king of Hell was, as he appeared, black and noble like Memnon and bejeweled like a mine where falls a pencil of sunlight, and your fingers, if you interpose them, drip fire.

"Jupiter guardian," he said solemnly, "guardian of the divisions of the world, strike him dead. For he has brought to life Lycurgus and Capaneus and Hippolytus and two or three more. They are lying; they do not make exceptions of cases but they steal whenever they can. Finally, he has taken leave of his wits and denies the evidence of his senses."

It thundered. The prayer was heard.

Even so we were not afraid, for there was in our master's voice a lilting tune of revelry as he said: "Presently! presently! I shall croak as I have heard so many others. I am inspirited now by my dispiritment then. I foresee in a few minutes my ending with a croak. The way is clear to me, I have often observed it, I am simply shuddering with terror. There is no alleviating circumstance. I hurry along and insist on the material fact. As a man is irresponsibly drunk with the awareness of nothing but the case how it is with him—farewell, sailors of the *Argo!*"

Never before had we heard from him two consecutive sentences about himself and himself, not attentive to some second person or demonstrating the nature of the case.

A bolt of lightning struck him and he fell forward.

"I can revive Hippolytus"—these were the last words of Aesculapius—"but me I cannot revive."

No! No! —we sing our joyous anthem —No! No! We deny it! We deny it!

It did not happen. There is no such thing. The past is always necessary, you cannot disregard it. But not this.

If he had been dead, how is he now alive?

Deny it! deny it! it is always a question how far you can deny the evidence of your senses and get away with it. As for us, we have a steady will for it to have been otherwise, as Aesculapius revived Hippolytus.

Afterwards who is right, they or we?

All along the shore the waves are regularly falling as loud as a conversational voice—it is the noise of drop on drop that thunderously accumulates to be this quiet music—as we lightly carry away our comrade: alas! except for us the line of the Asclepiades would be cut short. On the horizon far where the haze is, the tiny horses of Neptune are playing in the shining. The offshore islands are clear in detail where the lobster-men stop off to fuck the sheep. Their boats are beached.

No! No! we sing our joyful anthem; we deny it! we deny it! If he had been dead, how is he now alive? As for us, we go with a steady will for it to have been otherwise. (Afterwards who is right, they or we?)

As a man is irresponsibly drunk with the awareness of nothing but the case how it is with him—do you think we would be exerting an effort if we did not hope for success?

The day is clear as day and March like the start of spring. Everywhere the sky is spreading further than the earth. The clouds are shapes of vapor in the atmosphere. Sunlight is pouring down from the sun, the heat makes us warm. (That past day was. I recall it as a memory, and I have written it down in words.)

No! No! No! No! We deny it! We deny it! We stumble onward with a steady will for it to have been otherwise. As a man is irresponsibly drunk with nothing but the nature of the case—do you think we should deny the evidence of our senses if the non-existence of the fact were not necessary for us?

Not weeping for myself but my self weeping. My only world weeping myself away. My only world crying herself asleep. Not hurt, not lost, but waste. Not weeping for myself but my self weeping.

Therefore we deny it, we deny it. It did not happen, there is no such thing. We go right forward with a steady will for many things to have been otherwise.

OUR VISIT TO NIAGARA

> ※   "Meanwhile, the specious present, the
> intuited duration, stands permanent, like
> the rainbow on the waterfall, with its
> own quality unchanged by the events that
> stream through it."
>
> —WILLIAM JAMES

I.   THE NIAGARA RIVER

I was bored with the life from which we had come, I was
not interested in the family visit toward which we were
going; but on the way we drove by Niagara Falls. We
came to the Niagara River outside of Buffalo and turned
along it. I was keyed up, I thought the icy emerald of the
water peculiar and remarkable. My wife exclaimed with a
forced, yet not unfelt, enthusiasm. She had lived in these
parts when she was a girl. Now she was afraid—she was
afraid of me—that I might not be moved by Niagara
Falls, that I might consider it ordinary or childish or stupid (qualities that it seemed to me she could not distinguish)
to be moved by Niagara Falls. Out of her past, so poor,
she thought, in contrast to my past, she was about to offer me Niagara Falls, and I might regard that offering as
not much. But these fears that I guessed in her were
groundless, for although I have come to lead among people a spiteful and miserable existence, I still am simple
enough to be entranced by a geological splendor. I knew,
with a quiet confidence and a breathing expectancy, that
I should indeed be excited when I came to see Niagara
Falls. I looked hungrily at the deep and swift green river
as we rolled along. I drove erratically. "Keep your eyes

on the road," said Isobel, pleased at my interest. "Over there are all electro-chemical plants on the other side. Look, Ready," she said to our little boy, *"that's Canada!"*

"Where's Canala? I didn't see it—" cried the four-year-old, as if it were a herd of cows or a pair of horses that we had flown by on the road and called his attention too late, so that he was always desperately looking back.

"That land on the other side of the river. That's *all* Canada."

"We come to Niager Fa's in five minutes? You said so. You'll show me?" He was afraid that we should also fly by Niagara Falls. "Is they a bridge?"

"The Rainbow Bridge," repeated my wife still another time. "Lower down there's the Lewiston Bridge—that's the Gorge." Out of her childhood past she kept evoking, in a mesmerized tone, the words "Rainbow Bridge," "Gorge," "Goat Island," "The Whirlpool." I found it pathetic, but not antipathetic; my teeth were not set on edge. "Don't worry," she said, "you won't miss Niagara Falls. We'll get out of the car."

Out of the car! The child smirked with anticipation. We had been on the road two hard days. To alleviate his impatience, we had kept anticipating Niagara Falls— "Wait till we get to Niagara Falls! Tomorrow Niagara Falls!" Isobel obsessively repeated to him that from the middle of the Rainbow Bridge one got a good view of the Horseshoe Falls, and I kept trying to safeguard him from disappointment by explaining that we wouldn't go across a rainbow, it was just the name of a bridge. "Is they a rainbow?" asked Ready.

First he used to say "Nyaza Fa's." By the time we got to Skaneateles and Cayuga, he was saying "Niara's Fa's." And since Buffalo he had learned to say "Niager *Falls!* Niager *Falls!"*

The city grew thick around us and I paid attention to the wheel. We could hear the far-off booming of the Falls.

II.   APPROACH TO THE FALLS

Soon we could see the white mist shining through the trees and smell the ice-green spray; but I took my time looking for a place to park, for I no longer felt *eager* to see Niagara Falls. My face was flushed and my voice had heady tones, but I had lost contact with them. I could not hear the booming any more—the pedal-point had been held too loud and long—only confused murmuring, some one in the other room talking in his sleep.

If I had been alone, I think, I should have come to terms with my embarrassment as follows: I should have made a little bow to Niagara Falls when I saw him, and spread my lips in a smile, and sketched an informal salute, thus limiting the occasion to a small friendly encounter, as I am used to when I suddenly come on the moon on a country road. But now I was embarrassed for Isobel, to watch me encounter Niagara Falls according to some expectation of hers, as if she were the donor of Niagara Falls, for so she had appropriated it in her girlhood. I could not find a parking space and lost my temper; I cursed because it cost us fifty cents to park the car and we were poor.

"We'll stop only an hour," she said timidly, "just so you can see it. They expect us this afternoon."

My loyalty rose in me, I knew that Niagara Falls was important to *her*, and I said brutally, taking the blame on myself, "Oh drat your mother! she won't die this time either. Since we came so far—now that we're here—come, Ready, on to Niagara Falls!"

My wife was burning with impatience. I did not realize that it was despair, that she had already unconsciously given up hope of seeing Niagara Falls, as she sometimes decided at the very beginning of fucking not to have an orgasm. "We go out on Goat Island," she said. "That's—it's this way. It's this way." She led the way.

The boy was dancing. He was making the tiny bob of his head that he makes when a promise is really to be fulfilled; the chief part of his excitement is that his trust in us has been confirmed.

I could again hear the booming. To my surprise, I noticed that the smell and the rush of waters were coming from the other direction. *Up*stream. How was that?

"Niara's Fa's! Niara's Fa's!" cried Ready, as we came onto the stone bridge. I turned pale.—

"No, that's the river *going* to the Falls," said Isobel.

"The Falls is there where it's going over. We have to go out on the *island* to see."

But he was already throwing sticks into the boiling river and climbing on the parapet to watch his boats go under. He would whirl the stick with all his hard might and let go. Sometimes the stick flew, and sometimes it dropped at his feet while his own body tried to fly.

Isobel impatiently walked ahead and came back. She wanted us to see the *Falls*.

—As for me, I had turned pale. *The broad Niagara River was coming downhill toward us on the bridge.* There was a transporting smell of the oxygenated water. I had not counted on this slope of water. Seeing it, I quite forgot that I was meant to go on to see Niagara Falls. Obviously this, this *flow* of water bore everything before it, yet we persisted on the bridge. All of the Great Lakes was coming on. To me in my poverty it was this *copiousness* of water, visibly accelerating from the horizon and looming to engulf us, that promised—everything. I was not interested in either achievements or catastrophes. I do not need a spectacular Falls. The good smell was so strong it stank. Recovering from my astonishment, my ears ringing, I began to breathe evenly. Far off, at about eye level, the broad water was always dividing into its two channels.

My wife was puzzled that I was moved before the proper time to be moved. Yet automatically she found herself repeating a lesson of long ago, and she said, "It has all the power of the Great Lakes behind it." To her acute embarrassment she flushed and thrilled at the words, that were so evidently true. "Now that's *enough,* Ready!" she cried irritably, "let's go and see the Falls."

He jumped down from the parapet obediently; and I too was content to be led away, for I had had my Niagara Falls, as in a company of sailors on the town, one fellow is more calm and rational than the others because he has already had his party. So habitually, I have my party (I see to that) very quickly; and then, secure from disappointment, I am tolerant and serviceable.

III. ON GOAT ISLAND

As it is, we are protected by our social customs from
ever seeing Niagara Falls except by chance. There are
prescribed vantage-points and boat-rides and guided
tours, carefully fenced to be safe for the multitudes who
visit these dangerous Falls. These call attention to this or
that aspect of the Falls, and every such aspect is note-
worthy and, in the nature of the case, uninteresting, domesticated. Niagara Falls is shopworn. No doubt everybody feels the same and would like to exclaim, as Hawthorne did,

> "Oh that I had never heard of Niagara Falls till I beheld
> it! Blessed were the wanderers of old, who heard its deep
> roar, sounding through the woods, as the summons to an
> unknown wonder, and approached its awful brink, in all the
> freshness of native feeling. Had its own mysterious voice
> been the first to warn me of its existence, then, indeed, I
> might have knelt down and worshipped."

And still another century has passed since then, more
and more populous, more and more commercial.

It had been hard to find a parking space, and on the
rock ledge there was a great crowd elbowing to stand at
the fence and watch Lake Erie falling into Lake Ontario.
There was a lot of talk, that sunny afternoon, about Red
Hill who had just gotten himself killed going over in a
barrel made of inner-tubes and piano-wire. Red had
tried for the notoriety, in order to make a living and pay
for his beer; yet it was also the case that, like his father,
his life had been curiously bound up with the green
River. He was a "River man."

The color of that scene is extraordinary. The water is
emerald, the foam has a touch of yellow; the mist and the
air are shining; and the strata of rocks are a faded maroon streaked with gray-green. The vast amphitheater is
glowing. But then—superfluously, or like a bolt of magic
(perhaps it comes to the same thing)—shines the rainbow in the mist. One racks one's brains: where before has
one seen this unique coloration? And suddenly one re-

members: it was in a cheap chromolithograph of Niagara Falls! The violent caricature has betrayed its original to a T.

I stood at the fence. By experiencing it, I could see how a minute alteration of attention, a tiny false note, could change the magic Manitou into the vulgar postcard, not otherwise than those alternating figures-and-grounds of the psychologists flicker and make you sick. The scene did not fail continually to provide a false note. Far below in the basin the ridiculous little steamers, *Maid of the Mist I* and *Maid of the Mist II,* were busily chugging around and around.

"Well, it's the honeymoon's second disappointment, Niagara Falls," said a jocose fellow.

But Ready was smirking and bobbing his head in ecstatic recognition of the rainbow. It was there forever in the mist, it did not fly by. Beside himself with excitement, the boy fetched a stick from the thicket and flung it into the rainbow.

IV. THE CAVE OF THE WINDS

Now, however, I had a delicious and redeeming experience that has made me glad forever that I visited Niagara Falls. I say "redeeming" in a pregnant sense, for it was a kind of religious experience.

As a girl, Isobel had never descended to the *Cave of the Winds*. This was a guided trip among the fragmented rocks at the foot of the Falls, behind the sheet of water. We went to the pavilion. The fee was a dollar and a quarter each, and no children allowed. "It's not worth it, let's not—" she said (it used to cost half a dollar and they were too poor; now it cost a little more and we were too poor). I insisted. I parked Ready with an ice cream soda with the matron, and I laid down our sacrifice on the counter.

"Right this way, sir!" exclaimed at once a burly attendant, a kind of Turkish masseur. "Men this way! Women that way! You meet afterwards in front of the elevator." His tone was a command.

He led me to a clammy cell in a cold room. "You strip here. Underwear and socks too. Like your mother made you. I'll bring your duds. Put cash and valuables in this box and give it to me."

"I have no cash or valuables," I said.

"So much the better! No need to apologize."

I stripped. The floor and the stool were wet. I felt uncomfortable and exposed. He came back with a flannel monkey-suit, a pair of crude canvas slippers, and a flaming yellow oilskin and hood. "Put these on and go out to the elevator." The shoes were miserably wet.

When we were gathered at the elevator, men in yellow, women in black, I saw that we were neophytes. We were the fat and the lean, the tall and the short, of the Americans. At once our guide appeared and marshalled us into the cage. He was a large jolly fellow, in a habit that fitted; his manner was unmistakably malicious.

Ready caught sight of us in our strange costumes, he stretched out his arms and uttered a despairing wail; but the door slammed behind us and we descended.

"We are now going down through two hundred feet of solid rock—" began our guide. "Such and such tons of water are falling every second." The walls of the shaft were sweating like the tunnel of the IRT subway at 190th Street in New York City. Our shoes were wet and pinching. The fog, as we emerged, was thick. It was hard to see. There was nothing to see.

"This way!" roared our guide above the roar of waters. One could make out a boardwalk and wooden steps winding a short distance among the rocks; but nothing of any interest. He herded us out onto the walk and at once we began to be assailed by the wind and the shower. Nothing could be seen in the fog. We moved cautiously along, single file. "Watch your step! now for it!" roared our guide; and he led us where the buffeting was harder and the flood more blinding and drenching. That was "it." There was nothing to see.

It was evident that we were simply being hazed. The walk went on still a little way, where one could see still less and be still more uncomfortable. And now our shepherd was laughing at us.

According to their characters, some of the sheep began to be angry, some confused, some alarmed. I, identifying with the malice of the inventor of all this, began to be delighted. Once one accepted it *as* nothing; indeed it was even pleasant to face the furious sallies of cold water (though it was not worth a dollar and a quarter).

We came to the climax and stood on the last platform, drowning and gasping. Momentarily the fog blew away and through the downpour we could make out a rudely lettered sign:

```
┌─────────────────────────────────┐
│                                 │
│     No Smoking                  │
│                                 │
└─────────────────────────────────┘
```

Almost everybody was willing to laugh a little.

—This trip at Niagara Falls is our Mystery of Eleusis. One offers sacrifice and is taken in tow. One is stripped of his clothes and of the things of this world. One is subjected to the healing elements. And at last one is initiated into the American Hoax. . . . I should not record it here and give away the secret, except that it is precisely when the facts are known to us through and through that the gullible can feel most gullible.

"Well, and how did you enjoy your experience?" the Turkish masseur asked me blandly, as I dressed.

"Frankly, I enjoyed it very much. I enjoyed it immensely," I said, and gave him a quarter tip.

But some of the others, less established in philosophy, could be heard to mutter darkly, and they did not tip him at all.

V. THE HORSESHOE FALLS

Returning, I was holding my boy by the hand and we watched the Horseshoe Falls. Refreshed by my shower in the waters of Lake Erie, I was no longer perplexed by the notoriety and venality of Niagara Falls. The coloration of Niagara Falls did not oscillate into a chromolithograph of Niagara Falls; but the fact persisted as it was, continuously coming and becoming: that the ragged water rounding the deep bend under the cloudy sky was falling accelerating into the Gorge whence rose a strong voice, and mist. For his part, the small boy had played enough at throwing himself into the water in sticks and riding the current; he was content to stand still and watch like a grown person, but smirking none the less and bobbing his head in excited appreciation.

At a certain moment—I could tell by the tingling in his hand—his excitement gave way to orgastic wonder. He was very still, and then he said, "It keeps coming."

The Niagara kept coming; and without even the illusion of seeming to pause at the brink, the ocean spilled over. The weight of water gathered speed and crashed.

VI.   THE WHIRLPOOL

Isobel had, quietly, become frantic. Always looking for the Whirlpool. As we rolled northward along the Gorge —she was driving—suddenly she would pull over to the side of the road and jam the brakes, to see the Whirlpool. We would get out of the car to look at the Gorge, but this was not the place, and we went on. I assumed for a while that there really was a particular place she was looking for, that embodied her Niagara Falls. She referred vaguely to the Whirlpool; but it was not the Whirlpool plainly marked on our map that she was seeking. Also, she cast hardly a glance at the Gorge and rapids as they spread before us different around every turning, washed always with the colors of Niagara. She kept looking away to the other side of the road, where their house had been, if indeed it had been, if this was the road.

She had offered me her Niagara Falls, as a kind of peace offering or an appeasement, since she could not (would not) generously give me what I wanted and what was my due. The bother was that she did not *have* an available Niagara Falls for herself, nor to give. As for me, I am not altogether vindictive; I was quite willing to share her remembered enthusiasm and to admire Niagara Falls. But then, of course, I had to admire what *I* saw in Niagara Falls, and in the manner that I admire something, and this, of course, served only to estrange us further. What I could not (would not) do was to give to her my Niagara Falls, to share with her my impressions of Niagara Falls. (I am made anxious telling it with all the safeguards of literature.)

I refrained from raillery at her sentimental journey, and perhaps this was my mistake, for sometimes a burst of anger brings one sharply to the present actuality, to experience. If I had rallied her, her eyes would have flashed, her cheeks become hot, and her chin as stupid-stubborn as her mother's; nor is she unattractive when she looks that way. But as it was, we kept dutifully piling out of the car. I held the little boy firmly by the hand so he would not tumble down the slope, for he was fiercely yawning, hardly able to stand on his feet.

Nor was there a Whirlpool either, not in the sense of a maelstrom, a yawning spiral in the swirling waters that one could go down into if one had the courage (courage she had), as the Chinese magician descended via the whirlpool to hell, and danced his dance. What they call the Whirlpool is where the foaming Niagara makes an acute meander—that will soon cut the barrier and leave behind an oxbow—and everywhere there are confused and whirling waters.

I dared not look at her disappointment. Instead I looked at the mighty scene that did not disappoint, and recurs, shining emerald and maroon, in my spontaneous recollection, with the bellow of the Falls. All this scene, I could see, was fresh and recent and in the act of rapidly changing: the "ancient" Gorge was only a few thousands, a few scores of thousands, years old; soon it would again look different—the meander straight, the oxbow left behind; and the overthrust, the famous escarpment of Niagara, was being eaten away before one's very eyes, back toward Lake Erie, for the Falls erodes the softer understrata and the roof comes tumbling down. I could not help comparing Niagara against the standard of the Hudson of my own childhood, the valley cloven through pre-Cambrian granite, and the valley itself long ago drowned.

A tiny distant man was fishing on the bank. It was obscure to us how he had gotten down there.

I dared to look at her. I said gently, "Can you remember, Bella, who first told you that the Falls had behind them all the power of the Great Lakes?"

We could speak quietly for a moment, for Ready had fallen asleep at our feet, and so a burden had dropped from our shoulders.

Surprised by my question, she screwed up her face in a frown. She had a headache. She could not remember, neither who it was, nor how old she was, nor in what circumstances it was. But the tears started into her eyes, her frantic face relaxed, and she began to sob. She ran sobbing into the car, bawling.

All the years of her girlhood they had kept her at a strict boarding school, far from Niagara Falls. But she was first afraid, then ashamed, then she would not give them the satisfaction, to bawl for her loneliness. Nor was it any use. She had wanted to play the piano, but her widowed mother could not pay for lessons at the school and she was not allowed to touch the pianos, though there were six and they were idle. She was frequently "insubordinate," and the punishment was to sit up in the cold before dawn. There was a piano in that room and she once defiantly played on it loud through the night.

I carried the sleeping figure of our little boy to the car and laid him on the back seat.

She could not, by trying, give me the loyalty, the identification, that might perhaps have made living with a person like myself worthwhile. What she did for me—it was everything she did—she did as a duty that she had chosen, also for herself, that she had chosen but not that she wanted. Then when from time to time came a crisis and I happened to need affectionate support, she was disapproving and abandoned me to my detractors. Or again, she was sobbing for the fatality that exiled her to living with a person like myself who could only make her lonely and frightened, although there seemed to be other opportunities to live a little happier. (Just as I compel myself to live where I get not what I need, yet not nothing; except that I do not sob for it, but, bravely enough, hammer out my impressions of Niagara Falls.)

Or, simply, the headache in her temples made her whimper, a headache not to be alleviated by weeping, for it was the stretching of wide eyes of fright—near-sighted eyes behind horn-rimmed spectacles that she would not take off.

I took the wheel and we drove onward toward Ontario. Soon the river, as we glimpsed it, had become a gentle lovely river moving toward its sea. Our little boy was sleeping in the back seat. Finally, between two hills, we could see the inland sea. I was describing to my wife—sharing it with her—Lorado Taft's fountain-figure of *The Great Lakes* that stands in front of the Art Institute in Chicago. She had before her five great shells that cascade one into the other: Superior, Michigan, Huron, Erie, and Ontario—and so out to the open sea—all ingeniously placed and characterized to symbolize the actuality.

LAUGHING LADDY'S
SYMBOLIC ACT*

> ※ "The disharmony of the world seems, comfortingly enough, to be merely an arithmetical one."
>
> —KAFKA

I.

The Laddy liked to swim. So, being in Venice, he took the steamboat across the bay to Lido beach. Now the beach on Lido Island was divided into three zones.

The first, nearest the boat-station, was equipped with elegant private bathhouses that rented for 500 lire. Laddy could see at a glance the advantage of having such a little cottage to retire to if one had interesting company, and not far to walk. But he had come alone and had so far not met any one on the steamer who was both attractive and available. What set the Irish youth against the Exclusive beach, however, was that it was surrounded by a high wire fence to keep out those who did not have 500 lire. This was, he thought, an unwise economy; it importantly curtailed circulation and the probability, in this world that is statistically difficult, that a person would hit on what would make him happy. In his ignorance of the local situation, he was missing the point, for the Exclusive beach was designed by the canny Italians precisely for those lovers—bosses and secretaries or married folk with jealous spouses—who wanted to get away together for an afternoon, and comparatively quite cheap.

* This is a further chapter for Book V of *The Empire City*.

Laddy proceeded half a mile further down the island to
the Popular beach. Here came everybody, in all combinations, boys in bands and girls in bevies, placid wives
and hairy husbands slapping their nimble children and
feeding them sandwiches, teen-age lovers who did not
have 500 lire, and soldiers and sailors on the loose. For
a nominal fee, folk kept their belongings safe from
thieves in lockers, and there was a large congregation
around this pavilion washing the sand off their feet, and
where they also served wine and pasta and there was
music, so it was easy for anybody to strike up with anybody. Laddy's eyes sparkled with approval, and he en-
visaged such a community-building on his own beloved
Lough Neagh or on the sea at Dun Laoghaire, where the
Irish, who were not a whit less beautiful or lively, could
come to be populous and exist again, now that Saint Wayward had silenced the Jesuits. "But what," his mind raced
ahead, "when you *have* struck up with somebody? Ah—"

He saw that the procedure was then to leave this
Populare, where there were no private cottages, and go a
walk further along the shore to where it was wilder and
there were dunes. Surely this was also a grand thing for
a couple who had conceived an interest in each other and
who went for a walk in hope that that interest would increase and be practical. Trudging along the shore of the
blue sea washing their ankles, and stopping to pick up
shells, to where the landscape became wilder.

He approved of this decent agenda, but he was already a
wild one and he did not stop at the Popular beach and pay
his nominal fee. He hurried on, not impatiently but with
an excited laugh, to explore that Free beach itself, the
third zone, for it was called *la piaggia libra.* It beckoned
and he pressed on into the dune brush and the empty
waste of sand, to take his swim where the others didn't,
although he understood that this was not the decent
order to enjoy a practically happy day at the beach, since
the place to find an attractive partner is where there are
people, not where there are only rough pine trees and deserted bunkers from the War. But he was, I say, a wild
one. You could hear in his laughter an edge of wildness;
it was not, after all, a simple friendly sociable laugh. This
was not a likely sign for a man destined to become a cul-

ture-hero for the Irish folk, to laugh for himself alone
and to choose the Free beach to take his swim.

Nevertheless, this choice of his was part of a larger
plan, whereby in the wild he would learn to do his social
duty, and not just please himself from day to day.

II.

The Irishman undressed on the empty beach and put on
his bathing suit, as was *de rigueur* in that period, 1957,
and he heartily enjoyed his solitary swim. The water of
the Adriatic was soupy and unusually salty, not without
grapefruit-rinds and watermelon-rinds, but he was not
fussy. He stretched out in comfort on the dirty sand. (He
did not carry a towel to lie on like those sons of Ireland
whom you see on New York beaches, who seem to be
such toughs yet are afraid of a little grit, shit, and sperm.)

He had fallen asleep when, as if out of the blue, there
fell a thunderbolt, followed in a second by its deafening
thunderclap. The sky had clouded like a frown, the wind
was whipping the Adriatic. A bolt of lightning fell next to
him, with its roar simultaneous, and there burst such a
storm as was the inauspicious herald of the victorious
Moor to Cyprus, or hardly more fortunate (for her) the
tempest that drove Dido and Aeneas into the cave.
Laddy opened his startled eyes in the noise. The rain was
splashing down big as quarters. He sat up wild with joy
at the blue-black beauty of the scene and, seizing his
shoes and shirt and pants he bolted to his feet and ran
for a nearby bunker.

There were deserted bunkers from the War, redouts of
concrete scattered in the dunes, cylindrical, some greater
some smaller, strong enough to withstand the onrush of
armored tanks but now ruined and in rubble and put to
the uses of peace as hideouts where the Free-beachers
could make love in privacy. Seldom have swords been
beaten into more useful ploughshares.

Clutching his clothes, he ran for a big gray job with a
roomy hall of an entrance. There were others there—half
a dozen. The rain was coming down in sheets. By the
time he got under the roof he looked drowned and they

greeted him with hilarity and threw him a towel to dry his eyes.

He was, needless to say, an object of beauty and interest. *They* were three men, two women, and an adolescent boy. He looked about in admiration at the great concrete vault with its entrance overlooking the sea, the work of Italian masons, tip top, even in its state of rubble and ruin. He saw that there was also an entrance to an inner chamber that had been the magazine.

The man with the straw hat and the golden teeth joked to him in Italian. The man naked to the waist and covered with tattooes joked to him in German. The pretty lady smiled to him in French—she was from Geneva—and Laddy answered with an immediate hard-on in his swimming-trunks, a language universal. But at this her Swiss husband darkly scowled, and Laddy politely withdrew to the rear to explore the innards of the bunker.

The other two were strangely immobile—he did not like that. The heavy set German lady in the black dress with a heavy walking-stick looked with continually piercing eyes; she was not a beauty. The adolescent boy should have been a beauty, but he had a bad character, hostile and conceited.

The magazine of the bunker was dark and vast. It did not smell too good, people had shat in some of the corners. But other parts were not insalubrious and he saw—he lit a match—that in some coigns there were beds of straw and newspaper. He noted with approval, for although he himself preferred to make love under the wide eye of heaven, knowing that God smiled on him and it, yet he understood that there were others, not less worthy, who sought out darkness and shelter, the womb of night, safe from the prying of the Evil Eye. Why not, in a pinch, a corner of the inner chamber of the bunker? Laddy was easy-going, latitudinarian. He approved of those who stayed at the bathhouses and those who adventured into the wild, of those who fucked in the open air and those who hid in bunkers in order to fuck.

He returned to the company in the outer hall and two more had come in out of the rain, a teen-age couple strayed from the *Populare,* Beata and Paolo. Beata, dripping wet, was being bitchy to Paolo and she was acting this out by responding to the courtly attentions of the Italian gentleman with the straw hat and gold teeth, while the boy bit his lips.

"Nine of us!" thought Laddy enthusiastically. The entire company were indeed lugubriously watching the rain glistening on the dune shrubs in the silvery light and at best exchanging polyglot monosyllables. It was an atmosphere cold, cheerless, and uncomfortable. Yet Laddy could not help feeling enthusiastic to see what fine and plentiful human animals there were here—with *obvious* ways to get warm, and blessed Opportunity. He *took it for granted* that in this splendid company, segregated in a bunker waiting out the rain and nothing else to do, there were plenty of relations of attraction and possibilities of interesting action.

Some of the combinations leapt to the eye. The Italian gentleman was a pederast pursuing the conceited adolescent hustler whose name was Beppo; meantime he was stringing the little miss along. The tattooed German seemed to be a pederast too—but no, he was not interested in the boys, it was at Laddy's crotch that he was fixedly staring. Laddy himself was excited by the sidelong glance of the pretty Swiss, and this was having an erotic effect on her jealous husband who at this very moment wanted to knock her down and fuck her in full sight of all, saying "Mine! mine!" The steely German lady—she was a Countess—had begun to tap her cane and bite her lips.

There are two ways of looking at a scene like this. People are thrown together at random, to escape the elements; cheerlessly and bored they wait it out until they can again pursue the fair-weather purposes they are bent on; yes, that is one way of looking at it. But *in the nature of the case,* thought Laughing Laddy of Lough Neagh, here they *are,* now, live human animals brought together and sparks of spontaneous attraction, and leisure to devote ourselves to one another. This is the positive way of looking at it. There is no more heart-warming and promissory situation than to be stranded out of the rain with interesting people. The rain falls unheeded.

The peaceful and generous young Irishman was disturbed by the signs of hostility in the company, which he, for his part, was not going to exacerbate. Even so, he naively believed, given so many statistical chances, some good must eventuate for somebody. It was *obvious,* he *took it for granted,* it was *in the nature of the case:* such are the expressions of the innocent.

III.

The case, our human nature, was that no good was going to eventuate for anybody.

The erotic drama in that cave was idiotic. I do not intend to present it in its melancholy detail. It is the function of a poet to move and instruct, and not to freeze your marrow with the description of our usual plight that you know well enough. I would not tell this anecdote at all if it did not, finally, illustrate a higher plan.

The rather courtly Italian—his gold teeth flashed charmingly under his Panama hat; he was a journalist from Milan and his card said Ph.D.—had had a date here with the toughie hustler whom he usually paid 1000 lire. But today, to take him down a peg, he was willing to pay only 500. Meantime, while the young snot thought it over, he was flirting with Beata (who was more interesting anyway). She, the silly minx, was overwhelmed by so much grandeur and looked with unconcealed disdain at poor Paolo who had picked her up at the *Populare.*

Beppo, the hustler, disdained to pay attention to any one. Despite his acquaintance with gentlemen and scholars, he did not have a wide discourse. He responded to conversational advances by saying "Up yours!" or "Shut your trap!" Thoughtfully grinding his back teeth, he made up the plan to take the 500 lire but inhibit his orgasm, and then to come off with the *tedesco.* This would show who was boss.

The German was a remarkable and pathetic man. Naked to the waist and shivering, he was crudely self-tattooed in black and blue, every square inch, during long years in a Hamburg jail under Hitler. He was a world-famous cameraman. On him the first appearance of Laddy looming in the entrance against the dunes had had an extraordinary effect: he saw him as the Angel of

Death, swinging his bright blade forever on the boundary of Paradise. His knees were shaking and his teeth chattering with fear and desire as he essayed to stand near the Irishman and touch him. Laddy liked him, his cultured English and his intelligent eyes, and of course he was not unaware that the poor man wanted to touch his cock and get from it what strength he could. "You're cold, chum," he said, and laid an arm friendly across his shoulders, "why don't you put a shirt on?" With a cry the man started with fright and tore himself away, and stood out in the rain, biting his lips.

The Countess, who was his financier, had pursued him to Munich, from Munich to Lucerne, from Lucerne to Lugano, from Lugano to Venice, and in each place she looked at him with the same determined scorn.

Finally, in this sorry combination, there was Laddy and the pretty Swiss wife, so near and yet so far. But both were able to get a comic pleasure from the situation and to remain decent, and the irascible husband stiffly maintained his dignity.

At this moment the teen-age boy, Paolo, could contain his rage no longer and he slapped Beata across the eyes. This unleashed a frightful energy in the tattooed German and he threw the youth to the ground and began to pound him, till Laddy seized him by the hair and dragged him off. "Don't do that, chum," he said quietly.

"Oh Jesus!" he groaned from the bottom of his disillusioned heart, "I might as well be in an Irish pub." And he picked up his shoes and pants and shirt and retreated toward the inner room to dress and leave this place, for it was better to walk in the elements.

What a lesson he was learning! He knew that our existence is mathematically difficult, distances are great, it is not usual for lust to meet its best object, even less so in opportune circumstances. But he believed that it was possible to increase the probabilities of happiness, by multiplying one's efforts, by latitudinarian standards, by being satisfied with modest successes. It had not occurred to him that there existed a negative principle of defeat among people, that could nullify even brilliant promises.

He looked back at them from the threshold of the magazine. He loved them each one, and all together compassionately, they were fair or at least interesting. But he went in.

IV.

Full of somber thoughts and philosophy and compassion, he stripped off his bathing trunks and stood naked in the demi-darkness, undecided whether to put on first his left shoe or his right.

There appeared from the shadow a wizened old granny, toothless and bent, holding out her gnarled hand to beg.

"Soldi!"

"What! What? Do you want money, you poor granny? You gave me a turn." He took a couple of hundred-lire pieces from his jeans and gave them in her hand.

"Grazie!" She clutched them eagerly and pocketed them. *"Grazie! grazie!"* Nevertheless she persisted in getting closer to him and holding out her hand which now began to tremble violently.

"It's nooky you want too!" said Laddy with a flat but not unkindly laugh. He turned his body full toward her, so that his cock was nearer her outstretched hand. She fell on it with hot hands and kisses. She was inflamed by his nakedness. *"Bene? bene?"* she said, fearful, as though he might suddenly bash her brains in. He gently touched her harsh gray hair. *"Va bene,"* he said.

"Va bene," he said, *"since* you ask. Who'm I to turn ye down? But ye'll have to coax it up a bit, I'm thinking, because it's not looking at you, dearie, that will ever make him rise at a bound." Of course he courteously muttered this in English.

Now it's a poor kind of prick, not Laughing Laddy's, that can't be brought to life by a little fondling and kissing, and soon his rosy cock that had about it oh the bloom of youth, was big and strong. It was a hard-on wasteful alas for himself, since he was feeling nothing at all. But she pulled up her skirts excitedly; her cunt was dripping and pouting like a young wife's, remarkably, for she must have been seventy-five. Pathetically she showed off her shrunken buttocks, saying, *"Bello culo? no? Bello culo!"*

Since he undertook to be fucking her, the Irishman was not grudging about it. He put his penis in as if he meant it—he did not leave it to her to put it in—and he proceeded to give her a good workmanlike fucking, pressing her with his belly against the wall—still holding his pants in one hand and his shoes in the other. She squealed with delight. She clutched and scratched at his flanks, which was not his taste in love-making but he bore it with manly fortitude. Hopefully she looked up into his face, and he smiled down at her. When he judged that she had had enough, he gave in to a spontaneous interval to come off and fill her with something of himself, though to fertilize nothing.

During this interval of abstraction, she skilfully rifled the rest of the coins out of the pants that dangled from his limp hand.

He stood aside hygienically to urinate and he put on his pants. He noticed he had been rolled. "Give me back a hundred lire for the steamboat, grandmother," he said firmly, holding out his hand. She gave it gladly. She was frantic and vocal in her praises for his manliness and beauty and compared him to Michael the Archangel, or perhaps she was saying that he was like a figure of Michelangelo's—it is hard to guess what the Italians will say. He blushed.

V.

However it was, when he emerged again in the brighter vault—but Beata and Paolo were gone—he had as if increased in size, like one who has overcome a darling error and has done his duty. He spoke out at once. "There you have it!" he said bitterly.

Because he had a right to it, he allowed himself the following priggish homily, which he spoke with arrogance. Or rather, to do him justice, he could not help bursting out with it, since when a fellow has had a poor, not very feelingful, orgasm, he must vent his energy somewhere, in order not to turn it against himself and be sad, with what they used to call *post coitum tristitia*.

"There you have it! It's like a morality in a book. Here we were nine people, and six dozen ways to get a little satisfaction, but nobody got anything because nobody came across. But now back there the old piece wanted me and came across and asked, and I too came across. Gave her a good workmanlike fucking too. What skin was it off my ass? I trust I didn't catch a dose. There'll be another fuck in me in ten minutes, Saint Brigit! may it be more enjoyable."

He spoke this with arrogance, so that they looked at him with fear and astonishment. The Swiss wife began to weep, as if somehow he were upbraiding her, but he was not, and certainly she was the least to blame.

His anger was spent, and he went on more earnestly to his Sermon on the Mount. "Admitted that this world is mathematically difficult, that's all the more reason, isn't it? why you must not be impractical. To be practical is to come across. When you have a choice whether or not to reach out your hand, reach out your hand. When your friend does not bring himself even to make an appeal, then respond to the appeal that he does not even make.

"People say they *can't* come across. They are lying. The case is that they *won't*.

"Also, if you undertake to do something, don't be non and grudging about it, but do it in a committed and workmanlike way. Man, omit your fantasy, since it is your wife who is lying beside you. Wife, take his cock also in your mouth, if this is the kind of thing that pleases. Come across. Be practical."

He shook his head from side to side and said, "We certainly do not live in paradise. Yet it is not impossible to live in a modest kind of paradise. Our earthly paradise is not a place where we do what we want, and get what we imagine we want—God forbid, it would be disastrous. Earthly paradise is the place where people are practical and do not hold back from doing what they can. It's not our mother nature that is stingy with us, but ourselves."

Suddenly, as happened sometimes with him, he was so taken by his own blarney that he burst into tears. He was embarrassed by his emotion and also by the oratorical figure that he was presenting to them. He did not realize that he was standing before them suffused in an aura of blue light shot with orange. Awkwardly he bowed to the pretty lady and kissed her hand, and cordially shook her husband's hand to show that he meant no ill. Hastily he kissed the German on the brow and mumbled, "Why don't you call on us in town? We're at the Danieli, name of Alger." And he walked out into the unceasing rain.

VI.

Telling the story to St. Wayward back at the Danieli, Laddy was again in a jolly mood, and he did not spare thumbnail sketches of the irate husband from Geneva, the persecutory lady with the cane, and the hustler who had not a wide discourse.

But from the beginning, the boy Saint paid the closest attention. He made Laddy go back over it and fill in this detail and that detail. "There's no doubt of it!" he said finally.

"No doubt of what, Wayward?"

"Your act was symbolic. Notice. You passed by the concourse of the folk and chose the solitary walk in the wild, only to find yourself the more trapped in humanity, to suffer it. As if fleeing, you went into the inner room and fucked grandmother. There's no doubt of it at all, Laddy! you too will be a saint and one day wear a halo like myself."

When he had been pondering these things, Wayward's movable halo slanted forward over his eyebrows, like the cap of a sailor of the U.S. Navy on serious duty. But when he came to a conclusion, his halo tilted rakishly over one devilish eye, and the boy looked, if I may say so, like Champion Nunsoe Duc de la Terrasse, that white poodle with the malicious leer who year after year wins best dog in the show.

"You will be a saint because what happens to you is a pre-figure of what *will* happen to you, until the plan is fulfilled. Now, know that the granny you fucked in the back room—hah! and you say she picked your pocket too? while you were coming off? that's rich!—that granny is Ireland, and it is your part to bring her to life again, till she squeals with delight. And she rolled you too! that's good! that's really very good!" Wayward laughed his silvery laugh.

"I fail to see why that touch is so funny," said the Irishman.

"Back to Ireland!" commanded St. Wayward. "Your way is figured forth. You must leave here pretty soon and go home and begin. I wish I could say that I envied you the task. If I may judge by the symbol, it's not an attractive one."

"No, it's not," soberly agreed the Laughing Laddy of Lough Neagh.

"When *I* am grown to man's estate," said Wayward, "I trust I'll have more pleasurable duties. Oh, I'm sure I shall! The Creator of the heavens and the earth did not mean me to sweat and labor, but to be an exemplar of how all things conspire together to fall out just right."

New York City
February 1968

THE EMPEROR OF CHINA

　※　　*La Gaieté*
—BEETHOVEN,
superscription to Opus 127

I.

What does the Master infer? as he sits in his smallness on the swiftest of the claws of battling tigers; as he hovers in the middle of the whirlwind and so, the only one of us, is still in the storm.

　—That it's not the case, if we spend our strength for a free stroke, that there's no strength left for another! There is not a reservoir of force, but force is welling in the soul. If we *use up* our strength in love, there will be more strength for labor and collaboration. And always we are ready to the present.

　To the present: *Ow!* (I am now speaking not for the Master but for the Emperor of China who often says Ow!) The wild ducks flying southward rest in the same swamp as on their way northward: but the winter is upon us. Master, is not this a round, and for me at least not endless? Therefore the little yellowed man, the Emperor of China, is dreaming of immortality, and he has summoned to his court the Master, the sorcerer, to mix for *him* the potion of vitality. But will our Master come?

　Ah, as he lingers at his ease in the eye of the startled, swifter than fright, and therefore the only one of us who is not blind, what does the seer see?

　—That there is true invention, in social nature and art. It is not the case that what is done is only the hopeless palliative for an old wound. The games of the children are freely inventing the children, as slowly their red stockings flicker across the yard. Our Master waits smiling in the quick of the grievous wound, reveling in the knowledge that Destiny is Providence.

Is Providence: *Ow!* The Emperor knows it well; who can deny that Destiny has brought us one and all to the present moment? And we are rotating as in a whirlpool down into the black heart of our wound. Yes, the destiny of the Emperor of China and of the court of the Emperor of China is the providence of the sadness of all China. Who can deny it, as we slowly one by one slip to our death?

(But it is said that the *people* of China is immortal.)

The Master of the *Way!*—that we see only fitfully, when the curtain of the world happens to be ripped— what does he know, swimming in a gleaming spray-drop and sinking with it into the shining sea?

—He knows that what is best is easiest and what is easiest is best. Does it not rest and slide in the accumulated rage of the universe, and survive in the next motion of the universe as it trembles open into freedom and the present, not otherwise than the trembling daisy stretches to the tips of its many trembling petals? By the best, the easiest, and the latest moment, our friends will everywhere create small worlds of freedom.

But the ancient court of China turns in its tiresome ritual about its sullen wound. And those of the court most ancient and dignified are soonest sucked downward into black hell. It is these mandarins of the court who have said that the energy of the universe and the soul is conserved: that is, that it dribbles away in use, and if a man uses it for love or achievement, he will not have any left. They say, too, that a man becomes a man by giving up the ways of a child, rather than by growing into the glory of the next moment as it comes. So say these circlers of an old wound.

But our Master lay seventy years aforming in the womb, in safety, and *he* will never become a mere personality like you or me.

They imagine, in the red-lacquer court, that they are hoarding their strength. But watch close and you see that their ritual is made of thousands and thousands of pitiful fights with themselves, so minute that they cannot see them, but we see them in the taut tendons and strained eyes. "We cannot!" they cry, and meantime they are exhausting their power as hard as they can to whirl themselves around and downward into black hell. *Ow!*

The Emperor is bleeding. "That sage," he thinks, "is an immortal person"—the fool, for our Master is not even a person, and we doubt that he is immortal. "Send for him here, to mix me a potion of vitality, and perhaps I shall not die the moment after next."

Ay, send for him! beyond the Great Wall of the Empire. But will our Master come? lying stretched in his vastness as the circle of the horizon. What is our Master planning, as his thoughts drift across the blue heaven in clouds that are changeably seen as animals and junks, as they disperse?

—Silence and the Void. That into the silence and the void melt the gongs and the ritual, and the Great Wall of China itself. But from a crevice darts, quick as fire, an apprehensive salamander.

II. TRAVEL-SONG

Our Master has decided to answer the summons and go to Pekin.

As the Small Group, the humanity of our Master, goes up to Pekin, how shall I call it? what seems to be a small band of persons: children, parents, and friends, and some of these already dead, accompanying by their absence; and some not yet born, who accompany by our hope for them. This original humanity, not an individual and not a nation, but the social nature of the magician—as it goes among the fresh grass and reading by night the calligraphy of the Northern Bear trembling in the moist air —is dancing a travel-song.

Its name is *The Easiest, the Best, the Latest Moment*.

The Way is difficult ease. It is hard to do the easy thing, as to use the strength one has rather than to labor with the strength that one has not; to stand out of the way and let the power of the world crowd to our aid, rather than hinder it with obstacles; to go toward an end without using means that work away from the end. These easy things are hard to do. But is the easiest thing to do the hardest thing to do? No, there are many harder things, which we see people in fact busy doing, as we see people persevering with their last strength in a course which they know to be disastrous.

In general, there is an easy thing to do that is easy to do. This is not, to be sure, the easiest (which for us in our ignorance is always hard). But to do easily an easy thing is already a good step toward doing with less difficulty the easiest thing.

And sometimes, blessedly! the easiest thing to do is the easiest thing to do! often in moments of great stress, as we see people do immense and intricate heroic deeds, using the strength of the world that is crowding to their aid. Or habitually, in moments of quiet an artist draws the easiest line. Or reveling in despair, as our dear musician sang so lightly agreeing that he would die.

But always the easiest is the best. It is the Way.

So, demonstrating it by dancing it (for this is the easiest way), the social nature of the Master proceeds up toward Pekin.

Now in the opposite direction is coming a herd of sheep. All are in one impulse fleeing toward their slaughter. Each one of these sheep is alone in its rudimentary mind: it is hardly aware of its fellows, except in a few flashes of searing odor or a random urge of lust. Nevertheless all are bound in one direction and moving as one beast. They might be a herd of fifty or a hundred eighty million.

But the magical band of children, parents, friends, the dead, and the unborn has a certain small number, a certain variety of love and rivalry, of need and mutual aid, as on they trembling dance.

Now they are singing that the Latest is the best, the last motion of nature as it flickers through the present into the next motion after the latest. For who can deny that it is most available, it is present to hand, it is the easiest? It crowds upon us, whether we will or no, through all our senses and in our heartbeat, and even in our muscles taut to ward it off! O what are you warding off? Do you not recognize it? it is the present moment crowding into being to our aid, accompanied by the powers of all the past. A little living force, no bigger than a salamander, darting quick as fire from the crevice. A dragon, this present! lying in its vastness around the horizon, enclosing the world.

Let us watch them, dancing to Pekin. They are going on their legs. For they do not roll heels over ears like wheels, as once I thought to be the motion of Paradise before I considered the nature of Earth. For earth is textured, it is solid and uneven to the touch. By its solidity it offers support in order that its unevennesses may be spanned; so *we* proceed by making spans and bridges across the roughness.

And the music of dancing has four gaits: single-time of hopping and jumping, double-time of walking, triple-time of skipping, and quadruple-time of running. All these are native gaits, as you may tell by observing the locomotion of our children. And our social band goes all these gaits, hopping or jumping, walking, skipping or running to Pekin, and waiting up for the aged.

Accompanied too by some who are already dead and do not go these gaits; for the gayety of our natural band is made up somewhat by the presence of their absence.

III.

Our Master has come to the Great Wall. Let us go back to the Court.

The Great Wall of China is complete! and all China realizes with horror that it is imprisoned.

We in the Court have warded off the natural forces and projected them into bricks and commodities, and encysted them in true formulations; now these stand there glowering hostilely at us.

In the Court of the Emperor of China, they sound the gong of alarm. The Emperor is dreaming of not dying; he is dreaming of that immortal emperor who never died because he never lived. (But the *people* of China is immortal.)

The Emperor and the Chinese have been hoarding their strength brick by brick. Building the Great Wall of

China, feverishly, slowly, each man alone, brick alongside brick, and ordering the rows into a wall, and extending the wall along the survey lines. So one hoards
one's strength by deliberate calculation and builds the
Great Wall of China.

So an author orders the letters into a neat word. First
he has projected the threat of life into a thing, and he
denotes the thing in a neat word. Next he sets word next
to word in lines, he rules line under line to make up a
page. He has now encysted life in true formulations. He
arranges these pages in such a sequence . . . This is
called warding off the natural forces! protecting himself
from joy! hoarding his strength! building the Great Wall
of China.

But the Great Wall of China is complete and all China
realizes with horror that it is imprisoned. The natural
forces sit there, glaring hostilely.

Suddenly one is sensible that the whirlpool is turning;
and we see how already those nearest the center are being
sucked downward into black death. Good-bye to them!
one by one.

In the Court of the Emperor of China they sound the
gong. The Emperor of China is dreaming of not dying:
he is dreaming of that immortal emperor who never died
because he never lived.

See *here!* comes colored, motherly of carriage, and
floating a foot above the water, the junk of our silent
Master—on the escallops of the whirl and spray. The sails
are colored with the feelings Carefree, Omniregardant;
her flag is Super-Abounding and her pennons Toothless
Smiles. Patience Firmness Duty: these are her carriage,
the same as the endurance of the world: who rests in it
upborne more lightly than a babe.

She floats by Non-Attachment. She comes by the Dis-
closure of the Next Moment.

She pauses in mid-air in the maw of the whirlpool.
From the slippery wall of water is thrust a forearm with
a despairing clutch, but cannot touch her.

Nevertheless our Master makes himself heavy and
slowly sinks into the bite of pain.

IV.

※ *La Gaya Scienza*
—NIETZSCHE

While the wizard sinks, he swallows the space about and recreates a void.

While the diabolical magician brews the poison potion for the Emperor, he observes silence.

Silence: but the Silence! For there is a kind of lesser silence, when one does not talk or sing, as when a person is alone. Such a silence is not even refreshing, for one carries on silent wrangles and mutters his composition. Deeper than this there is a better silence that, if one observes it, is indeed refreshing, yet it is not the Silence: this is when a person listens and does not think of answering, as when we listen to frogs in the marsh and look at everything attentively. This silence is recreative, and finally we break it with a melody from nowhere. A good sign, but still it is not the Silence.

For always we are still forming concepts and judgments and inwardly saying: "It is the croaking frog—" "The interval is a minor third—" "See the dark line of the hills." This inward speech, that seems to be only listening and taking in the scene, is betrayed by our small gestures, the motions of swallowing, of darting eyes, as we say to ourselves, "this" and "next?"

How to be silent? and not always forming concepts and judgments? As for me, I am *expert* in formulations; these I can always make and say, "there it is!" "that is what it is!" "it is only that, don't fear!" "Next?" There is no doubt of it, that I talk and think too much, and write too much. Yet let me speak no evil of the creator spirit, listening to whom, over my shoulder, and taking in the scene, I joyfully make my true formulations. But it is *not* meant that I should use them to ward off the world.

The Silence of the magician is before he has learned to speak, as we speak; before he is formed a personality, as we are personalities.

The images float across his sky like clouds. They split with fire and there is a crack of thunder. It is raining. For in the Silence, our Master, who lay seventy years in the womb, is playing with the milk, the drool, the turds, the piss, the blood, and the semen.

In the void, in the quick of the wound, where the wizard has swallowed up the space, he is dancing the Creation of the Things Before They Have a Name.

—That the drool and the milk and so forth are the Rivers of Paradise.

That when he masturbates he opens high and wide the dome of Heaven.

That sinking and losing the weight of his body, he divides into territories at his bony joints, and these are the six Continents and their mountain ranges.

That from turds he fashions out the elephants and the bears.

That when he fucks, the electric friction makes the sky blue. The thick lightning.

From the seed the magician is born again, that lay seventy years in the womb. The Master of *La Gaya Scienza!*

(As for me, natural things are no longer so hostilely glowering.)

In the Silence, in the Void, things fall of their weight. They drop lightly into place. They tremble open to the most space to the present flowers of May. The wild ducks are flying northward. The moments are flying thick and fast, but they are not flying by, they are not flying by. The Master of *La Gaya Scienza* is dancing us the things that do not yet have a name. Thick and fast the moments are not flying by.

Now, in the hole of the vortex, in the clenched jaws of death, the hellish wizard is spinning like a dervish and his skirts fly out. He has made his excrements into missiles and is destroying those who love him. He sucks their breasts and will not let loose with his teeth. They are drowned in the searing piss, beaten by his virile club, and jumped on up and down. All things are flying from him as he spins: he spins alone: his skirts fly out. Can we ever restore to place those things flung far from their center?

Too late! Our future has been swallowed up by a wizard.

We were omnipotent when we destroyed it; but now when we would restore it, we are not omnipotent. *Never* can we make restitution. *This* is the grievous wound by which we are bleeding to death.

V.

Wifely, high: like the moon rescued from the slime after a fortnight we did not see her and all at once shining at a bound in the top of heaven, such are the full sleeves that offer to the Emperor the cup of vitality. The beverage that is brewed of animal spirits, that is fermented for the duration of the world, and distilled into presentness. The revolution that is frothing at the brim never ceases. Drinking, our natural band will go the wandering way that does not err.

But the Emperor of China sips this poison and straightway he falls down in death agony, croaking.

For the Emperor of China summoned the Master of the Way and bade him brew for him the elixir of immortality; but drinking it, he is poisoned and falls down in his death agony. Is this the fault of the elixir?—The Master is impassive.

The Emperor of China cries out, croaking: "*Ow!* I *know* that destiny is providence; my brain is seared with it, as a tongue of fire licks from the window and envelops the house. Hurrying on, I have come back again and again to my wound, and who can deny that the past is crowding into this present moment and the next and last? Am I supposed therefore, in the jaws of death, to sing out joyfully, 'Ah! providential!' *Ow!* Yet indeed, the natural forces are no longer glaring at me so hostilely. They are impassive. Even the Great Wall of China is only a broken wall. What drink is this that you have poisoned me with? The revolution frothing at the brim does not cease. Ow! I know! Is it not the same thing to say Ow! and I know? Who is this impassive dragon lying around the circle of the horizon with his tail in his mouth? It means that my time is complete. I am the immortal emperor, who never died because he never lived. Tell me, is it *thus* that the people of China will be immortal?"

He is dead. What? are they not going to proclaim another?

The Master says: "Why didn't he drink of it a second time?"

VI.

The Master says, "Why didn't he drink of it a second time?"

He says: "Is not every natural force violent? Violent clashes with violent, and there emerges, trembling, what was not known before. This is called Brotherly Conflict and Invention.

"When a man is in prison himself, must not nature seem to be the destruction of the world?

"When a man is imprisoned, this is called Dreaming of Immortality.

"But 'the hounded hare takes pleasure in his leaps, in his dodges, in his speedy course.' "

The mandarins of China—looking each man with wide eyes at his startled friend—say to one another: "*Therefore* let us set free the people of China.

"It is said that the people of China is immortal. Perhaps they can teach us to be immortal. Or at least! at least that we, in our yellowed age, may have a little comfort in watching the inventive games of the children of the people of China, as slowly their red stockings flicker across the yard.

"That we may rest from building the Great Wall of China, no longer hoarding our strength and making true formulations.

"In order that the natural things may not glower at us so hostilely.

"To cease to turn about our grievous wound.

"To dance into the present with the force of the endurance of the world."

NOAH'S VINEYARD

(after Michelangelo)

I.

After the Flood, the world was dirty and washed.

Noah began to be a farmer, and planted a vineyard.

"How do you dare to do it, Noah?"

"Because," he said, "one day the prophet Isaiah shall arise and prophesy: 'They shall build houses and inhabit them. They shall plant vineyards and eat the fruit of them.'"

"When will *that* come to pass?"

"It will come to pass!" cried Noah. "It will come to pass, saith the prophet, when God creates new heavens and a new earth. Then a man will build and inhabit, and plant and eat the fruit."

"But Noah! look about! is *this* new heavens and a new earth?"

"No. Now we are just practicing."

The world was dirty with silt and new washed with water. The sun was hot and the plain was steaming. The farmer wore a straw hat, and bending his back to the spade he wore a little smile, as though he too had been promised something.

"What did He promise *you*, Noah?"

Noah leaned on his spade and said, "He promised me that while the earth lasts there will be seed-time and harvest, hot and cold, and night and day. There was a rainbow."

"He did not promise that you would plant and eat the fruit?"

"No, certainly He did not promise that. But that the seasons would henceforth be regular, and that *something* would come of it. A rainbow."

"Ah. Is this enough?"

He did not answer that, but fell to work. *Fell* to work, for in planting the vineyard Noah did not spade with his hands and wrists as if disdainfully; he did not work with merely his biceps and shoulders while holding his head away; but he bent his head and back to the spade, attending to what he was doing. And the power of gravity flowed up through his legs and back, and then around down into the spade into the clay. The spade shone lurid, and he remembered

II.

how the first flash of lightning had disclosed an instant face that seemed fixed at its widest scream. Simultaneously, whenever the successive lightnings flashed, that mouth had opened to its widest scream and so seemed stroboscopically fixed.

Because he remembered the Flood, Noah planted his vineyard in order to drink and get drunk. He was nagged by the long instant image of the scream, that lasted a frantic half hour. He was not much haunted by day when he was working the hot field, nor if, used up by his forthright labor, he ate and fell on his straw bed and slept. But if, being a man, he stood apart awhile, to look at the reviving earth, the spears of grass; and especially when he quit work early on the Sabbath eve. Then he was nagged, he nagged himself, with memories.

How the Ark is already afloat in the rain! This is occurring not all at once but for a frantic half hour, that the thousand-mile-long stormcloud has opened and the river spills over. Men and women have swum out to the Ark and are clinging to the plank; and the sons of Noah are swinging their oars to crush their fingers and get them off. One man is *unable* to let go in his despair, and one of the wives of the sons of Noah has lifted an axe. In the noise the screams cannot be heard, but in the lightning you can see an instant face fixed at its widest scream.

The intermittent lightning is blazing at every second, and simultaneously, the man sobbing and yelling is yelling out at every second: then his instant face out of the dark seems fixed at its widest scream for half an hour.

A man's memory is such a stroboscope.

After, there was a rainbow.

When he is bending his back spading, Noah is entirely occupied in the rhythm of himself and the hot field. But if—like a man—he notices that the earth is reviving, and he himself is helping it to revive, he cannot but see that the spade is lurid.

Our father is planting his vineyard in order to drink and get drunk. Especially when, on the Sabbath, he raises high the stone goblet for all to behold and sings in his warbling and joyous bass, like the erotic bullfrog in the marsh:

"Sixth Day! and *finished* were heaven and earth and all their hosts. Blest art Thou, Lord our God and King of the Universe, who createst the fruit of the vine!"

Eagerly he drinks the cup and drains it.

III.

Now it is night. Noah is Pan, the leader of the bullfrogs in the marsh. It is night. Bigger beasts, the musk-ox and water-buffalo, have come down to listen, standing in the marsh, their belly-hair drenched. The hippopotamus is wallowing to his hips and shoulders. The frog is booming G-sharp in the bass. The moon is squirming in her sky-lake of light coffee, but in the mirror of the marsh the bright button of the moon is fixed and provocative: *you* must do it, O my lover, unbutton this tantalizing button and mobilize the breathing mud-depths.

Begoom, croaks our swollen father, on his great frond gently heaving—prophetic of later Moses in the bulrushes. The circles are spreading slowly to the fringed shore where only the nostrils of the hippopotamus are snuffling above water, yes and his gleaming eye in conjunction with the moon. The spreading concentric waves languish in the rushes; but tirelessly the patriarch thunders his *begoom* G-sharp in the bass, and the water-beasts are drunken with the song of Noah: he sings,

"Close your too bright eye, ferocious hippopotamus; do not look at us. So, let me unbutton—you! my world, my only one!—your garment too freshly laundered, it smells too fresh. Your garment, my only world! clasped by this bright button. My fingers are fumbling and you smile queenly at me. But I am persistent, no? Begoo-ooom!"

The moon is pale and he is booming on a single note in

C-sharp minor while, for a swelling moment, the arpeggio soars and sinks.

It is still. Noah is unbuttoning the too freshly laundered garment of our only world in order to drown. His fumbling fingers have unbuttoned it. The splash that you hear is his diving from his black frond into the depths. He is squatting at his panic ease on the mud bottom. You cannot see him, but the bottom is exhaling bubbles of methane breaking at the surface. And the veil of the world is lying in a discarded and disregarded heap.

From his muddy home Noah the Pan is looking out with goggling eyes. Our world our only one has no clothes on. So passes a long time. The bottom is exhaling bubbles of methane that idly break at the surface. Our amphibious father is abiding a long time in the home of the drowned.

IV.

Ham, that mocking son, whose name means Hot, looks in on him and sees his father's nakedness uncovered. For Noah is lying there sprawled in his drunkenness, leaking away as if it were tears.

"Whatcha doin' in there, daddy?" cries Ham, pretending to have a conversation with the stoned man.

"Who? me? Just pee-in."

"Well, for Chrissake, dad, you don' needa pump it out!"
Merrily Ham runs to tell the others, and they come to the door, to peep and exchange limericks.

But the frog's eyes are popping with attentiveness, awe-struck, as if he is seeing, we not. But indeed our only world has no clothes on, and you too might see her as well as Noah if you plunged into the black and sat there still, and breathed in softly the methane of the drowned.

"Mademoiselle!" sings out Ham,

> "Mademoiselle! let me persuade
> you to *a tergo* be laid,
>   so if, heaven forfend,
>   we are stuck in the end,
> out of here we can *walk* for first aid."

Shem more drily recites,

> "Prim, a poodle, trotting at random
> saw bicyclists riding a tandem.
>   With a horrified wail
>   she emptied a pail
> of hot water on 'em to disband 'em."

And Japheth, finally, favors them with the abstract theory of all limericks:

> "A character from a place
> is doing what's a disgrace,
>   is hurried rapidly
>   to a catastrophe,
> and in the dénouement loses face."

V.   THE SCREAM AND DANCE OF NOAH SOBER

Awakening, Noah screamed,

"My desire's left the house! It is alive. Here is the dis-carded garment of my only world, too freshly laundered, yet such as it is! still warm from her body——" And he plunged his face and all his senses into that senseless landscape, squeezing the strong cloth, sniffing for a little odor. He was sick with longing for his only world.

Apprehensively he looked about, to see if he was observed. He was thinking, "Dare I put this dress on? the discarded garment of my only world, and feel my belly and my breast in hers?" But he did not care whether or not he was observed and he dared to slip into the garment, the senseless landscape. And so the patriarch danced, writhing and squirming, the Dance of Putting on the Senseless Garment of His Only World.

The dancer writhed and panted and the sweat broke out on his face. How close were they two now! His prick was standing up into the lap. So he danced Unable to Breathe Because of Waves of Trembling. He danced With Fumbling Fingers Undoing the Button on the Garment of My Beloved. He urinated and the hot water stained the lap of the robe and ran down between his legs. He danced The Hero Who Has Put On a Poisoned Garment.

Noah planted a vineyard in order to drink and get drunk. (After the Flood everything was both dirty nd new washed.) "It will come to pass!" cried Noah, "when God creates a *new* heavens and a *new* earth, *then* will a man build and inhabit, and plant and eat the fruit thereof!" And Noah unbuttoned the garment of our only world.

Afterwards Noah screamed: "My desire has left the house!" And he danced the dance of putting on the senseless garment of the only world.

> What is that lovely rainbow that abides
> upon the dripping moments till it fades?
> > God promised me, though I am old,
> > if I will work this new-washed field,
>
> while my future vanishes past,
> something will come of it at last.
> > This is the rainbow that abides
> > on the dripping moments—till it fades.

VI.

In the course of time the very silt and debris of the Flood themselves grew grass and flowers. And it was all one again. One could hardly guess what had occurred. That there had been a rainbow.

But we paleontologists dig savagely for the antediluvian. Bones. We dig savagely for antediluvian bones. As if we said, "Brothers! this is inadmissible, what we see about us. It is incomprehensible. Therefore let us dig."

"Yes. I am a psychologist and this patient dares to come into my office as he is! How else should he come there? But this is inadmissible, how he is. I cannot tolerate it. Let us rather dig for the antediluvian."

So we dig savagely for bones. We dig.

"Brothers! as for me, I am living a life with my family and friends in this city that is inadmissible. We cannot be persuaded, we *will* not be persuaded, that this makes sense. It is incomprehensible, how it is."

Therefore we paleontologists dig savagely for antediluvian bones. We dig up bones.

Darlings! look at one another; this is simply inadmissible. It is inadmissible. Therefore we dig for the antediluvian. We dig savagely for bones. We dig for the antediluvian, and what we dig for is bones. We dig *for* bones and we dig up bones.

THE GALLEY TO MYTILENE

(after Thucydides)

※ "Take me up, sailors, into your great ship and I'll tell you a story to bring you peace."

I.

In chains, but still trying to gesticulate with his chained hands, as if he still had something to say, but he had nothing to say and could not utter a sound, the envoy from Lesbos watched the preparations.

The galley was equipped. The oarsmen began to climb in and take their places. To Mytilene was a voyage of a day and a night, and they would arrive tomorrow morning, carrying the sentence of doom.

As the twelve men and their captain got in, the ship settled low in the water.

The captain clambered back onto the pier and cried angrily. "What kind of tub have you given us here?"

"The fastest ship in the Piraeus, and you know it," said the port inspector, checking it off.

"I count twelve men and food for twelve and me," said the captain, "and it's like a cargo of lead."

"The men's hearts are heavy, that weighs you down."

The captain aborted a gesture. He jumped in and she listed, and when she righted she had settled to the oarlocks. "This won't get us there in a week," said the bearded captain, whining like a child.

There was also no wind.

It was soon after sunrise, but the port of Athens already lay as if in black noon. The customs building and the warehouse were white blocks and their shadows swallowed men up like holes in space. There was no color anywhere.

There was movement. In the absence of atmosphere and reflection, the far-off of the Acropolis smashed forward like a fist that slowly from afar hits you suddenly between the eyes. The water spread to the edge and fell.

The Lesbian envoy, who had failed in his plea for clemency, had been brought to witness the departure. Chained, he was guarded by two stony boys. They would not let him onto the pier and he stood at the edge of the shore, in the water up to his knees. His face was haggard but he could no longer weep. He had no more language. They had crushed him in the Council by repeating monotonously their one sentence, "Teach others not to rebel."

As if he were speaking to men of affairs, to men of letters, he urged arguments of rational, imaginative, devious policy, but they said only, "Teach others not to rebel." Very soon he came to wailing and gnashing his teeth and hugging their knees, but they repeated only, "Teach others not to rebel." The Athenians were stupid.

He could not weep because they did not offer him, even in his defeat, a consoling handshake.

To his hot dry eyes his lovely native town, with its porticoes and colonnades of rose and blue, was already flaming and razed. The women were shrieking in his ears. The men were dead. He did not feel for any of this, the shock of it was past. Indifferently he watched the last haze of smoke on the horizon.

They unwound the lines. The galley scraped the bottom and lurched. The captain angrily shouted.

II.

Once under weigh, out of sight of the ambassador, they rowed hard forward. The naked oarsmen sat in benches of two, and they rowed ten strokes to the minute. They rowed the *actual* minute (it was counted) and after it the minute after it.

The galley made slow progress.

The oarsmen for such an important mission were not slaves but free athletes, past their ephebic years of service, but it was wartime. Indeed, they were the best of the best, the strongest of the fairest. Yet they rowed away the actuality as if they were naked slaves and as if their captain were beating them in anger. They, who were used to go armed and merrily to their idiotic battles.

But we must distinguish between the actuality, the reality, and the existing. (Try! you will never be able to distinguish them.) The hot sun lit the ship, the sea, the oars, the fists of the oarsmen: the actuality was how it *was*, this was the reality.

Ordinarily, however, we can imagine away, we have already somewhat imagined away, from the actuality how it is, and the reality is also this imagination. But *their* imagination was frozen to the actuality, and they rowed. They did not let themselves think of the one thought that prepossessed them, and no two on a bench spoke. They made slow progress.

The rapid rhythmic rowing itself was exhilarating. They began to sing a loud chantey.

"Don't you think that something is coming after us?" an oarsman asked his fellow.

They both looked back over their shoulders.

Naturally others looked back, to see what they were looking at. (There was nothing.) For a moment the count was broken and they stopped rowing. At once the ship came to a dead stop.

The men looked at one another with the whites in their eyes showing. For ordinarily a body floats on a little by momentum; it has inertia and therefore velocity. This is its reality. It is *springing* forward, it is *reaching* toward. But not their ship. They were adding stroke by stroke to a dead weight that did not come alive.

Their heavy hearts were now at sea. In a towering anger the captain brought out his bull-whip. But it was noon and they sneered at him and elected to eat.

The food was tasteless.

Their imagination was pinned to the actuality because

of an idea in the actuality that they would not let themselves think. Yet this idea was no secret to anybody.

"It's a rough deal," said one of the oarsmen finally, meaning the sentence of doom that they were carrying to Mytilene; or perhaps meaning the actuality that *they* were carrying the sentence of doom.

"To what are you referring," said his fellow carefully, because he was thinking of the same idea.

"Do you know anybody there?"

"Don't you know somebody there?"

Another sailor asked his fellow without prelude, "Do you know anybody there?"

"Don't *you* know somebody there?"

"What are you referring to?" said another, because his mind was blank. "One!—one!—one!—one!"

They rowed hard forward, stepping up the beat to twelve, and they laid a minute of it on another minute on another on another. They worked up a certain speed, so far as one can do this without blessed velocity. But persistently it kept seeming to them that there was another ship, some other ship, *not* this ship, not *this* ship. Pursuing them. They kept looking back. They hastened forward because they were being pursued. On the wide sea was nothing. The sun lit what there was, the one heavy galley and the sweating oarsmen.

III.

At Mytilene on Lesbos, the Athenian garrison stayed to themselves on the peninsula, neither fraternizing with nor harassing the populace, while they waited for the mandate from home. They expected no leniency, and perhaps they were even conniving for the Lesbians, thinking, "Let them vanish in the hills, if they can." But the Mytilenians were imprisoned by their own terror and made no effort.

No one felt this terror, the shock of it was past. It worked within and inhibited motion before it arose. Looking at them, constrained by no visible guards, one came to ask in surprise, "Why don't they act on impulse? why don't they run away?"

Instead, they were *confident* that the Athenians did

not seriously intend totally to destroy them. They interpreted in this sense the withdrawal of the garrison. Yet by withdrawing, the garrison had become uncanny to them. What was up?

During these days, the Mytilenians, a people famous for pleasure and license, did not make love. If they had felt their terror and sweated and trembled, many would likely have rushed into license for a little comfort. But they were frozen. They felt nothing.

Some went to the temple of Apollo Savior of Orpheus. The statue of the god was, as always, smiling, and they interpreted this as a good omen, during the very hours that the galley with the mandate of doom was looming across the water toward them.

Yet late in the afternoon, when the galley, we know, had come only *half* way and was making no rapid progress, there suddenly spread the rumor that the ship *had* arrived, and it had brought the expected sentence of doom. At once some of the men cut their throats, before they could feel their terror. The women felt their terror and shrieked. The fear unfroze in the marrow of their bones and many rushed into love for a little comfort.

"I told you so!" said a man to his partner.

She shrieked with delight.

A neighborhood was set afire, the black smoke hung in the dusk. The soldiers of the garrison had to come to control the flames and save the city, whose people they soon expected to kill. It was not yet time for it to burn down.

No ship was to be seen, but everywhere arose grief and wailing. It was bitter to them to notice the ironical smile of the god, and they cursed him and blasphemed.

IV.

Heavy between the two worlds, the galley rowed hard— pursued, rushing toward the goal, making no haste on a horrible errand.

But when the dusk came over the water and the sun no longer lit their hands and faces, it was no longer so easy to identify as one the actuality and the reality.

The surrounding world was dark. The inner place was blue. Their faces and fists were blue. The wooden oars were pale. The men had put on their woolen cloaks.

Behind them, the sky was still white and they kept looking back into it.

They had eaten the confused amalgam of the actuality and the reality and now, in the cool evening, they began to be sick. Suddenly a man would haul in his oar and lean over the side and vomit. The ship drifted sideways. Ashamed, the angry captain was racked with cramps. He let go the governor and, with the tears streaming from his eyes, he vomited up the actuality.

"I told you so!" said a sailor, referring to the idea that another ship was coming after them, "*there* she is! my shy one! my wood-dove!"—And indeed, against the fading whitening behind them, that was whitening itself into darkness, you could not see what there was or was not, in the sea's gray holes. "*See* how she skims and flies! my beauty! my new ship! my new ship approaching in the sunrise! Her name is *Dolphin*. Do you know anybody on her? *Don't* you know somebody on her! Hurry, fellows, let's get on—because she never comes when you wait! She never comes when you look back at her! My gull! my delight! One!—one!—one! dammit! This is the last time I ever go to sea."

He spoke a little beyond their vital belief, and they jeered him good-naturedly.

They stepped up the beat, because it was very cold. They tried again a chantey. And to any one a few hundred yards away (but there was no one) would have come the sound of music on the water, welling from that dark ship, wasting in the holes of the sea. The first stars began to come in.

They kept looking back at the progress of the other ship that was bearing down on them.

V.

It is night and the city of Mytilene is at rest. Its heart is bounding. The knocking bones in fright have loosed the electric currents of vegetation, and they are flowing. There is no sign of life—

"All that mighty heart is lying still."

But it is *still* beating! Therefore the sentence of the poet is sublime. For indeed the mighty heart of the sleeping city is not still but is quietly beating. Even as you perceive that it is still, you know that it is not still.

VI.

At sea the existing is gently arriving into the next moment. The existing is blazing here like the Burning Bush of the Jews where if you plunge your hand, you take it out your existing hand. The fire is colored the color of passing-thought-over-a-face. So the fists of the oarsmen are lit up, and their faces are lit up and arriving.

Around midnight the other ship, named *Dolphin,* overtakes them.

They are hailed.

Blazing in the existing, the *Dolphin* lies off a way; she rides high in the water; her sail is bellying in the wind of desire. The tired oarsmen look at her with aching hearts.

"What do you want?" calls our captain.

The answer comes at once, loud and clear: "The Athenians have relented. The order to destroy Mytilene is countermanded. We are carrying a more hopeful message."

"How do we identify you? Do we know anybody aboard you?"

And the reply comes clear and loud: "*Don't* you know somebody aboard us? don't *you* know somebody aboard us?"

Circling, the *Dolphin* draws closer to us and comes their cry: "It makes no difference what you choose to believe, for you are about to sink, and we are on our way. So come aboard!"

It is true. Stopped dead, overtaken, without even the forward impulsion of the actuality, our ship is sunken to the gunwale and is certainly foundering.

"Hurry, damn you!" cries *Dolphin,* "before you all drown."

"Move closer!"

Will tack as close as she dares, the sail flapping angrily and the sheets whistling in the inhibition. The sail drops. "Come! jump!"

The moon rises at a bound and we'll see how it is! We jump into the suddenly spangling sea. Angry father our captain is standing there, to see us safe away. Then he too jumps and swims for it.

Dripping with the moment we joyfully clamber aboard the *Dolphin*, filling out her crew to twelve and one.

A moment later, the other galley will have sunken.

Safe on our new ship, we men are beginning to weep, to burst out crying, and soon we shall be sobbing and bawling, and it feels good.

It is because of relenting. Some one has relented. Something has been relented.

We see that our misery was not inevitable, there have been other possibilities. Our imagination is no longer pinned to the one actuality. But of course the actuality itself has now changed, and this is the reality. (Try! and I shall never be able to distinguish them.)

Having let go, we have nothing to hold on to. It is for ourselves that we are crying, because of everything that has been lost. We are sobbing in self-pity, but we are bawling absolutely, in darkness and blackness. In newness and darkness and the void. Keeping our eyes open or shutting them seems to make no difference.

We, the strongest of the fairest! bawling on our new ship, and we do not know another minute to add to this minute. Opening our eyes or shutting our eyes makes no difference.

I am not at ease on the strange ship. The *Dolphin* rides too light in the water; a man does not feel himself sitting *in* her with his weight. Looking about, we recognize one another. (Where are the others?)

. . .

A favoring gale. Put up the sail. Pick up speed. After a while, take up the oars and also row. Desire! desire!

But for the moment we are doing nothing. Looking, not at one another, with open eyes. We are guilty because we have forgotten the *other* mandate, whatever it was. "Don't look at me!" cries the captain, as a teacher flinches before a child's imploring eyes when the problem is too hard, "the answer isn't written on *my* face." Rubbish! he doesn't know the answer either.

"Isn't there anything to eat? We're empty. We vomited up the actuality back there. Surely they didn't send a ship after us with nothing."

Will feed on the oranges of arriving.

VII.

As our new ship approaches in the sunrise—
coming around the promontory
The sunrise is washing all rose and blue the colonnades and porticoes of Mytilene.

Before a favoring gale, leaning hard on the oars, adding yards and bursts of time and speed to the momentum and the previous and the wake, we have skirted the cliff and are already bearing down on the beach. Shall we anchor off or risk it and plunge through the surf?

At first flash, the colors of the city seemed to be almost baby blue and pink, but there is a depth of darkness in them that the sight gropes into, trying to touch solid. Navy blue and blood red.

The townspeople have sighted us! They are pouring down to the shore. As for us, we are *un*afraid to act out the resolutions made by night!

They are wading into the water. Obviously they count on good news—but this they could already guess from the rapturous rhythm of our rowing, the *added* bursts of our gale-borne flight—yes, as the swan regularly yet with a *steady* augmentation, drawing on no failing source, leaves the water, and flies, dripping the moment from his feet.

The gulls are so thick about us that it is hard to see. But the people can see *us* in the cloud of gulls. They are crying out confused sounds. The gulls are screaming.

Twin Castor O! and twin of Castor! what a thing it is to arrive!

The people's hearts are pounding as only with those bursts of confident hope touched by the uncertainty of the final moment. Let us be careful, for it is just such persons who recognize their happiness and drop down dead.

Now *here* is the surf. We are going to risk it and plunge through the surf and beach her. Our ship, our *Dolphin,* was designed by experience, that makes bold choices. The curve of desire is built into her hull. He found out our mother in the heart of the tree.

We have touched.

They crowd around, silent. The wash of the breaker is wet on the glad faces of our sailors and they are so bright and beautiful that I am struck blind.

Carefully—not delaying, but avoiding producing an exaggerated impression—we say: "The mandate from the citizens of Athens is not unfavorable to you; you need not fear the worst."

Hermes, thank you. You have given me to deliver a message that relieves fear. I say to a man, "Thank Hermes."

"Ah! we need not fear?"

"You say," says another man carefully, "that we need not fear the worst."

"We knew that they would repent!"

"The other ship was a mistake!"

"I told you so! that the *Athenian*s could not let the other order stand." He speaks of them proudly, as if they were not the tyrants of his people!

Some of the women were leaving the beach with tears trickling down their cheeks.

"Repent?" one of our sailors caught the word. "*Other* order? What other ship?"

"The order brought by the other ship. The first ship."

"*Was* there another ship?!" we cried in consternation. "What? did *they* get here?"

We ourselves had *seen* that other ship sink in the sea. "*How* did they get here before us?"

"Oh, it was not so bad, not so very bad," they reassured us. "Please don't be upset. In the first panic, as if the order had to be carried out at once! and by our own hands! a few killed themselves. A few houses were set afire—hard to know by whom. But *I* said, Wait! And now, thank God, you have come . . . Please! don't disturb yourselves so. A handful. Not too bad. I assure you."

I looked at my fellow. "They are here. We'll meet them. It's inevitable, in a small place like this. All of a sudden —coming round a corner—" Already in anticipation, vividly imagining it, the guilt of it had me by the throat.

"Oh, he's as afraid of you as you are of him. Did you know anybody on her?"

"Didn't *you* know somebody on her?"

So (otherwise than the history tells it) the galley brought to Mytilene a message of clemency.

By this time the Athenians too had relented.

A STATUE OF GOLDSMITH

I.

I spent a few months in rainy Dublin, lonely and malcontent as elsewhere. For I contrive, often with ingenuity and boldly seizing opportunities, to get into a situation where I can be alone and do as I please, and then I am lonely and "doing as I please" does not get me what I want. Yet while I was in Dublin I finished work on a fine book that often touched me and moved me to love and admiration for itself, so that when I had indeed finished the last sentence I fell on my knees, and prayed that my book would have an easy access and an understanding reception in the world.

During the lonely days and nights when I was not doing that work, however, I tried, as I do, to make human connections of friendship in Dublin, rarely getting anywhere, usually let down when I got somewhere, and fearful of the consequences of such inappropriate connections as I did make. I am very inept. It is not interesting to report it.

My favorite haunting—for I love rivers, and ships and trucks, and to watch the heavy work of loading and unloading cargoes—was to go along the Liffey and try to mix with the stevedores and sailors. I guess I was in love with a crew of workmen at the far end, who were dismantling for scrap-iron the ancient freighter *Kyleglen*. The scrap is important for the Irish, since they have no native iron of their own; it was a big and useful job.

Of the half-dozen, with their torches and their crane, one was a grand workman. I gazed at him with an aching heart. He had a plain open smiling face and a tall straight easy bearing every pose of which was graceful. But he was not so beautiful off the job—at lunch, playing soccer as they did with a small rubber ball.

His name was Jerry. When Jerry leaned on the crow-bar, the mass moved, even though the others could not budge it. When he gave a smash with the stone mallet, the iron broke, though the others had hacked in vain. He was perhaps stronger than the others in a lithe way, but it was more that he knew what he was doing; he had the confidence and follow-through that come from paying attention. If there was a task that was out of the routine and either more delicate or difficult, they spontaneously drew back and let Jerry do it. He was too good. He knew the job even too well for the job—he knew more than the foreman—although it was big and dangerous work. There was a pathos in his excellence.

"You know," I said to him during a cigarette, "you're a grand workman."

"You mean, I work hard?" He didn't especially.

"No. I mean you know what you're doing. You're better than the others—and it shows. I just wanted to tell you how it looks from outside." The fact is that I love to praise, and to have something to praise.

He lowered his face and blushed. "Some of them *will* get themselves killed sooner or later" was his comment.

Of course I wished he would be interested in me too, but he always politely contrived to move away from me, as if chary of me. The boundary of education and so forth that meant nothing to me meant a lot to them.

I watched them with longing: how the iron obstacles that thwart us, *they* cut through with their acetylene torches.

And it would begin to rain again and they would go below, leaving me forlorn on the dock. In love with the crew of wreckers dismantling the *Kyleglen,* what kind of thing was that to be in love with?

I walked away from there back into the city and I thought to visit Trinity Library and see the famous Book of Kells. I entered the University close between the statues of Burke and Goldsmith.

II.

Once up in the long hall of the Library, it was not long before I began to hum and breathe deeply, as I do when there are interesting things to see, passing from showcase to showcase. The ancient vellum books were of course remarkable, but it was the display and honor accorded to our authors that absorbed my attention. I was pleased by the judicious evaluation of Goldsmith:

> He went to Trinity College and after graduation tried to make a living in various ways without success. As a hack writer he produced a large number of works on subjects of which he knew little. His literary reputation, however, rests securely on *The Vicar of Wakefield, The Deserted Village,* and his play *She Stoops to Conquer,* one of the great comedies of the English theatre.

The school-grades of Jonathan Swift for 1685: Natural Philosophy *Male,* Greek and Latin *Bene,* Theme *Negligenter.* There was food for thought in that. Samuel Lover's *Handy Andy.* I was interested to notice that Bernard Shaw's handwriting was as tiny and unbroken as my own, with bold descents below the line; of course marching on with fuller and more regular impulse than mine; but with a tell-tale leftward slant, holding back. He did. That is, our manuscripts were comparable, with different prizes to be given to each. He had reaped his reward and I was going to win mine.

They had on show many an Irish novelist of no merit, yet it was a fine thing to see honor done to them all in this hall of scholarship, by a people that has always esteemed wit and learning and daring eloquence, despite the appalling bigotry and censorship that they are subject to.

I spent a couple of hours, I guess, swiftly taking in and musing on all these things—and the harp of Brian Boru —during which time I did not think whether or not I was happy. Having seen enough, I went out with a nod at the armorial bearings of Elizabeth preserved from the original buildings of the College, long since destroyed.

III.

As I came out of the Library, it was the sight of the statue of Lecky seated, that set me off into a jolly mood. It was surprising to see a statue of Lecky, and there he was, boots and side-whiskers, with a solemn face about to break into a grin. Really very good.

However it was, as I looked about at the close, where the young were hurrying to classes on the hour, at that moment I felt completely, alarmingly, *finally* at home in Trinity College, Dublin. I didn't know a soul, yet my loneliness dropped from me as if it would never return. Knowing nobody made no difference, since I securely belonged to the inner company of these authors, scholars, and doctors. I needed only to reveal myself, so to speak, to be welcome. My doctorate was a sound one, through (I think) Yale and Cambridge back to Paris; likely they had my thesis somewhere on their shelves; and I had the prerogative to go into one of those classes and join in the disputation. Nor would I have disputed, but rather supported and underscored what the professor was trying to tell them, for our company are trustworthy on our home grounds, though we often sell out off-campus.

Trinity was a university after my own size. Its tradition and slightly ragged Irish spirit were after my own style. Nowhere except in Ireland have I ever felt appropriately dressed, neither too shabby nor too careful. It did not hurt, either, that I have always found Irish young people the most attractive; they have been my type since childhood on 151st Street. And they were set off by a good sprinkling of Nigerians, Thailanders, Jews.

Here came a professor with his satchel of books, a burly man in a hurry, resembling Richard McKeon. He looked confident of himself but short-tempered because of the chances of life, not enough time for lunch. I was just as glad that it was he and not I who had to get to that class.

I stood in the angle of the archway and lit my pipe and enjoyed my solitary anonymity in that square where I was at home. Obviously it was there that it was right, and fated, for me to be in love, except that therefore there was no need for me to be in love or to feel any particular emotion whatever, except as a particular occasion might call for it. Yet I must have been a striking figure standing at my ease there, solitary, alertly watching, drawing on my pipe, for many of the kids who passed looked at me with curiosity in which there seemed to be respect. I had authority.

The next moment I began again to feel my loneliness, my placelessness, my inactivity; the impossibility of everything I wanted in the world; how my natural spirits and health were in ruins and the hour about to strike. And, as if beaten in a battle and evacuating the fort, I went out through the archway worse off than I had come in. Between Burke and Goldsmith.

IV.

Now it was in these circumstances that I came, that afternoon, to pose myself the question: *What is the meaning of this statue of Goldsmith? Why have they put it here?*

For as I emerged from the archway, on my left stood the statue of Goldsmith. The pose relaxed but about to move; his right arm slightly retracted and with a pen for a weapon, about to stab at the book that he is holding; a sweet Irish face and beginning to lose his hair.

That metal man: what connection did he have with Goldsmith who was dead? None whatever. How did Goldsmith who used to be alive, as I felt myself alive (and perhaps not with any happier feeling about it than I had), how did that Goldsmith survive in this bronze statue of Goldsmith? In no way whatever. This statue was present with us. A living Goldsmith was in no way present with us.

No doubt it was just this that people were unwilling to tolerate, that the man whose relics were important to them, touched them even to laughter and tears and insight, should in no way be really here. Such a thing is eerie, it makes us anxious. Therefore, to alleviate their unease, people erected a statue of Goldsmith and wrote on the pedestal "Goldsmith." But this did not immortalize Goldsmith; it did not do *anything* for Goldsmith.

Popular philosophers will speak of the man living on in our hearts, in our thoughts, in the influence of his works; we live in our culture and Goldsmith is our culture. Such philosophers seem to envisage a kind of shadowy mental and social immortality for the poet: and then that bronze figure (as one passed by) was a symbol, a memento, to call up such associations and make the "immortal Goldsmith" glow with a little more substance: literally a figure in the living culture. This has been argued, and oh, I suppose there is something in it; namely, very little.

For as I stood there and thought of gone Goldsmith and thought of myself, it did not seem to me that, in my case, my existence as an object or influence for other people, added much to *my* life at all. Quite the contrary; in the instances where my words or deeds were for the good, I felt diminished by them rather than enhanced—*they* were not myself—they occurred as if on their own, though at the expense of myself; they gave me no grounds of pride or satisfaction. When I had finished a work, I felt that much more exhausted, and I knew it was not even I who made the work. And so far as my things worked in other people and gave them something useful, those people by no means responded by giving anything to me. Rather, moved by the poem, they envied its author. Certainly no one stretched a hand to relieve my animal distress. I doubted that it was very different with Goldsmith. *I* would (now) have loved him and felt sorry for him, but he was dead.

What did they mean to be doing when they erected the statue of Goldsmith? Was it merely for guilt that they had not enough loved Goldsmith?

v.

These were bitter thoughts I had as I looked up at the statue of Goldsmith springing out of the green grass of Ireland; but at least they were natural thoughts. But when the true answer came to me, it froze my soul, for it was not even natural.

It was so simple. They put up the statue of Goldsmith in order to have a statue. Like a clench of the fist. Just for the immortality of it.

Not *his* immortality, nor even theirs; it was even more abstract than that.

Nothing to do with Goldsmith. Or rather, they made their statue as an effigy of Goldsmith, taking his name and inventing an unlikely pose, not otherwise than a painter who is making a painting pretends to be painting a landscape with figures, but he is really making a painting. They wanted a statue and they took advantage of Goldsmith, after his death just as during his life, except that now at least it did him no harm.

Good; they had their statue; oh, and it was immortal like the Emperor of China "who never died because he never lived."

Nevertheless it was a statue of Goldsmith, and served him right! It was Goldsmith first who taught them to take advantage of Goldsmith. Just for the immortality of it. Like a clench of the fist. *He* willed it. Because it was not from nothing, it was from the martyrdom of Goldsmith, that "his literary reputation rests securely on *The Vicar of Wakefield, The Deserted Village,* and his play *She Stoops to Conquer,* one of the great comedies of the English theatre." The play was certainly his; it was written by Goldsmith who was dead. But *whose* literary reputation is it that "rests" so securely in that present tense? The statue of Goldsmith!

And suddenly the horror swept over me, and froze my soul, of those lonely months that I had spent working in rainy Dublin (in Florence, in Paris, in New York); and the horror of this frightful day that I was even now spending like a ghoul of immortality. Every part of it was chilling. How I loved to praise, and to have something to praise—just because I could not tolerate the common waste and death. (The young workman was instinctively chary of me.) And I thought of us ghouls in the University close, who passed on our culture, just for the immortality of it. Like a clench of the fist. Like the statue of Goldsmith.

My animal spirit has left me; I am without lust; I could

be pushed this way or that way or just left to lie; and with detachment I remember how I fell to my knees and prayed that a book I wrote would have an easy access and an understanding reception in the world.

ADAM

I.

Wanting to talk about love and awaken
in me longing again and bawl,
what sailor hot because of the sea
and death shall *I* recall, or which
of women to win and be her man?

For I was in a company of young people and they were
talking about their loves, as they do, to cheer and excite themselves, some telling wistfully what they want,
some boasting about what they have, others lying. They
became very merry, one man talking about a whore, a
woman about a milkman. One father sweetly mentioned
his children, and another man said that he was in love
with a dog. I too wanted to talk that way and be cheered
and I blurted out, "The one I love is red—" and I burst
into tears and began to bawl. For whom I love is Adam.
He is the only thing I am in love with in this whole world,
and I cannot find him. I could not continue speaking.

For nearly fifty years, I have been tirelessly seeking in
the city and the country and in Europe. I have grown
tired and I am still seeking. Listening to those young people, I understood my life work. Therefore let me describe
also this beloved of mine in a mixture of prose and verse,
imitating how long ago Dante wrote about Beatrice in

The New Life; but I am doing it in order to console, with this beautiful subject, my aging and frustrated life. In order, being a poet, to have something to praise that I love, as other poets do; better than being dumb.

> —What loyal animal that hardly
> understands love dumb like my penis?
> what child of mine exciting because likely
> or giant for his size is lovable?

> *None* of these provokes me. Only you
> Adam, my red lover made of earth,
> I am in love with in this world.
> I talk about you and awaken
> in me longing again and bawl.
> My hard eyes soften when I look at
> your likeness by Michelangelo
> and my soul is mad with your surprise,
> namer of the beasts.

> Sailor hot with sea and death!
> farmer on the mountainside!
> animal dumb like my penis!
> child whose other name is Likely!
> giant for your size is lovable.

So I make verses about him, because a poet has to have *something* to praise. But the truth is that I don't know whether Adam exists or is a figure of the mythological past or is a figment of my mind. I walk the streets, and even the fields and woods where no one at all is to be found (as if, if I found some one there, it would be more likely to be Adam). Naturally people gossip about this inept behavior of mine, but I don't care about that; though when I think of my wasted life, I am mournful. It is stupid what I do; but it has kept me naive and my will for mankind alive. Man-like my god I make—

> Man-like my god I make nor fear
> to be an idol's fool, for
>   so hard I think of man the thought
>   crumbles into absolute
> un-Nature. Oh and he will save
> me in the little work and love

> I lust in day by day until
> my name he elects to call.

What I do know, however, is that my friends, such as regard me, say that I am a sad man; and even I can judge that the books I write are sad.

II.

In common day, my Adam is surprised; everything happens to him for the first time. With present eyes he says, "Lo, here you are."

Oh, no doubt that his eyes are present as the brooks flow into eternity (as Rilke said of the animals). Nevertheless, he is shaking his head from side to side and, being a man, doesn't know which way to turn. "Lo! lo!" he says and his forehead is perplexed, "here now you are for me and here am I responding as who can?"

An explorer to whom each new turning opens out a broader wilderness is finally afraid that he is getting lost and may not find his way home. But Adam is going in the only world that there is, even though to his grief and confusion. *He* is not lost. He goes firmly.

He does not, as in a hostile company, turn to each blow *after* it has struck, but he is ready where it comes like a fist between his eyes. My Adam is not insulted by being amazed, as if it were the part of dignity to be in the know, for he does not make a comparison between himself and others, what it is appropriate for a man to be like.

Adam is not disappointed when he is confounded, for he has not had any expectations. The tears that start into the eyes of my beloved do not come from hurt feelings. As firmly he continues on his way to work, I wish that I could walk beside him silently a mile. In common day.

> When Adam woke a boundless surprise
> was his, to see his own flesh red,
> to see the as-yet-nameless zoo parade,
> and red the sunset and the white moonrise.
> He was astonished when before his eyes

sat Eve, and afterwards both shame and dread
were news to him, and with uplifted blade
Michael at the door of paradise.

Everything that Adam fell was new.
When like himself the setting sun he shone
red on the hill and there stood Cain his son
but Abel on the field whom Cain slew,
he was amazed that him the quiet one
did not acknowledge as he used to do.

   With Adam firmly walking to
   the farm-work that he knows to do
      in deep confusion, for the grim
      news of everyday to him
   happens each thing by surprise
   like a fist between the eyes
      —let me day to day work on
      in this thick cloud that has sunk down.

In the Sonnet I remind myself that Adam is amazed, and
in the Little Prayer I pray that I too shall be able to continue working even in this confusion that I cannot shake
off. In the following poem I express the wish that I could
share in his surprise:

       Day! save me! I am entranced
       by the Eternal Forms;
       by love and loss are they strong,
       by love and then by loss.

       By love they came to be
       and by death they are.
       O unpeople me, my Day
       my only one, this place

       of sorcery where I lie,
       and let only surprise,
       surprise and falling asleep,
       surprise and sleep be my gait,

       surprise as when forth cast
       from the finger of God the Man
       looked back at him with boundlessly
       boundlessly open eyes.

III.

This image of the creation of Adam that haunts me is in the picture of Michelangelo's on the ceiling of the Sistine Chapel in Rome. Yes, it is that trust-drunken face and its present eyes that I am looking for in the factories and the fields.

And I have had the thought to arrange Michelangelo's picture as a dramatic tableau for the stage. The stage is divided into two, and stage right (the spectator's left) is at first concealed with a scrim.

Slowly from Left Rear appears the great cart of God and his Angels, moving in an arc toward the center. It is wrapped and blown round by the fluttering cloak of Whirlwind who spoke to Job, noisily agitated by a wind-machine. But the machine quiets down when the Angels begin to speak.

What are the Angels saying, as their cart swings toward the center? For at the decisive moment at which Michelangelo chose to portray them, their countenances are expressing the most various thoughts, as if they had excitedly been talking to one another; and there is no doubt that thus the poetic painter meant to tell us *his* different thoughts about the creation of Adam. The fat boy, attentive over God's right shoulder, is wide-eyed, a bit alarmed. The three who are looking over his left shoulder are like three youthful scientists, one wonderstruck with mouth agape, one with his lips grimly intent, and the third, looking straight at it, excitedly curious, with the small smile that we wear for the crucial experiment. But the lovely youth (or is it Eve?) about whose shoulders God's left arm is familiarly flung, and who is clutching at God's forearm for support and almost as if to check him, surely his face is big-eyed with dismay. What does it mean? And lastly, the chubby child on the right, whom God is touching with a bent forefinger, he is purposely *not* looking on at the scene but seems to be in a kind of daydream. And besides these, there are faces hidden in the shadows.

As the cart of God and his Angels approaches the Center of the stage, God has stretched out his right arm and forefinger, and now as if by the sweep of his gesture the scrim is opened, disclosing Adam on the hillside with his extended hand. There is no doubt that at some instant their fingertips have touched, but already the cart is continuing in its slow arc toward the exit Left Front, although God, as he goes, does follow with his eyes his creature.

At the moment of touching, too quick to be noticed, God has thrown Adam into being, and this is expressed by opening the scrim revealing him on the hillside. But there is no need for the actor of Adam to imitate the countenance of that moment, nor did the painter paint it, nor can we guess it; for already it is past, and Michelangelo has painted us the countenance of Adam at the instant *after* their fingers have touched.

This is the trust-drunken face of Adam with boundlessly open eyes, for his soul is pouring through his eyes looking into God's face that has not yet vanished. (As it has not yet vanished.) The look of my Adam is more alive than the solemn look on an animal's face; but it is more melancholy than the simply serious look of a man absorbed in his concerns. Adam has on his face the trusting and boundlessly-drinking look of separating from God, as if to say, "Lo! here now you are for me—going away, and here I am responding as who can." Not a look of grief, for God cannot be altogether lost. Nor a look of disappointment, for Adam has not had any expectations. But it is the look toward God going away, separated from us, just as it is. And after the cart has made its exit, this look does not change, but it is what the spectators take home with them, as the curtain falls.

This is the face and the eyes of my Adam, in his portrait by Michelangelo, that is fixed in my soul, and I do not know what to do.—

> Creator of the worlds! O joy
> of speed! and when the powers that lie
>   latent, into being break,
>   I shall not fear the onward wreck
> because I am in love with
> the nature of things unto death,
>   and as they loom say, "Lo!"
>   Lord favor me, the road I go.

Father! guide and lead me stray
for I stumble forward straight my way
    undeviating, I do not
    notice the pleasant bypaths that
make us this world surprising nor
the precipice that sinks before.
    O give me ground for next a step
    to stagger walking in my sleep.

As I think of my Adam thrown into this world whose resources I have assayed for fifty years of my life, to God I
pray for faith, for conviction that I have ground underfoot for a next step.

IV.

So into this paradise that is a world for him, though often
to his grief and confusion, my Adam has awaked-like-the-
slow-avalanche-softly-snapping-trees. In common day
when-after-the-hurricane-everything-is-dirty-and-washed.
Whichever way a man looks-he-is-confronted-by-the-
oval-wall-of-closely-fitted-adjacent-colors. He cannot find
a door in the day to go through and come outdoors. Yet
in-whichever-direction-a-man-moves-he-brings-into-
being-a-new-space.

Or if, sitting on his hillside, he is scrutinizing a stone
that he has picked-up-for-it-is-to-hand, suddenly empty
freedom has departed from him; he is pinned-in-the-at-
tention-that-he-chooses. But when he flings away the
stone, the scenery has bounding-leaped-toward-him-up-
the-hill and joins onto his unbroken space quietly-as-a-
great-jumper-comes-down-and-just-walks-away. And into
this unbroken space he steps.

Now Adam and the Sun are staring-at-one-another-
each-waiting-for-the-other-to-volunteer-to-do-what-both-
wish-but-are-not-able-to-begin. Adam's sun is bigger than
mine, occupying nearly one eighth of his sky. It is because
he does not have so many other ideas in his field of
vision, to crowd out the sun. The sun's hot rays come to
him quicker than the eight seconds that they take to tra-
verse to me.

Therefore Adam has made a plain gold disk about five inches in diameter. It is only metal hammered thin, but being a disk and being of gold it is an adequate image of the sun. One can gaze on it a long time as if warmed by its rays. I have seen many such sun-disks in the museums, coming from Central America or Ireland. I seek them out because my soul is cold, and I gaze at each one a long time and am warmed by its rays.

As a man of letters I have thought a lot about how Adam speaks, and I am persuaded, with Otto Jespersen, that his language consists of complex words, "inseparable irregular conglomerations that he is forever crooning." And Adam means his language to be a magical act in the world and change the situation, you, the thing, himself; he is not left, like me, with an empty poem. So we may (imitating his own speech) describe him naming the animals in paradise: His-sensitive-surfaces-have-become-moist-and-he-is-reaching-standing-at-the-edge-not-quite-willing-to-dive waiting-out-the-interval-between-the-flash-of-lightning-and-the-crash-of-thunder. He-comes-down-softly-like-a-great-jumper-who-just-walks-away and copiously-as-the-warm-semen-spurts he calls out Tiger-tiger-burning-bright-in-the-forests-of-the-night thank-you-it-is-now-my-grateful-privilege-to-oblige-*you*-how?

But alas! the tiger, who has small speech nor need for friends, crashes-away-through-the-brush, leaving Adam with the Name that he has acted.

Adam and the Name are staring-at-one-another-each-waiting-for-the-other-to-volunteer-to-do-what-both-wish-but-are-not-able-to-begin, and Adam flaming with shame from his toes to the roots of his hair, having dared to create something in blinding forgetfulness of who he is, wants-to-drop-out-of-sight. But he is consoled by the approving embrace of the Creator Spirit who hovers in the garden made for Adam, though often to his grief and confusion. Let me pray.

> Creator Spirit, who dost lightly hover
> whence I know not and why to me I never
>   questioned, come. Do visit thy lover
>   after thy long absence. I turn over
> awaking in the morning, thou art not
> there to my touch, nor is a substitute

there, but nothing nothing at all to talk
to and make love when I awake.

O Spirit wise, shine, somewhere shine
so I can squander me again!
I ask it if ever I tried hard
to eke me out a livelihood
from a grudging city, or if ever
I have been patient to preserve
Opportunity my sweet
muse, my darling, my flirt.

Adam is alert-to-the-noise-of-a-snake-in-the-grass. But
it is the snake himself, and Adam softly follows his swift
curviline arrow-straight to where, as D. H. Lawrence once
saw him, he is sipping at the water trough. Delighted
with the beauty of his guest, yet Adam holds-back-with-
patient-courtesy-in-order-not-to-disturb-somebody-eating.
At length, however, the snake looks up at him with his
hard bright eyes. There is an eerie-of-unresponsive-eyes,
of looks-holding-one-another-at-more-than-arm's-length.
Adam is-frigid-at-the-presence-of-a-spirit-whom-he-does-
not-want-warmly-to-embrace; yet he is-profoundly-respect-
ful-of-the-equal-king-of-another-realm, he himself being
a fearless lord and king. The snake not-swiftly-and-not-
slowly slithers into a black crevice in the rock and vanishes
into the burning bowels of the earth, leaving Adam with-an-
empty-thought. Adam and the Black Hole stare-at-one-
another-each-waiting-for-the-other-to-volunteer-to-do-what-
both-wish-but-are-not-able-to-begin. While the prophet-birds
in the branches are wildly hopping about, peeping and
grieving.

A dog is watching there, wagging his tail uncertainly,
not knowing if he is going to be regarded, more than
ready to make friends and be the dog of his master.
Finally Adam cannot not notice the dark limited gaze
following his every move as though it were a great matter.

So Adam stretches out, noblesse oblige, his great hand
and lays it on the dog's head, with the-slight-abstracted-
ness-with-which-one-gives-a-sufficient-satisfaction-to-the-
other-when-it-is-no-great-matter-to-oneself. He is pierced
by the woeful pang of being a superior being and alone.

But the dog leaps up on him in ecstasy, frantically wagging his plume, and barking ear-splitting volleys echoing in the valley, until the man is flustered.

V.

But *those* were, you say, the deeds of Adam in paradise, if he ever was. I tell you flatly, my Adam is as much in paradise as he ever was.

To my mind the most dismaying moment in John Milton's story about Adam, and one of the most awful moments in all literature, is when, in the Tenth Book, God bids his Angels to derange the world as "sorted best with present things." Then some of the Angels laboriously push askant the axis of the earth twenty degrees and more, entailing the consequences of that; and others sow discord among the beasts. And the world becomes just as it is. The world becomes just as it is. It is hard work to accomplish it, Milton says so, but he does not show us, like Michelangelo, the expressions on the faces of the Angels doing that work. Naturally to me as an artisan, with our obsession to conserve the least object of creation, this command of God is the most sickening and shocking possible, to derange what has been created good. I freeze with horror when I read of those great Angels with their great crowbars; and when I think how what Milton says is also true, I burst into tears of woe.

It is then that I think, with tears of joy and longing, that my Adam is practical, and he is firmly going to his farmwork that he knows to do, even though in deep confusion and surprised and balked.

I do not like it when people speak of Adam's "fall"; there is no such language in the Bible. How did he fall? from what dignity? how humiliated before whom? I agree with Pascal that his misery proves his greatness, for only a great man has such misery; but he is not a "deposed king," he is always a king, only his kingdom is in permanent insurrection. It is possible to construe the Biblical sentences about knowing and nakedness to mean that Adam has lost his innocence; but to me at least, this does not seem to be our universal fact. For although many people are knowing, ashamed of their nakedness, or otherwise no longer innocent, many of us are still innocent and ignorant, surprised and confused. Naked, we are not ashamed but vulnerable.

But that the world is no longer very practicable for us, if it ever was, *this* is our universal fact. It does not offer us opportunities for our best capacities; it is rare among men that an occasion occurs at the right time (so that, when it does, we regard it as a gala day in history). And neither I nor the people I consort with are practical to seize even such opportunities as there are. But my Adam, whom alone I am in love with in this world, is practical. And if one day I have gold to give him, *he* will not demand but silver. Or nothing. Or be suspicious of counterfeit.

By "paradise" I mean nothing but the world practical. It is a matter of degree. Some people at some times have a more practicable world than others, and we say that they have Grace or Luck. The world is a world for them. Naturally they have abounding faith, the conviction that there is ground underfoot for a next step. Others, by character or destiny (it comes to the same thing), have less luck; and I am one of those. I am in the middle rank, for I have been able to work, and therefore it must be that an area of the wide world is for me, in which I work. Goethe said, A man must do not what he wants but what he can—though he, to be sure, commanded a commodious area that was for him. Others, again, seem to have no luck at all. The world is not for them. And when I notice this, I do try to help and be some luck for them, in order that my world shall be more like paradise. (But with the best will in the world, it is hard to be somebody else's luck. The trouble is that I do not simply love them, thoughtless of paradise, for it is only Adam that I love.)

> Despairing to be happy any more,
> on the other hand I am not much in pain,
> I can work, and sometimes from my pen
> such lovely sentences of English pour
> as I am proud of for their casual grandeur
> nor will, when I am dead, they be forgotten:
> I look about and I am as most men
> as happy. Yet my spirit is still sore

with disappointment of the paradise
lost that I could not enter; a hard question
haunts me, "Is life worth it as it is?"
like a baffled man looking for the direction
from side to side I shake my head—and oh
notice! my toes are tense, to go, to go.

On the highroad to death
trudging, not eager to get
　　to that city, yet the way is
　　still too long for my patience,
teach me a travel-song,
Master, to march along
　　as we boys used to shout
　　when I was a young scout.

In the Sonnet I wonder whether or not I can indeed
continue in the unhappy way I am in, and in the Little
Prayer I pray to God to teach me a travel-song.

VI.

Guard me from hope. Give me days of labor and a few
moments of joy, but spare me the poisonous hours of
hope in which I have fantasies and lose touch with my
only world, such as she is. Let the moments of joy be
scattered, so I may not forget that that exists; but guard
me from my feverish expectations that have never yet,
and will not, come across in my real world. Wishes are
chaos and—I don't know how it is with others—the
color of my chaos is pain. I am not unobservant, and I
know from experience the modest degree of success that
comes to me, at what grade of paradise I live. Just enough
to keep me going. Then, Lord, let me aspire according to
my experienced judgment. (But if it be your plan, as you
seem to have marked out, for me to exist periodically in
the crazy distraction and torment of hope like a fever, I
have been able to survive it till my forty-eighth year.)

Thou invigorating poison
that while I flush and pant
tossest me sleepless
Hope! only last night

in pain and joy I forethought
to wryly praise thee dread
drug I could not sleep,
and now tonight I neither
can sleep until at last
I'll cry myself to sleep
and let go of my life,
for thou hast not so much
vanished as grimly shone
thine other thy real face
Expected Disappointment.

O answering Luck! us who are agile souls,
who do the necessary and think up
new things—and sometimes we have adventured
into rough places among enemies,

then do you, O subtile O understanding
answering Luck! smile at and accompany
some of us, and they are laureate with
shining success and roseate with pleasure;

we others, though, look after wistfully
as you two vanish and the door closes;
it tastes us bitter and we would to God
we had been idle, we should be less hurt.

Tell me, Lord, is not my longing for his beauty the only
direct awareness that I *have* of paradise? How else can I
know it? It is the kind of knowledge that moves to action,
and that unlooses also energy in me to squander.

But in my city, knowing about paradise I have become stupid. I am a mono-maniac for Adam. (Everything
else is a lie.) The streets I walk are now my jail.

My anger has become
a settled rage. I look calm
but I no longer wish to touch
any flesh with tender lust.
Lord, give me back my lust to touch
beautiful flesh, or else teach
me some otherwise to make sense
of my experience.

Now dare I anything! O Warden
of the Drunk and Careless, guard me!
   for the reins that stay my course
   and hinder me are loose.
When forth I go, for forth I shall,
my blond and black horses gallop
   toward the wreck that I forecast
   with little interest.

Such is the history of paradise that I have been able to tell in verses out of my life, better than being dumb.

VII.

But Adam will make me take him seriously, and so stay my drunken and careless course.

It is hard for me to take other people seriously as existing, because I am smug and know it all, and I attribute to others needs out of my own ideas. (So finally I lose my attachment to my own life.) But Adam will not allow this to happen, he will not allow me to do it, and thereby he will give me a great surety in the world and an unaccustomed peace. Even if I am not going to be happy.

For we across these plains of hell are like the spinning dust-filled winds. My desires are fitful gusts, and I pay for them with airy efforts to serve people according to my preconceptions. My works vanish in eddies and whispers. Yet most of the people that whirl by seem to me even worse off than myself, whistling vortices of personality. And everywhere, mounting high into the sky and blotting out the sun, are cyclones of dead leaves.

Adam is substantial. I cannot treat him, surprised and confused, as if he were an idea of mine. "I regret that I have not been of any good to you, Adam," I say. "I love you and I should be proud to see you happy and great, but I don't know how."

I don't say this to cajole a response from him, but simply because, when I am with some one I love, I cannot keep silent but compulsively need to express my affection in every word and act, and apologizing if I haven't been able to prove it. This behavior of mine is oppressive.

But Adam takes it simply as how I am. He does *not*, like the others, disregard my abject longing for him, as if I did not exist. (Because he acknowledges me, it will not so much matter if he loves me.)

"No, Everyman," he says, "you do me a lot of good. And you *do* make me feel that you love me. I cannot disregard it. Everyman."

Oh! then I shall not have to talk bitterly about myself for my own ears as if I were a third person. *He* is substantial and *I* am substantial. The fitful winds calm down, and the strong sun of autumn is pouring upon us.

"You make a mistake, Everyman, to search for me so hard as you do. You could really sit quite still and I would know you by your work, how you love me. But it's a harmless mistake; I am not put off by it."

I will have lowered my eyes.—"Do you know my work? I am inscribing this present work to you, Adam."

There is a long pause. Yet I am *not* threatened by it, wondering what he is thinking. Adam can think his own thoughts.

"It has been peaceful, Adam, having you in my house this past week. Nowhere to go, having arrived. Also—" suddenly I am embarrassed—"your presence shines like a star."

(I *understand* that he does not love me; but this does *not* bring death to my heart, as I should have thought. Simply, that I in this world am not going to be blest and that—no newsy story—many a thing possible for others will not be possible for me.)

But to my stupefaction—as a man is understood and *therefore* the ground sinks from under his feet—Adam has said, "You have revived my purpose to succeed."

At this moment my hairs have stood up, electrified.

We are staring at one another each waiting for the other to volunteer to do what both wish but are not able to begin.

"Adam! let me pray!" and I shall pray the Little Prayer

> God of the Fullness! who in hours
> hast, after my starving years,
>   filled my bowl and with garlands
>   laden my outstretched hands,

teach me again what it is
to want, that I by long disuse
and disappointment have forgot
and my brain is slow with surfeit.

Naturally he is practical, and especially in this misfit-
ting world where it is necessary to make an extra effort,
he gives me and takes from me what satisfaction is possible, whatever the measure of it. And lo! suddenly! as
a man is stung on the threshold by a wasp—I shall have
been stunned by a sweet winged joy whose poison has
now worked on me swiftly with such irresistible fire and
power that I fell down as if I were dead. Among the
howling and whining whirlwinds and the fitful gusts.—

I lustily bestrode my love
    until I fainted near and poured my seed
    and then I lay in sweetness like one dead
whom angels sing around him and above.

I lay with all my strength embraced
    and swiftly to a quiet grave withdrew
    most like a grotto with the sea in view
surging and pounding, till the spell was past.

Since when my hours are empty of
    everything, only beauty touches me
    but is like pain to hear and see.
Absent among the tribes of men I move.

I am no longer careless of my life given to me and not
made by me, as absent among the tribes of men I move.

VIII.

But I have had the thought that Adam is working all an
afternoon tarring a roof in a clearing near Tenafly, across
the river from New York City where I live. As he works
and looks up he can often see, from the cliff-top, the slate
expanse of the lordly river spreading northward, not
spangling, for the sun is sinking behind him.

Finally, having finished his day's work, he jumps down

from the roof. And there, at the edge of the clearing, in a shaft of sunlight, stands the Angel Dogwood.

Adam is surprised. "Lo! here now you are for me," he says readily.

The resourceful Angel is one of those who come down from heaven and visit the world, wearing his white petals that are my bland joy. He is alive with empty spaces and shadows, and on him fall the shafts of sunlight as he stands here and there in the little wood, to make Adam smile. He is a resourceful and powerful Angel.

And Adam, tired with his day's work, gladly follows the Angel here and there in the wood and is surprised, espying the white dogwood in the sunlit woods. But when suddenly, as if to tease or excite him, the Angel puts on his pink petals, then Adam lowers his head stolidly and closes his eyes in pain, and turns to go home.

"Why, what's the matter, Adam?" asks the Angel pleasantly. "Why do you refuse in this way?"

And Adam says, "Your pink dogwood is too beautiful; it makes me yearn for the reunion of the separated and I hurt. But dogwood white is my bland joy. I look at you with an open face of wonder in the sunlit woods just on the border of the possible, and this doesn't make me unhappy."

So Adam was tarring a roof in the clearing of the possible and there stood, just on the border of the possible, the Angel Dogwood with his white petals, and Adam was not unhappy.

IX.

And I have had the thought that it is sunset. Cain is standing in the field near the body of Abel whom he slew, when he notices his father Adam approaching on the road, returning from his work. Then Cain, his mind wandering a little, asks himself, "Lo! which of the creatures made by God in the Six Days is coming this way slowly? Is it the Sun down-going in the evening, when he was new and did it the first time? Or the red Earth arising from the sea? He has the look of one who had no father—fearless! the

first namer of the beasts: it is the Man, Abel's father."
And as Adam draws near to where the murder is hovering near the ground, Cain has begun to shudder and be present in the world again.

Adam, acknowledging Cain, is surprised that Abel, the other son, does not greet him, is not present. He calls out to the body Abel's name, but the body does not respond, and Adam is amazed. He does not choose to see the murder hovering near the ground.

"Lo!" he says, "lo! here now you are for me." For he knows that Abel is dead like other animals, many of whom he himself slew. And he says to the Death of the first man to die, "Lo! lo! and here I am responding as who can." He too has begun to wander in his mind a little and to speak of himself in the 3rd person, and says to Cain, "Is Adam to be always learning? Everything that falls him is new."

But Cain says, "An Angel was here and we conversed. He put this sign on my forehead." He shows the mark on his forehead to his father, who examines it with wonder and curiosity.

"How comes Abel to lie still and not acknowledge me?"

"Because he is dead. I killed him with my hands, like a calf. He cannot move or talk or recognize *anything*."

"Let me look again at that mark on your forehead, son," says Adam, and he examines it again with attention and curiosity. He keeps saying, "Lo! lo! here now you are for me." His son is dead. He mutters, "My son is dead." His mind is wandering.

It is a bad prospect, for he foreknows that Eve is going to weep and mourn for the son whom she gave birth to with pain. The thought of it casts him into gloom.

Seeing the trouble on his father's face, Cain feels excluded from his father's intimacy and is disturbed more than he can bear. (But in fact the murder that was hovering near the ground has gone away.)

Cain and Adam are staring at one another each waiting for the other to volunteer to do what both wish but are not able to begin.

But Adam helps him by asking a practical question. "What shall we do in this new case, I mean with the dead boy?"

And Cain says, "Let us carry the body back to my mother."

It is dusk, and where a man turns are holes in the oval wall of closely fitted adjacent colors. There are loud holes like bells.

In the deepening dusk the holes are spreading, like loud bells. They are like loud holes, like bells. While Adam, carrying the body, says, "Lo! lo! here now you are for me—not. And here I am responding as who can?" I have had the thought of Adam going confronting this only world that is for him, and he and she are staring at one another each waiting for the other to volunteer to do what both wish but are not able to begin. I cannot think, now when my son's dead, of any next thing. But Adam is practical and makes a gesture.

Such are some of the thoughts that I have had to praise Adam, whom alone I am in love with in this world, in order to console myself as I grow old.

Thee God we praise, for this complete
work that over-use and doubt
    and pain could mar but not prevent
    because thy spirit still was sent.
Such as it is, this now belongs
also among the created things
    whilst I relapse, thy dying fact
    more spent, more sullen, and more wracked.

Heavy silence, Lord, dim eyes,
dull ears, and dubious a guess,
    I offer thee as that which is.
    My tithe is this blind daze
as I to work return
without regard for past work done
    and for the work I do begin
    without reward or hope. Amen.

PAUL GOODMAN, a native New Yorker, was born in 1911. After graduating from City College in New York, he received his Ph.D. in humanities from the University of Chicago. Mr. Goodman has taught at the University of Chicago, New York University, Black Mountain College, Sarah Lawrence, the University of Wisconsin, and has lectured widely at various universities throughout the country.

Mr. Goodman has written for *Commentary, Politics, Kenyon Review, Resistance, Liberation, Partisan Review*, etc. His novels include *Parents' Day, The Empire City*, and *Making Do*. He is also the author of *The Young Disciple, Faustina* and *Jonah: Three Plays*. He has published two volumes of verse, *Hawkweed* (available in Vintage Books) and *The Lordly Hudson. Kafka's Prayer* and *The Structure of Literature* are books of literary criticism. Vintage Books has reprinted several of Mr. Goodman's well-known works of social criticism, among them *Growing Up Absurd; Utopian Essays and Practical Proposals; The Community of Scholars* and *Compulsory Mis-education* (in one volume); and *People or Personnel* and *Like a Conquered Province* (in one volume).

Adam and His Works contains most of the contents of Mr. Goodman's three volumes of short stories: *The Facts of Life* (with the exception of *Jonah*, which is available in *Three Plays*), *The Break-Up of Our Camp*, and *Our Visit to Niagara*, as well as five new stories.